EVERYMAN, I will go with thee,

and be thy guide,

In thy most need to go by thy side

THOMAS DELONEY

Born probably at Norwich *c.* 1543. His son, Richard, was christened at St Giles, Cripplegate, October 1586. Died in 1600.

ROBERT GREENE

Born at Norwich in 1558. Matriculated to St John's College, Cambridge, 1575, B.A. 1579, travelled in Italy, Spain, Denmark, and Poland. Cambridge M.A. 1583. He married, but deserted his wife soon after the birth of her first child. Died in 1592.

THOMAS NASHE

Born at Lowestoft in 1567. Matriculated to St John's College, Cambridge, 1582, B.A. 1586, travelled in France, Germany, and Italy, and settled in London *c.* 1588. Died *c.* 1601.

Shorter Novels: Elizabethan

INTRODUCTION BY
GEORGE SAINTSBURY

NOTES
ON THE AUTHORS BY
PHILIP HENDERSON

DENT: LONDON
EVERYMAN'S LIBRARY
DUTTON: NEW YORK

NO. *824*

INTRODUCTION

THAT Everyman should be provided with a collection of Short
or Shorter Novels (one might rather like to have a pedantic
little battle over the respective appropriateness of the Positive
and Comparative) is obviously proper: for Everyman should
have everything proper provided for him.

The present writer is unhappily at some variance with
two distinguished dead critics, friends of his own, as well
as with others, as to the merits of Nashe's *Unfortunate Traveller*.
Both Sir Edmund Gosse and Sir Walter Raleigh *Secundus*
thought very highly of it and, partly from their estimate,
partly from that of others, it has sometimes received the
always dangerous place of 'first' novel with—even more
widely—the primacy in time, if not rank, not only of fiction
but of journalism. Now that there was a great deal of the
journalist in Nashe no critic could possibly deny. He was,
two centuries and a half beforehand, and with alterations to
time, one of the not quite best class of 'newspaper men'—
Thackeray's Bohemians. He had a great deal of satirical
power, and a little dramatic. But he does not seem to me
quite to have known how to tell a story, though his apparent
'realism' has bribed people of the present and the later last
generation. He pops in clever anecdotes, true or false, of
historical persons; he bustles his hero about from this place
to that. He does to some extent discard that amazing
euphuistic jargon which has made his brother tale-tellers and
pamphleteers impossible to read to so many people. But he
does not seem to me to present life and carry on story as they
should be presented and carried on. It is, of course, the fault
of the whole class. It is not till Bunyan that the people are
thoroughly alive; that their actions are what they would do
if they were alive; and that their speech, slightly altered in
mere diction, is what they would say. But Nashe does not
seem to me much, if at all, in advance of his fellows in some
respects, though it requires considerable audacity to say so
and some strong argument to make it good. Greene—slender
and romantic merely as is his substance, and fantastic as is
its style—seems superior as a tale-teller to his not ungenerous
defender after his death.

The comparative appreciation of *The Unfortunate Traveller*, which has been referred to, is perhaps partly due to what has recently been called its realistic as opposed to sentimental character. The former adjective has rather usurped its name, for killing is not in the least more real than kissing, nor are descriptions of outrage and torture more so than descriptions of dances and Watteau-like picnics. On the other hand Nashe, though beyond all question a master of the art of collecting what is likely to various classes to be interesting matter, seems to me not quite such a master of that art of *telling* which almost necessitates the possession of an art yet higher in itself—the art of creating personality. When in Greene's *Card of Fancy* 'the disdained Gwydonius' writes to 'the desired Castania' (they are in fact extremely fond *of each other*) and she answers him that the very remembrance of his person makes her fall into most hateful passions and comparatively reminds her of the well-known scientific facts that no serpent can abide the smell of hartshorn; that the panther escheweth the smell of the ounce; that the vulture is a mortal enemy to the eel, and that it is impossible to hatch up a swan (or one would suppose any other bird) in an eagle's nest, one is rather sorely tempted first to laugh and then to be bored. Yet somehow or other Greene communicates personality, which one supposes implies reality if not realism, to Castania and Gwydonius in a way which Nashe does not (at any rate in some estimates) to anybody in *The Unfortunate Traveller*. Of course it may be said that Greene was a better dramatist than Nashe, and that drama and novel are only allotropic or allomorphic forms of the same thing. Yet it is curious that as these two forms have gone, it has become, till quite recently at any rate, less and less common for a really good dramatist to be a really good novelist and vice versa. Goldsmith is the chief exception, and Goldsmith was an exception in most things.

It must have struck not a few people of those who have reflected at all upon the history of English literature, that its course in respect of prose fiction, and indeed of fiction generally, has been curiously broken and irregular, not exhibiting anything like perfection till very late. The comparison with French is most remarkable, all the more so because no small portion of French romance before Chaucer's time was pretty certainly written by Englishmen. Further, when our country began to furnish itself in the various departments of literature from its own resources of language, the amazing developments in poetry and drama, accompanied by fewer but still great things in serious prose, did not succeed in providing anything at all masterly in prose fiction: and for nearly three centuries seemed to be conducting a series of blind or half-blind experiments. True, in our worst century of all, the fifteenth, there *had* been a masterpiece—the 'childish,' as I think I once saw it called, achievement of Sir Thomas Malory: but this had no companions. Even later than the Restoration, things in themselves first-rate, the performances of Bunyan, Defoe, and Swift were, in the first and last cases especially, 'side-shows'—as it were in fiction—allegories—a great word, which one might almost translate 'side-show' in one of its senses. People translated, as by many hands from Anthony Munday downwards, the long romances of French and Spanish, and imitated the short ones, as, for instance, in that *Incognita* of Congreve's, which has been so differently estimated and which perhaps we shall give. The 'strong contagion' of world-exploring which showed itself mainly in Defoe, had minor symptoms such as that curious *Isle of Pines* of Neville's which the Continent, if not England, also took for history. Head's and other people's disreputable *English Rogue*, putting its disreputableness aside, is an attempt at a novel, and though a long one is made of short things put together: and when we come to the great quartet of the mid-eighteenth century we seem to have stumbled into competence never quite to stumble out of it again, though to go through many ups and downs of individual accomplishment or failure.

If, as has been thought, Deloney's prose stories are the work of the last few years of his life, and if he was a ballad-monger during the greater part of it, one may certainly say that the last part of this man's life was better than the first. *Jack of Newbury* and the rest are not masterpieces. They are quite evidently written for a class of people of whom it used to be rather rashly presumed that they would not be likely to read anything. Though by no means obscene, they are certainly rather coarse: and there is not the slightest attempt at developing either plot, character, description, or polished dialogue in them. But there is a certain hearty joviality and occasionally a healthy sympathy in them, and they can rarely be called merely dull.

Now the versified portions of history, hagiology, or actual romance which seem to have undergone the process of versification at Master Deloney's hands merit no part of this praise and would be justly awarded some of the severest terms of abuse allowed in a respectable critic's vocabulary. One could hardly, before the experience, believe in the possibility of such stuff: and the only satisfaction that the acutest and hardest working student can get out of it is the discovery, if he has not previously discovered it, of the fact that metre— that is to say regularised rhythm—has a power of causing the reverse of delight which is beyond the reach of rhythm left free, that is to say prose, in its worst state.

One point which seems to me of some interest: and that is the relation of tale or novel, and drama which is so noteworthy in these Elizabethan stories. It may be said to be mere accident, but that I think is a superficial judgment. Everyone who has made any real study of literature generally must have come to the conclusion that the relations of the two kinds are rather complicated and also rather curious. They seldom flourish together: and though constant efforts have been made to make one a supply-tank for the other, these efforts have by no means been invariably successful. The two have much in common: but the points of community seem to require management and development in very different ways. Sometimes, as in this very Elizabethan case or vice versa in our own Victorian times—when we could write the best novels in the world and not a decent drama to save our lives—the current goes wholly on one side or the other: sometimes it mixes, but almost always there appears to be an odd difference between the kinds. At times when no special division of literature is at its healthiest condition and highest reach, but when the 'man of letters' is abundant, fairly trained and industrious, there may be a considerable joint production of both. France has been the chief scene of this joint mass-production of a rather mechanical product, and we seem to be trying at it ourselves now. But that is probably a mistake, or rather, as these things happen at the will of destiny, an evidence, perhaps not the only one, that England is not 'in pudding-time' as far as letters are concerned. On that, however, it is not necessary to say much. We have had pudding-times in plenty: fortunately they are capable of being gone back to when only bare bones or scraps appear in the contemporary menu, and we have not *quite* got to that yet.

GEORGE SAINTSBURY.

NOTES

THOMAS DELONEY

THE novels of Thomas Deloney represent the first consistent attempt in English literature at drawing material for fiction from the everyday life of ordinary people. They are the first step towards the novel as we know it to-day.

Unlike Greene and Nashe, Deloney belonged to no circle of 'university wits.' He was, for the greater part of his life, a silk-weaver at Norwich and a pedlar tramping the roads of East Anglia, famous for his ballads voicing the popular wrongs of the day after the manner of Elizabethan journalism, and when, at the end of his life, he turned his attention to more serious writing, he was concerned more with profitable story-telling than with the stylistic refinements of his contemporaries. For this reason his novels are more valuable to us to-day on account of the picture they give us of our ancestors living their normal lives and going about their daily work than are the moral and alliterative tales of Lyly's school, so popular with the cultured reading public of that time. But Deloney was not courting the favour of the 'Courteous and Courtly Ladyes of England,' and the 'Gentlemen Readers' like Lyly, Greene, and Sidney; his works are addressed to the 'Famous Clothworkers' and cobblers of England, a public whom the writers of Arcadian romances would have despised as 'base mechanicals.' Indeed, Nashe and Greene speak of him most disparagingly. In the former's *Have with you to Saffron Walden* we read of 'the balleting silke-weaver of Norwich,' and Greene refers to his 'trivial trinkets and threadbare trash.'

There is no evidence in Deloney's works that he was touched by the new learning of the Renaissance, and apart from a few incidents from Boccaccio, of whose origin he was probably unaware, his novels deal purely with the town and country life of old England, being written in a plain, unaffected style, yet at the same time reaching moments of a transparent lyrical beauty, and breathing always the natural atmosphere of everyday life. Unconsciously, he achieved a triumph of realism, his dramatic restraint and sureness of touch being unsurpassed by any other contemporary novelist. Although realism was not altogether disdained in this poetic age, as we can see from such jest-books as *Long Meg of Westminster*, the pamphlets and satirical tracts of Greene, Nashe, Dekker and notably in Riche's *Farewell to Militarie Profession* (1581), Deloney was the first writer to apply such methods to the novel. Yet he makes a few concessions to the popular taste of his time by introducing the romantic story of Duke Robert and the Fair Margaret into *Thomas of Reading*, and the story of Sir Hugh in *The Gentle Craft* is a knight-errantry romance of the usual kind. Like Nashe in *The Unfortunate Traveller*, he makes use of historical figures from Holinshed to lend a greater actuality to his story, utilising and inventing history as it suits his fancy, telling us in *Jack of Newbury*—which otherwise is made up entirely of local tradition and professional experience—how Henry VIII, Cardinal Wolsey, and their company with Will Summers, the jester, were entertained at the house of the famous weaver.

Beside Deloney's subtle sense of drama Nashe appears crude and melodramatic, and Shakespeare may well have been indebted to him for the scene of Old Cole's murder in *Thomas of Reading*—the most solidly constructed of Deloney's three novels—a scene that Swinburne in his *Age of Shakespeare* describes as 'worthy of Defoe at his very best.' But reading it we are still more forcibly reminded of *Macbeth*, where another host and hostess plot the murder of their guest and where strange premonitions of foul death haunt the night just as they do the mind of Old Cole before he lies down to sleep for the last time at the 'Crane Inn.' Local tradition at Colnbrook identifies this inn with that now known as 'The Ostrich,' and retells the story of the murder with almost the exact details of Deloney's narrative. Also the epitaph of John Winchcomb is to be seen at Newbury Church, where his memory is still cherished by the inhabitants.

A whole literature sprang up in the tradition that Deloney created. His novels went through many editions before 1600, and their popularity lasted all through the seventeenth century and survived in chap-book form during the eighteenth. But since that time they have been strangely neglected, their author having been, till now, repeatedly denied a place in the history of the English novel.

Born probably at Norwich. Silk-weaver. Published *A Declaration Made by the Archbishop of Collen* (i.e. Cologne) *upon the Deede of his Mariage*, etc. (translation), 1583; topical ballads (succeeded William Elderton as chief ballad-writer in 1592). Married and living in London, 1586. Perhaps married again, 1594. Itinerant ballad-monger, 1596. Collected his ballads in *A Garland of Good Will* (three parts), 1593–6, and *Strange Histories, Of Kings, Princes, Dukes, Earles, Lords, Ladies, Knights, and Gentlemen*, 1602 (earlier?). Published *The Pleasant Historie of John Winchcomb, in his Yonguer Yeares called Jack of Newbury* and *The Gentle Craft* (the first part), 1597; *The Gentle Craft* (the second part), 1598; and *Thomas of Reading*, 1600. Died, 1600. *Canaan's Calamitie*, 1618. *A Batchelars Banquet* (translation), 1598 or 1599 (1603), may be his.

Jack of Newbury reprinted 1859, 1904 (in Germany), 1912, 1920, 1929, 1953.

Thomas of Reading reprinted 1622 (4th ed.), 1632 (6th ed.), 1828, 1912, 1920, 1929, etc.

Works, ed. F. O. Mann, 1912.

ROBERT GREENE

'*Greene's Carde of Fancie*, wherein the Folly of those carpet knights is deciphered, which guiding their course by the compass of Cupid, either dash their ship against most dangerous Rocks, or else attain the haven with pain and peril,' was Greene's third novel, entered in the 'Stationers' Register' 11 April 1584 and published in the same year. It is probable that Greene borrowed the plot from the Italian novelists, but an indication of the spirit of the work is set forth on the original title-page, where lounging cupids are to be seen playing on lutes, hautboys, and serpents among sections of heroic architecture and growths of palms, apples, and counterfeit fruit. For in his 'love-pamphlets,' Greene was above all things, musical and gracefully euphuistic, so much so that some critics have said his fame rests chiefly in the lyrics scattered through these romances. This, perhaps, is rather unjust, unless these critics are unwilling to allow the Elizabethan reader his share of literary taste—a strange deficiency in the greatest age of our literature—for at that time moralistic romances like Lyly's *Euphues* and Greene's *Card of Fancy* were absolutely the craze of the more cultured reading public who turned away from reality with a poetic scorn and lost themselves among improbable adventures in Egypt, Greece, or Bohemia. As Greene tells us in *A Groat's Worth of Wit*, the penning of love-pamphlets had brought him much fame—'who for that

trade,' he says, 'was so ordinarie about town as Robin Greene?'
and in truth he soon earned the reputation of the 'Homer of
Women.' In fact, the idealisation of women who, then, as
now, were by far the greater reading public, was the secret
of his success. Developing the theme of romantic love, his
heroines recall those of Shakespeare's early period and there
is no doubt that *The Two Gentlemen of Verona* was written
under Greene's influence. In spite of their strange rhetorical
gesticulations, on the whole we feel his characters more than
we do those of Nashe, and Castania's lament in prison is
genuinely moving, although 'Floods of tears . . . fell from
her crystal eyes.' At times her wailing rises to a kind of
humorous sublimity: 'Nay, what creature ever was clogged
with the like calamitie? Have the spiteful destinies decreed
my destruction, or ye perverse planets conspired my bitter
bane?' But although the alliteration is as heavy as Lyly's,
and the similes from natural history as abundant, there runs
through Greene's work a much lighter spirit, and there is
a lyricism not present in *Euphues*. Indeed, the truth is contrary to fashionable criticism, for Greene's prose is not at all
unreadable to modern minds, but on the contrary, for those
with an ear for sheer musical writing and a sense of humour,
it is nearly always delightful. And to say that it is bad
because modern authors do not write in this way, or that
those great ones of the seventeenth century did not, is no
more criticism than condemning the elaborate polyphony
of Byrd or Gibbons because they have not Purcell's simple
clarity. There was a luxurious exuberance in Greene's mind
as there was in other Elizabethans, and he was an extremely
rapid writer: 'in a night and a day would he have yarked up a
pamphlet as well as in a seven year,' says Nashe, 'and glad
was that printer that might be so blest to pay him dear for the
very dregs of his wit.' In his later novels Greene exhibits a
more natural restraint, as in the graceful tragedy of *Pandosto*.
If he was sometimes a little trite in his moralising generalisa-
tions it was the fault of his age; when, in courtly circles, such
sentiments were on everybody's lips. Greene exalts virtue in
his novels to such heights because he knew from experience the
misery of the reverse of virtue; and that clearness of conscience, that he denied himself in life he was able to enjoy to
the full in his writings, usually beginning with a moral on the
title-page.

Reading his novels there would be an excuse for thinking

Greene as far out of touch with real life as any writer of fairy tales, but that this was not the case is shown by his coney-catching pamphlets and Repentances that command a powerful realism and a close observation of life. In fact, these writings were so faithful in their portrayal of the vices of low life that they very nearly occasioned their author's assassination at the hands of the thieves and pickpockets whose tricks they exposed.

But in drama Greene was not so successful. He set himself to rival Marlowe, pitting his *Alphonsus* and *Friar Bacon* against the latter's *Tamburlaine* and *Dr. Faustus*. But although he failed in this intended triumph his development of the current dramatic forms prepared the way for Shakespeare by contributing with Lyly, Peele, and Kyd a greater flexibility to the form of comedy than it had possessed while following the classic models of Plautus and Terence.

He had many followers and imitators and while his death was still the latest sensation of the literary world, many 'feigned repentances' appeared. His most significant followers, however, were the novelists Nicholas Breton and Emanuel Ford.

Born 1558 at Norwich. Matriculated as sizar at Corpus Christi College, Cambridge, 1573; at St John's, 1575. B.A. 1580. Travelled in Italy, Spain, France, Germany, Poland, and Denmark. Returned to England and Cambridge. M.A. 1583. Published *Mamillia*, 1583; *Arbasto, Greenes Carde of Fancie, Morando*, and *The Mirrour of Modesty*, 1584; *Planetomachia*, 1585. Married in Norwich, but deserted his wife after she had borne him a son. Loose life in London. *Euphues his Censure to Philautus* and *Penelopes Web*, 1587; *Alcida, Pandosto*, and *Perimedes the Blacksmith*, 1588. Incorporated M.A. at Oxford, 1588. *Ciceronis Amor, Menaphon*, and *The Spanish Masquerado*, 1589; *Greenes Never Too Late, Franciscos Fortunes, or The Second Part of Greenes Never Too Late*, and *Greenes Mourning Garment*, 1590; *Greenes Farewell to Folly, A Maydens Dream*, and *A Notable Discovery of Coosnage* (*The Art of Conny-Catching*), 1591; *The Second Part of Conny-Catching, The Thirde and Last Part of Conny-Catching*, and *A Disputation betweene a Hee Conny-Catcher and a Shee Conny-Catcher, The Blacke Bookes Messenger, Philomela*, and *A Quip for an Upstart Courtier*, 1592. Died 3 September 1592. Posthumously published: *Greenes Vision, Greenes Groats-worth of Witte, Bought with a Million of Repentance*, and *The Repentance of Robert Greene*, 1592; *Mamillia: The Second Part of the Triumph of Pallas*, 1593; *The Historie of Orlando Furioso, A Looking-Glass for London and England* (with Lodge), *The Honorable Historie of Frier Bacon, and Frier Bongay*, 1594; *The Scottish Historie of James the Fourth, Slain at Flodden*, 1598; *The Comicall Historie of Alphonsus, King of Aragon*, 1599 (five plays); *Greenes Orpharion*, 1599.

Works ascribed to Greene: *The First Part of the Tragicall Raigne of Selimus*, 1594; *A Pleasant Conceyted Comedie of George a Greene, the Pinner of Wakefield*, 1599; *John of Bordeaux, or The Second Part of Friar Bacon*, (MS, ? 1590).

The Life and Complete Works in Prose and Verse, ed. A. B. Grosart, 15 vols., 1881–6.

THOMAS NASHE

The Unfortunate Traveller or The Life of Jack Wilton was published in 1594, when Nashe was twenty-seven years of age. It represents his single adventure into the novel form and has the double distinction of being his most ambitious piece of work and the first picaresque novel in the tradition of Lazarillo de Tormes to appear in the English language. Written with that good-humoured truculence which is Nashe's most attractive quality and so much the spirit of his age, it at once gained popularity, fulfilling the Elizabethan stay-at-home's appetite for foreign adventure, bloodshed, and perilous amours, and a second impression was published before the end of the year. Like the novels of Deloney, it is partly founded on actual experience and makes use of an historical background from Lanquet, Sleidan, and Holinshed, introducing the Earl of Surrey and well-known figures of Henry VIII's period. But unlike most other picaresque writers, Nashe understood that life was not all rollicking merriment, and he combines practical jokes and lurid horror with long passages of an ingenious lyrical beauty. At the beginning we are introduced to the Falstaffian figure of the cider-merchant, allowed a glimpse of 'Arabian spiceries of sweet passions' and towards the end caught up in the growing conflagration of tragedy and melodrama.

The Unfortunate Traveller, its author tells us, is 'in a clean different vaine from other my former courses of writing,' and up till the time of its appearance Nashe was regarded as a kind of 'young Juvenal,' chastising the follies and vices of his age with a lash of scorpions and carrying in his pen, as Dekker says, 'the deadly stockado' and 'all the furies of Hercules.' But his literary style, as he justly claims, is entirely his own, being careful to defend himself against the influence of Lyly and Greene. 'Did I talk of counterfeit birds, or herbs or stones?' he asks in *Strange News*. 'This I will proudly boast . . . that the vaine which I have is of my own begetting and calls no man father in England but myself.' And indeed his works have the freshness of the adolescent English in which they are written and all the gorgeousness of the Renaissance, his images often being as hyperbolically extravagant as the fardingales and monstrous ruffles of his age. In the piling up of synonymous words into a final burst of rhetoric he resembles Rabelais and Robert Burton, and Aretine with the Italianate endings of his verbs. Yet for all that, Nashe had a peculiar dislike of bombast. He ridicules it, in spite of his own early euphuistic *Anatomy of Absurdity*, in the preface to Greene's *Menaphon*, making Kyd, it is supposed, the butt of his satire and even censuring Marlowe for 'embowelling the clouds in a speach of comparison.' He excuses himself for the *Anatomy of Absurdity* by suggesting that it belongs to a time when he was 'a little ape at Cambridge,' and it is possible that the greater restraint exhibited in *The Unfortunate Traveller* is, to a large extent, due to his study of the Scriptures before the composition of *Christ's Tears over Jerusalem* which was published in the preceding year to his novel.

Nashe's power as a picaresque writer lies mainly in the living, actual quality of his prose that, for vigour, is often equal to Shakespeare's. But he was also capable of vivid characterisation and possessed a powerful sense of melodrama which enabled him to write such a scene as Cutwolfe's revenge and subsequent torture that ranks among the most moving passages in all Elizabethan prose. At the same time he was, for a novelist of character, unforgivably biased towards his creations, and, as a plain story-teller, he has the supreme defect of sometimes interrupting his narrative with long irrelevant moral discourses. Moreover, his novel is really only a collection of tales and events that owe their unity merely to the fact that they occur within the experience of one person. In spite of that, *The Unfortunate Traveller* has an appearance of continuity, due more, it is true, to the welding fire of the style than to the development of the subject matter. It is generally admitted to be the best specimen of the picaresque tale anterior to Defoe, its tradition being carried on in the work of Fielding and Smollett.

PHILIP HENDERSON.

Born at Lowestoft, 1567. Matriculated as sizar at St John's College, Cambridge, 1582; afterwards a scholar. Graduated B.A., 1586. Mainly in London from 1588. *Flytings* with Thomas Churchyard

and with Gabriel and Richard Harvey. Engaged in the Martin
Mar-Prelate controversy. Published a Preface to Greene's *Menaphon*, and *The Anatomie of Absurditie*, 1589; *An Almond for a Parrat*,
1590; a Preface to Sidney's *Astrophel and Stella*, 1591; *Pierce Peni-
lesse his Supplication to the Divell*, 1592; *Strange News, of the Inter-
cepting Certaine Letters*, and *Christs Teares over Jerusalem*, 1593;
*The Terrors of the Night, The Unfortunate Traveller, or, The Life of
Jacke Wilton*, and *The Tragedie of Dido Queene of Carthage* (with
Marlowe), 1594; *Have With you to Saffron-Waldon*, 1596. Part-
author of *The Isle of Dogs* (satirical play, lost), 1597. Fled to Yar-
mouth to escape prosecution. *The Barbers Warming Pan*, 1598
(not published?). *Nashes Lenten Stuff, the Praise of the Red Herring*,
1599. Books suppressed. *A Pleasant Comedie, Called Summers
Last Will and Testament*, 1600. *The Choise of Valentines* (poem,
MS). Died *circa* 1600.

The Unfortunate Traveller reprinted 1594, 1892, 1926, 1927, 1929,
1953, etc.

Works, ed. R. B. McKerrow, 5 vols., 1904–10.

For this edition a revision of the preliminary material
has been made by R. G. Howarth, B.A., B.Litt., F.R.S.L.,
Professor of English Literature in the University of Cape
Town.

CONTENTS

SHORTER NOVELS : ELIZABETHAN

The pleasant Historie

OF

IOHN WINCHCOMB,

In his yonguer yeares called

IACK of NEWBERY,

The famous and worthy Clothier of
England; declaring his life and loue,
together with his charitable deeds
and great Hospitalitie.

And how hee set continually fiue hundred poore
people at worke, to the great benefite of
the Common-wealth.

Now the tenth time Imprinted, corrected and enlarged
by *T. D.*

Haud curo invidiam.

LONDON,
Printed by H LOWNES, and are to be sold by *Cuthbert
Wright* in S. *Bartholomews*, neer the entrance
into the Hospital. 1626.

To all Famous Clothworkers in England, I wish all happiness of life, prosperity, and *brotherly affection.*

AMONG all manuall Arts used in this Land, none is more famous for desert, or more beneficiall to the Commonwealth, than is the most necessary Art of Clothing. And therefore as the benefite there of is great, so are the professors of the same to be both loved and maintained. Many wise men therefore, having deeply considered the same, most bountifully have bestowed their gifts for upholding of so excellent a commoditie, which hath been, and yet is, the nourishing of many thousands of poor people. Wherefore to you, most worthy Clothiers, do I dedicate this my rude worke, which hath raised out of the dust of forgetfulnesse a most famous and worthy man, whose name was *John Winchcombe,* alias *Jack* of *Newberie,* of whose life and love I have briefely written, and in a plaine and humble manner, that it may be the better understood of those for whose sake I took pains to compile it, that is, for the well minded Clothiers; that heerein they may behold the great worship and credit which men of this trade have in former time come unto. If therefore it bee of you kindly accepted, I have the end of my desire, and think my paines well recompenced: and finding your gentlenesse answering my hope, it shall move mee shortly to set to your sight the long hidden History of *Thomas* of *Redding, George* of *Glocester, Richard* of *Worcester,* and *William* of *Salisbury,* with divers others; who were all most notable members in the Commonwealth of this Land, and men of great fame and dignity. In the meane space, I commend you all to the most high God, who ever increase, in all perfection and prosperous estate, the long honoured trade of English-Clothiers.

Yours in all humble service,

T. D.

THE MOST PLEASANT AND DELECTABLE HISTORIE OF JOHN WINCHCOMBE

Otherwise called *Jacke* of *Newberie:* and first of his love and *pleasant life.*

CHAPTER I

In the daies of King *Henrie* the eight, that most noble and victorious Prince, in the beginning of his reigne, *John Winchcomb*, a broad cloth Weaver, dwelt in *Newberie*, a towne in *Barkshire*: who for that he was a man of a merry disposition, and honest conversation, was wondrous wel-beloved of Rich and Poore, specially, because in every place where hee came, hee would spend his money with the best, and was not at any time found a churle of his purse. Wherefore being so good a companion, hee was called of old and yongue *Jacke* of *Newberie*: a man so generally well knowne in all his countrey for his good fellowship, that hee could goe in no place but he found acquaintance; by meanes whereof, *Jacke* could no sooner get a Crowne, but straight hee found meanes to spend it: yet had hee ever this care, that hee would alwaies keepe himselfe in comely and decent apparell: neyther at any time would hee bee overcome in drinke, but so discreetly behave himselfe with honest mirth, and pleasant conceits, that he was every Gentlemans companion.

After that *Jack* had long led this pleasant life, beeing (though he were but poore) in good estimation: it was his Masters chance to dye, and his Dame to be a widow, who was a very comely ancient woman, and of reasonable wealth. Wherefore she, having a good opinion of her man *John*, committed unto his governement the guiding of all her worke-folkes for the space of three yeares together: In which time shee found him so carefull and diligent, that all things came forward and prospered woundrous well. No man could entice him from his businesse all the weeke, by all the intreaty they could use: Insomuch that in the end some of the wild youths of the town began to deride and scoffe at him.

Doubtlesse (quoth one) I thinke some female spirit hath inchaunted *Jacke* to his treadles, and conjured him within the compasse of his Loome, that he can stirre no further.

You say true (quoth *Jacke*) and if you have the leasure to stay till the Charme be done, the space of sixe dayes and five nights, you shall finde me ready to put on my holy-day-apparell, and on Sunday morning for your paines I will give you a pot of Ale over against the Maypole.

Nay (quoth another) Ile lay my life, that as the Salamander cannot live without the fire, so *Jack* cannot live without the smel of his Dames smock.

And I marvell (quoth *Jacke*) that you being of the nature of a Herring (which so soon as he is taken out of the Sea, presently dyes) can live so long with your nose out of the pot.

Nay *Jacke*, leave thy jesting (quoth another) and goe along with us, thou shalt not stay a jot.

And because I will not stay; nor make you a lyer (quoth *Jacke*) Ile keep me here still: and so farewell.

Thus then they departed: and after they had for halfe a score times tryed him to this intent, and saw he would not bee ledde by their lure, they left him to his owne will. Neverthelesse, every Sunday in the afternoone, and every Holy-day, *Jacke* would keep them company, and be as merry as a Pye, and having still good store of money in his purse, one or other would ever be borrowing of him, but never could he get pennie of it againe: which when *Jacke* perceived, he would never after carry above twelve pence at once in his purse: and that being spent, he would straight returne home merrily, taking his leave of the company in this sort.

> My masters, I thanke you, its time to packe home,
> For he that wants money is counted a mome:
> And twelve pence a Sunday being spent in good cheare
> To fifty two shillings amounts in the yeare;
> Enough for a Crafts-man that lives by his hands:
> And he that exceeds it, shall purchase no lands.
> For that I spend this day, Ile work hard to morrow.
> For woe is that partie that seeketh to borrow.
> My money doth make me full merry to be;
> And without my money none careth for me:
> Therefore wanting money, what should I doe heere?
> But hast home, and thanke you for all my good cheere?

Thus was *Jackes* good governement and discretion noted of the best and substantiallest men of the Towne: so that it wrought his great commendations, and his Dame thought her selfe not a little blest to have such a servant, that was so obedient unto

her, and so carefull for her profite: for shee had never a Prentise
that yeelded her more obedience than he did, or was more
dutifull: so that by his good example, hee did as much good as
by his diligent labour and painfull travel: which his singular
vertue being noted by the widow, shee beganne to cast a very
good countenance to her man *John*, and to use very much talk
with him in private: and first by way of communication, she
would tell unto him what suters she had, as also the great offers
they made her, what gifts they sent her, and the great affection
they bare her, craving his opinion in the matter.

When *Jacke* found the favour to be his Dames Secretarie, he
thought it an extraordinary kindnesse: and ghessing by the
yarne it would prove a good web, beganne to question with his
dame in this sort. Although it becommeth not mee your
servant to pry into your secrets, nor to bee busie about matters
of your love: yet for so much as it hath pleased you to use conference with me in those causes, I pray you let me intreat you
to know their names that be your sutors, and of what profession
they be.

Marry *John* (sayth she) that you shall, and I pray thee take
a cushion and sit downe by me.

Dame (quoth he) I thanke you: but there is no reason I should
sit on a cushion till I have deserved it.

If thou hast not thou mightest have done (said she): but some
Souldiers never finde favour.

John replied, that maketh me indeed to want favour: for
I never durst try maydens because they seeme coy, nor wives
for feare of their husbands, nor widowes doubting their
disdainfulnes.

Tush *John* (quoth she) he that feares and doubts womankinde, cannot be counted mankinde: and take this for a principle,
All things are not as they seeme. But let us leave this, and
proceed to our former matter. My first sutor dwels at *Wallingford*, by trade a Tanner, a man of good wealth, and his name is
Crafts, of comely personage and very good behaviour, a widower,
wel thought of among his neighbours: he hath proper land, a
faire house well furnished, and never a childe in the world, and
hee loves me passing well.

Why then Dame (quoth *John*) you were best to have him.

Is that your opinion (quoth shee)? now trust mee, so it is not
mine: for I finde two speciall reasons to the contrary: the one
is, that he being overworne in yeares, makes me overloth to
love him: and the other, that I know one neerer hand.

Beleeve me dame (quoth *Jack*) I perceive store is no sore, and proffered ware is worse by ten in the hundred than that which is sought: but I pray who is your second sutor?

John (quoth she) it may seeme immodesty in me to bewray my lovers secrets: yet seeing thy discretion, and being perswaded of thy secrecy, I will shew thee: the other is a man of middle yeares, but yet a Batchellor, by occupation a Taylor, and dwelling at *Hungerford*: by report a very good husband, such a one as hath crownes good store, and to mee he professes much good will: for his person, he may please any woman.

I dame (quoth *John*) because he pleaseth you.

Not so (said she) for my eyes are unpartiall Judges in that case: and albeit my opinion may be contrary to others, if his Art deceive not my eye-sight, hee is worthy of a good wife, both for his person and conditions.

Then trust mee Dame (quoth *John*) for so much as you are without doubt of your selfe that you will prove a good wife, and so well perswaded of him, I should thinke you could make no better a choice.

Truly *John* (quoth shee) there be also two reasons that move mee not to like of him: the one, that being so large a ranger, he would at home be a stranger: and the other, that I like better of one neerer hand.

Who is that (quoth *Jacke*)?

(Saith she) the third Suter is the Parson of *Spinhom-land*, who hath a proper living, he is of holy conversation and good estimation, whose affection to me is great.

No doubt Dame (quoth *John*) you may doe wondrous well with him, where you shall have no care but to serve GOD, and to make ready his meate.

O *John* (quoth she) the flesh and the spirit agrees not: for he will bee so bent to his booke, that he will have little minde of his bed: for one moneths studying for a Sermon, will make him forget his wife a whole yeare.

Truly Dame (quoth *John*) I must needs speak in his behalfe and the rather, for that he is a man of the Church, and your neere neighbour, to whom (as I guesse) you beare the best affection: I doe not thinke that he will bee so much bound to his booke, or subject to the spirit, but that he will remember a woman at home or abroad.

Well *John* (quoth she) I wis my minde is not that way: for I like better of one neerer hand.

No marvell (quoth *Jacke*) you are so peremptory, seeing you have so much choice: but I pray ye Dame (quoth he) let me know this fortunate man that is so highly placed in your favour?

John (quoth shee) they are worthy to know nothing, that cannot keepe something: that man (I tell thee) must goe namelesse: for he is Lord of my love, and King of my desires: there is neyther Tanner, Taylor, nor Parson may compare with him, his presence is a preservative to my health, his sweete smiles my hearts solace, and his words heavenly musicke to my eares.

Why then Dame (quoth *John*) for your bodies health, your hearts joy, and your eares delight, delay not the time, but entertaine him with a kisse, make his bed next yours, and chop up the match in the morning.

Well (quoth shee) I perceive thy consent is quickly got to any, having no care how I am matcht so I be matcht: I wis, I wis I could not let thee goe so lightly, being loth that any one should have thee, except I could love her as well as my selfe.

I thanke you for your kindnesse and good will, good Dame (quoth hee) but it is not wisedome for a yongue man that can scantly keepe himselfe, to take a wife: therefore I hold it the best way to leade a single life: for I have heard say, that many sorrowes follow marriage, especially where want remaines: and beside, it is a hard matter to finde a constant woman: for as yongue maides are fickle, so are old women jealous: the one a griefe too common, the other a torment intolerable.

What *John* (quoth she) consider that maidens ficklenesse proceedes of vaine fancies, but old womens jealousie of superabounding love: and therefore the more to bee borne withall.

But Dame (quoth hee) many are jealous without cause: for is it sufficient for their mistrusting natures to take exceptions at a shadow, at a word, at a looke, at a smile, nay at the twinkle of an eye, which neither man nor woman is able to expell? I knew a woman that was ready to hang her selfe, for seeing but her husbands shirt hang on a hedge with her maides smocke.

I grant that this fury may haunt some (quoth shee) yet there bee many other that complaine not without great cause.

Why, is there any cause that should move jealousie (quoth *John*)?

I by *S. Mary* is there (quoth she): for would it not grieve a woman (being one every way able to delight her husband) to see him forsake her, despise and contemne her, being never so merry as when he is in other company, sporting abroad from morning till noone, from noone till night, and when he comes to bed, if hee turnes to his wife, it is in such solemnesse, and wearisome drowsie lamenesse, that it brings rather lothsomnesse than any delight? can you then blame a woman in this case to be angry and displeased? Ile tell you what, among brute beasts it is a griefe intolerable: for I heard my Grandame tell, that the Bel-weather of her flocke fancying one of the Eawes above the rest, and seeing *Gratis* the Sheepheard abusing her in abominable sort (subverting the law of Nature) could by no meanes beare that abuse; but watching opportunity for revenge, on a time found the said Shepheard sleeping in the field, and suddenly ranne against him in such violent sort, that by the force of his wreathen hornes, he beat the braines out of the Shepheards head and slew him. If then a Sheepe could not endure that injury, thinke not that women are so sheepish to suffer it.

Beleeve mee (quoth *John*) if every horne-maker should be so plagued by a horned beast, there should bee lesse hornes made in *Newbery* by many in a yeare. But Dame (quoth hee) to make an end of this prattle, because it is an argument too deepe to be discussed between you and I, you shall heare me sing an old song, and so we will depart to supper.

> A maiden faire I dare not wed,
> For feare to have *Acteons* head.
> A maiden blacke is often proude:
> A maiden little will be loud.
> A maiden that is high of growth,
> They say is subject unto sloath.
> Thus faire or foule, little or tall,
> Some faults remaine among them all:
> But of all the faults that be,
> None is so bad as jealousie.
> For jealousie is fierce and fell,
> And burnes as hot as fire in hell:
> It breedes suspicion without cause,
> And breakes the bonds of reasons lawes.
> To none it is a greater foe,
> Than unto those where it doth grow.
> And God keepe me both day and night,
> From that fell, fond and ougly spright:
> For why? of all the plagues that be,
> The secret plague is jealousie.
> Therefore I wish all women kinde,
> Never to beare a jealous minde.

Well said *John* (quoth she) thy song is not so sure, but thy voice is as sweete: but seeing the time agrees with our stomackes, though loth, yet will we give over for this time, and betake our selves to our suppers. Then calling the rest of her servants, they fell to their meate merrily, and after supper, the Goodwife went abroad for her recreation, to walke a while with one of her neighbours.   And in the meane space *John* got him up into his chamber, and there began to meditate on this matter, be-thinking with himselfe what hee were best to doe: for well hee perceived that his Dames affection was great towards him: knowing therefore the womans disposition, and withall, that her estate was reasonable good, and considering beside, that he should finde a house ready furnished, servants ready taught, and all other things for his trade necessary, hee thought it best not to let slip that good occasion, lest he should never come to the like.   But againe, when hee considered her yeares to be unfitting to his youth, and that she that sometime had been his Dame, would (perhaps) disdaine to bee governed by him that had been her poore servant, and that it would proove but a bad bargaine, doubting many inconveniencies that might grow thereby, hee therefore resolved to be silent, rather than to proceed further: wherefore he got him straight to bed, and the next morning settled himselfe close to his businesse.

His Dame comming home, and hearing that her man was gone to bed, tooke that night but small rest, and early in the morning hearing him up at his worke, merrily singing, shee by and by arose, and in seemely sort attyring her selfe, shee came into the workeshop, and sate her downe to make quills.

(Quoth *John*) Good morrow Dame, how doe you to day?

God a mercy *John* (quoth shee) even as well as I may: for I was sore troubled in my Dreames.   Mee thought two Doves walked together in a corne field, the one (as it were) in com-munication with the other, without regard of picking up any thing to sustaine themselves: and after they had with many nods spent some time to their content, they both fell hard with their prety bills to pecke up the scattered corne, left by the weary Reapers hand.   At length (finding themselves satisfied) it chanced another Pigion to light in that place, with whom, one of the first Pigions at length kept company: and after returning to the place where she left her first companion, per-ceived hee was not there: shee kindely searching up and downe the high stubble to finde him, lights at length on a Hogge fast asleepe, wherewith mee thought, the poore dove was so dismaid, that presently shee fell downe in a trance.   I seeing her legges faile, and her wings quiver, yeelding her selfe to death, moved with pity ranne unto her, and thinking to take up the Pigion, mee thought, I had in my hands my owne heart, wherein mee thought an arrow stucke so deep, that the bloud trickled downe the shaft, and lay upon the feathers like the silver

pearled deaw on the greene grasse, which made me to weepe
most bitterly. But presently, mee thought there came one to
mee crowned like a Queene, who told me my heart would dye
in time, except I got some of that sleeping Hogs grease to
heale the wounds thereof. Whereupon I ranne in all haste to
the Hog with my heart bleeding in my hand, who (mee thought)
grunted at mee in most churlish sort, and vanisht out of my
sight. Whereupon comming straite home, mee thought, I
found this Hog rustling among the Loomes, wherewith I presently
awaked, sodainely after midnight, being all in a sweate and
very ill: and I am sure you could not choose but heare mee
groane.

Trust mee Dame, I heard you not (quoth *John*) I was so sound
asleepe.

And thus (quoth shee) a woman may dye in the night before
you will have the care to see what she ailes, or aske what she
lackes. But truly *John* (quoth she) all is one: for if thou
shouldest have come, thou couldest not have got in, because
my chamber door was lockt: but while I live this shall teach
mee wit: for henceforth I will have no other locke but a latch,
till I am married.

Then Dame (quoth he) I perceive though you be curious in
your choice, yet at length you will marry.

I truely (quoth shee) so thou wilt not hinder me.

Who I (quoth *John*)? on my faith Dame, not for a hundred
pounds, but rather will further you to the uttermost of my
power.

Indeede (quoth shee) thou hast no reason to shew any dis-
courtesie to me in that matter, although some of our neighbours
do not stick to say, that I am sure to thee already.

If it were so (quoth *John*) there is no cause to deny it, or to bee
ashamed thereof, knowing my selfe farre unworthy of so high
a favour.

Well, let this talk rest (quoth shee) and take there thy quils,
for it is time for mee to goe to market.

Thus the matter rested for two or three dayes, in which space
shee daily devised which way shee might obtaine her desire,
which was to marry her man. Many things came in her head,
and sundry sleights in her minde, but none of them did fit her
fancy, so that she became wondrous sad, and as civill as the nine
Sibbels; and in this melancholy humour continued three weekes
or a moneth, till at last it was her lucke upon a *Bartholomew*
day (having a Fayre in the towne) to spie her man *John* give a

paire of Gloves to a proper maide for a Fayring, which the maiden with a bashfull modesty kindly accepted, and requited it with a kisse: which kindled in her an inward jealousie: but notwithstanding very discreetly shee covered it, and closely past along unspied of her man or the maid.

Shee had not gone farre, but she met with one of her sutors, namely the Taylor, who was very fine and briske in his apparell, and needes hee would bestow the wine upon the Widow: and after some faint deniall, meeting with a Gossip of hers, to the Taverne they went, which was more courtesie than the Taylor could ever get of her before, shewing her selfe very pleasant and merry; and finding her in such a pleasing humour, the Taylor after a new quart of wine, renewed his old sute: the Widow with patience heard him, and gently answered, that in respect of his great good will long time borne unto her, as also in regard of his gentlenesse, cost, and curtesie at that present bestowed, she would not flatly deny him. Therefore (quoth shee) seeing this is not a place to conclude of such matters, if I may intreate you to come to my poore house on thursday next, you shall be heartily welcome, and be further satisfied of my minde: and thus preferred to a touch of her lips, hee payed the shot and departed.

The Taylor was scant out of sight, when she met with the Tanner: who albeit he was aged, yet lustily hee saluted her, and to the wine she must, there was no nay. The Widow seeing his importunacy, calls her gossip, and along they walked together. The old man called for wine plenty, and the best cheere in the house: and in an hearty manner hee bids the Widow welcome. They had not sitten long, but in comes a noise of Musitians in tawny coates, who (putting off their caps) asked if they would have any musicke. The Widow answered no, they were merry enough.

Tut (quoth the old man) let us heare good fellowes what you can doe, and play mee *The beginning of the World*.

Alas (quoth the widow) you had more need to hearken to the ending of the world.

Why Widow (quoth hee) I tell thee the beginning of the world was the begetting of Children: and if you finde mee faulty in that occupation, turne mee out of thy bed for a bungler, and then send for the Sexton.

Hee had no sooner spoken the word, but the Parson of *Speen* with his corner cap, popt in at the doore, who seeing the Widow sitting at the table, craved pardon, and came in.

(Quoth shee) for want of the Sexton, heere is the Priest if you need him.

Marry (quoth the Tanner) in good time, for by this meanes wee neede not goe farre to be married.

Sir (quoth the Parson) I shall doe my best in convenient place.

Wherein (quoth the Tanner)?

To wed her my selfe (quoth the Parson).

Nay soft (said the Widow) one Swallow makes not a Summer, nor one meeting a marriage: as I lighted on you unlookt for, so came I hither unprovided for the purpose.

I trust (quoth the Tanner) you came not without your eyes to see, your tongue to speake, your eares to heare, your hands to feele, nor your legs to goe.

I brought my eyes (quoth she) to discerne colours, my tongue to say No to questions I like not, my hands to thrust from mee the things that I love not, my eares to judge twixt flattery and friendship, and my feet to run from such as would wrong mee.

Why then (quoth the Parson) by your gentle abiding in this place, it is evident that here are none but those you like and love.

God forbid I should hate my friends (quoth the widow) whom I take all these in this place to bee.

But there bee divers sorts of loves (quoth the Parson).

You say truth (quoth the Widow): I love your selfe for your profession, and my friend the Tanner, for his curtesie and kindnesse, and the rest for their good company.

Yet (quoth the Parson) for the explaining of your love, I pray you drinke to them you love best in the company.

Why (quoth the Tanner) have you any hope in her love?

Beleeve me (saith the Parson), as much as another.

Why then Parson sit downe (said the Tanner): for you that are equall with mee in desire, shall surely be halfe with mee in the shotte: and so Widow, on Gods name fulfill the Parsons request.

Seeing (quoth the Widow) you are so pleasantly bent, if my courtesie might not breede contention between you, and that I may have your favour to shew my fancy, I will fulfill your request.

(Quoth the Parson) I am pleased howsoever it bee.

And I (quoth the Tanner).

Why then (quoth shee) with this cup of Claret wine and Sugar, I heartily drinke to the Minstrels boy.

Why, is it he you love best (quoth the Parson)?

I have reason (said shee) to like and love them best, that will bee least offended with my doings.

Nay, Widow (quoth they) wee meant you should drinke to him whom you loved best in the way of marriage.

(Quoth the Widow) you should have said so at first: but to tell you my opinion, it is small discretion for a woman to disclose her secret affection in an open assembly: therefore, if to that purpose you spake, let mee intreat you both to come home to my house on Thursday next, where you shall bee heartily welcome, and there be fully resolved of my minde: and so, with thankes at this time, Ile take my leave.

The shot being paid, and the Musitians pleased, they all departed, the Tanner to *Wallingford*, the Parson to *Speen*, and the widow to her own house: where in her wonted solemnes shee settled her selfe to her businesse.

Against Thursday shee drest her house fine and brave, and set her selfe in her best apparell: the Taylor nothing forgetting his promise, sent to the Widow a good fat Pigge, and a Goose. The Parson being as mindfull as hee, sent to her house a couple of fat Rabbets and a Capon: and the Tanner came himselfe, and brought a good shoulder of Mutton, and halfe a dozen Chickens, beside hee brought a good gallon of Sacke, and halfe a pound of the best Sugar. The Widow receiving this good meate, set her maide to dresse it incontinent, and when dinner time drew neere, the Table was covered, and every other thing provided in convenient and comely sort.

At length the guests being come, the Widow bade them all heartily welcome. The Priest and the Tanner seeing the Taylor, mused what hee made there: the Taylor on the other side, marvelled as much at their presence. Thus looking strangely one at another, at length the Widow came out of the Kitchen, in a faire traine gowne stucke full of silver pinnes, a fine white Cap on her head, with cuts of curious needle worke under the same, and an Apron before her as white as the driven snow: then very modestly making curtsie to them all, she requested them to sit downe. But they straining courtesie the one with the other, the Widow with a smiling countenance tooke the Parson by the hand, saying, Sir, as you stand highest in the Church, so it is meete you should sit highest at the Table: and therefore I pray you sit downe there on the bench side. And Sir (said shee to the Tanner) as age is to bee honoured before youth for their experience, so are they to sit above Bachelers for their gravity: and so shee set him downe on this side the

Table, over against the Parson. Then comming to the Taylor,
she said, Batcheler, though your lot bee the last, your welcome
is equall with the first, and seeing your place points out it selfe,
I pray you take a cushion and sit downe. And now (quoth she)
to make the boord equall, and because it hath been an old saying,
that three things are to small purpose, if the fourth be away:
if so it may stand with your favour, I will call in a Gossip of
mine to supply this voide place.

With a good will (quoth they).

With that shee brought in an old woman with scant ever a
good tooth in her head, and placed her right against the Batcheler. Then was the meate brought to the boord in due order
by the Widowes servants, her man *John* being chiefest servitor.
The Widow sate downe at the Tables end, betweene the Parson
and the Tanner, who in very good sort carved meate for them
all, her man *John* waiting on the Table.

After they had sitten awhile, and well refreshed themselves,
the Widow, taking a Chrystal glasse fild with Claret Wine,
drunke unto the whole company, and bade them welcome.
The Parson pledged her, and so did all the rest in due order:
but still in their drinking, the cup past over the poore old
womans Nose; insomuch that at length the old woman (in a
merry vaine) spake thus unto the company: I have had much
good meate among you, but as for the drinke I can nothing
commend it.

Alas, good Gossip (quoth the Widow) I perceive no man hath
drunke to thee yet.

No truly (quoth the old woman): for Churchmen have so
much minde of yongue Rabbets, old men such joy in young
Chickens, and Batchelers in Pigs flesh take such delight, that an
old Sow, a tough Henne, or a gray Cony are not accepted:
and so it is seen by mee, else I should have beene better
remembred.

Well old woman (quoth the Parson) take here the legge of
a Capon to stop thy mouth.

Now by *S. Anne*, I dare not (quoth she).

No, wherefore (said the Parson)?

Marry, for feare lest you should goe home with a crutch
(quoth shee).

The Taylor said, then taste here a peece of a Goose.

Now God forbid (said the old woman) let Goose goe to his
kinde: you have a yongue stomacke, eate it your selfe, and
much good may it doe your heart, sweet yongue man.

The old woman lackes most of her teeth (quoth the Tanner): and therefore a peece of a tender Chicke is fittest for her.

If I did lacke as many of my teeth (quoth the old woman) as you lacke points of good husbandry, I doubt I should starve before it were long.

At this the Widow laught heartily, and the men were striken into such a dumpe, that they had not a word to say.

Dinner being ended, the Widow with the rest rose from the Table, and after they had sitten a pretty while merrily talking, the Widow called her man *John* to bring her a bowle of fresh Ale, which he did. Then said the Widow: My masters, now for your courtesie and cost I heartily thanke you all, and in requitall of all your favour, love and good will, I drinke to you, giving you free liberty when you please to depart.

At these words her sutors looked so sowerly one upon another, as if they had beene newly champing of Crabs. Which when the Taylor heard, shaking up himselfe in his new russet Jerkin, and setting his Hat on one side, hee began to speake thus. I trust sweet Widow (quoth hee) you remember to what end my comming was hither to day: I have long time beene a sutor unto you, and this day you promised to give mee a direct answer.

'Tis true (quoth shee) and so I have: for your love I give you thankes, and when you please you may depart.

Shall I not have you (said the Taylor)?

Alas (quoth the Widow), you come too late.

Good friend (quoth the Tanner) it is manners for yongue men to let their elders bee served before them: to what end should I be here if the Widow should have thee? a flat deniall is meete for a sawcy sutor: but what saiest thou to me, faire Widow (quoth the Tanner?)

Sir (said shee) because you are so sharpe set, I would wish you as soon as you can to wed.

Appoint the time your selfe (quoth the Tanner).

Even as soone (quoth shee) as you can get a wife, and hope not after mee, for I am already promised.

Now Tanner, you may take your place with the Taylor (quoth the Parson): for indeede the Widow is for no man but my selfe.

Master Parson (quoth shee) many have runne neer the goale, and yet have lost the game, and I cannot helpe it though your hope be in vaine: besides, Parsons are but newly suffered to have wives, and for my part I will have none of the first head.

What (quoth the Taylor) is your merriment growne to this reckoning? I never spent a Pig and a Goose to so bad a purpose before: I promise you, when I came in, I verily thought, that you were invited by the Widow to make her and I sure together, and that this jolly Tanner was brought to be a witnesse to the contract, and the old woman fetcht in for the same purpose, else I would never have put up so many dry bobs at her hands.

And surely (quoth the Tanner) I knowing thee to bee a Taylor, did assuredly thinke, that thou wast appointed to come and take measure for our wedding apparell.

But now wee are all deceived (quoth the Parson): and there-fore as we came fooles, so we may depart hence like asses.

That is as you interpret the matter (said the Widow): for I ever doubting that a concluding answer would breede a jarre in the end among you every one, I thought it better to be done at one instant, and in mine owne house, than at sundry times, and in common Tavernes: and as for the meate you sent, as it was unrequested of mee, so had you your part thereof, and if you thinke good to take home the remainder, prepare your wallets and you shall have it.

Nay Widow (quoth they) although wee have lost our labours, we have not altogether lost our manners: that which you have, keepe: and GOD send to us better lucke, and to you your hearts desire.   And with that they departed.

The Widow being glad shee was thus rid of her guests, when her man *John* with all the rest sate at supper, she sitting in a Chaire by, spake thus unto them.   Well my masters, you saw, that this day your poore Dame had her choice of husbands, if shee had listed to marry, and such as would have loved and maintained her like a woman.

'Tis true (quoth *John*) and I pray God you have not withstood your best fortune.

Trust mee (quoth she) I know not, but if I have, I may thank mine owne foolish fancy.

Thus it past on from *Bartholmewtide*, till it was neere Christ-mas, at what time the weather was so wonderfull cold, that all the running Rivers round about the Towne were frozen very thicke.   The Widow being very loth any longer to lye without company, in a cold winters night made a great fire, and sent for her man *John*, having also prepared a Chaire and a cushion, shee made him sit downe therein, and sending for a pinte of good Sacke, they both went to supper.

In the end, bed time comming on, she caused her maid in a merriment to plucke off his hose and shooes, and caused him to be laid in his masters best bed, standing in the best Chamber, hung round about with very faire curtaines. *John* being thus preferred, thought himselfe a Gentleman, and lying soft, after his hard labour and a good supper, quickly fell asleepe.

About midnight, the Widow being cold on her feet, crept into her mans bed to warme them. *John* feeling one lift up the cloathes, asked who was there? O good *John* it is I (quoth the Widow); the night is so extreme cold, and my Chamber walles so thin, that I am like to bee starved in my bed, wherefore rather than I would any way hazzard my health, I thought it much better to come hither and try your courtesie, to have a little roome beside you.

John being a kind yongue man, would not say her nay, and so they spent the rest of the night both together in one bed. In the morning betime she arose up and made her selfe readie, and wild her man *John* to run and fetch her a linke with all speede: for (quoth shee) I have earnest businesse to doe this morning. Her man did so. Which done, shee made him to carry the Linke before her, untill she came to Saint *Bartholmewes* Chappell, where Sir *John* the Priest with the Clark and Sexton, stood waiting for her.

John (quoth she) turne into the Chappell: for before I goe further, I will make my prayers to *S. Bartholmew*, so shall I speed the better in my businesse.

When they were come in, the Priest according to his order, came to her, and asked where the Bridegroome was?

(Quoth she) I thought he had been here before me. Sir (quoth she) I will sit downe and say over my Beades, and by that time hee will come.

John mused at this matter, to see that his Dame should so suddenly be married, and he hearing nothing thereof before. The Widow rising from her prayers, the Priest told her that the Bridegroome was not yet come.

Is it true (quoth the Widow)? I promise you I will stay no longer for him, if hee were as good as *George a Green*: and therefore dispatch (quoth she) and marry mee to my man *John*.

Why Dame (quoth he) you do but jest.

I trow, *John* (quoth shee) I jest not: for so I meane it shall bee, and stand not strangely, but remember that you did promise mee on your faith, not to hinder mee when I came to the Church to be married, but rather to set it forward: therefore set your link aside, and give mee your hand: for none but you shall be my husband.

John seeing no remedy, consented, because hee saw the matter
*B 824

could not otherwise bee amended; and married they were presently.

When they were come home, *John* entertained his Dame with a kisse, which the other servants seeing, thought him somewhat sawcy. The Widow caused the best cheare in the house to bee set on the Table, and to breakfast they went, causing her new husband to be set in a chaire at the tables end, with a faire napkin laid on his trencher: then shee called out the rest of her servants, willing them to sit downe and take part of their good cheare. They wondring to see their fellow *John* sit at the tables end in their old masters chaire, began heartily to smile, and openly to laugh at the matter, especially because their Dame so kindly sate by his side: which shee perceiving, asked if that were all the manners they could shew before their master? I tell you (quoth shee) he is my husband: for this morning we were married, and therefore hence forward looke you acknowledge your duety towards him.

The folkes looked one upon another, marvelling at this strange newes. Which when *John* perceived, he said: My masters, muse not at all: for although by Gods providence, and your Dames favour, I am preferred from being your fellow to be your master, I am not thereby so much puft up in pride, that any way I will forget my former estate: Notwithstanding, seeing I am now to hold the place of a master, it shall be wisedome in you to forget what I was, and to take mee as I am, and in doing your diligence, you shall have no cause to repent that God made me your master.

The servants hearing this, as also knowing his good government before time, past their yeares with him in dutifull manner.

The next day, the report was over all the Towne, that *Jacke* of *Newberie* had married his Dame: so that when the woman walked abroad, every one bade God give her joy: some said that she was matcht to her sorrow, saying, that so lusty a yongue man as hee, would never love her being so ancient. Whereupon the woman made answer, that shee would take him downe in his wedding shooes, and would try his patience in the prime of his lustinesse: whereunto, many of her Gossips did likewise encourage her. Every day therefore for the space of a moneth after shee was married, it was her ordinary custome, to goe forth in the morning among her Gossips and acquaintance to make merry, and not to returne home till night, without any regard of her houshold. Of which, at her comming home her husband did very oftentimes admonish her in very gentle sort, shewing what great inconvenience would grow thereby: the which sometime shee would take in gentle part, and sometime in disdaine, saying.

I am now in very good case, that hee that was my servant but the other day, will now bee my master: this it is for a woman to make her foote her head. The day hath beene, when I might have gone forth when I would, and come in againe when it had pleased mee without controulement, and now I must be subject to every *Jackes* checke. I am sure (quoth she) that by my gadding abroad, and carelesse spending, I waste no goods of thine. I, pittying thy poverty, made thee a man, and master of the house, but not to the end I would become thy slave. I scorne, I tell thee true, that such a yongueling as thy selfe, should correct my conceit, and give mee instructions, as if I were not able to guide my selfe: but yfaith, yfaith, you shall not use me like a babe nor bridle me like an Asse: and seeing my going abroad grieves thee, where I have gone forth one day, I will goe abroad three; and for one houre, I will stay five.

Well (quoth her husband) I trust you will be better advised: and with that hee went from her about his businesse, leaving her sweating in her fustian furies.

Thus the time past on, till on a certaine day she had been abroad in her wonted manner, and staying forth very late, hee shut the doores and went to bed. About midnight shee comes to the doore, and knockes to come in: to whom hee looking out of the window, answered in this sort:

What? is it you that keepes such a knocking? I pray you get hence, and request the Constable to provide you a bed, for this night you shall have no lodging here.

I hope (quoth shee) you will not shut mee out of doores like a dogge, or let me lye in the streetes like a Strumpet.

Whether like a dogge or drab (quoth hee) all is one to mee, knowing no reason, but that as you have staied out all day for your delight, so you may lye forth all night for my pleasure. Both birds and beastes at the nights approach repaire to their rest, and observe a convenient time to returne to their habitation. Looke but upon the poore Spider, the Frog, the Flye, and every other silly Worme, and you shall see all these observe time to returne to their home: and if you, being a woman, will not doe the like, content your selfe to beare the brunt of your owne folly: and so farewell.

The woman hearing this, made pittious mone, and in very humble sort intreated him to let her in, and to pardon this offence, and while shee lived vowde never to doe the like. Her husband at length being moved with pitty towards her, slipt on his shooes, and came downe in his shirt: the doore being opened, in she went quaking, and as he was about to locke it againe, in very sorrowfull manner she said, Alacke husband, what hap have I? my wedding Ring was even now in my hand, and I have let it fall about the doore: good sweet *John* come forth with the candle, and helpe me to seeke it.

The man incontinent did so, and while hee sought for that which was not there to bee found, shee whipt into the house, and quickly clapping to the doore, she lockt her husband out. He stood calling with the candle in his hand to come in, but she made as if shee heard not. Anon shee went up into her chamber, and carried the key with her: but when he saw she would not answer, hee presently began to knocke as lowd as hee could at the doore. At last she thrust her head out at the window, saying: Who is there?

Tis I (quoth *John*) what meane you by this? I pray you come downe and open the doore that I may come in.

What sir (quoth shee) is it you? have you nothing to doe but dance about the streetes at this time of night, and like a Spright of the Buttery hunt after Crickets, are you so hote that the house cannot hold you?

Nay, I pray thee sweet heart (quoth he) doe not gybe no longer, but let mee in.

O sir, remember (quoth shee) how you stood even now at the window, like a Judge on the Bench, and in taunting sort kept mee out of mine owne house. How now *Jacke*, am I even with you? What, *John* my man, were you so lusty to locke your Dame out of doores? Sirra, remember you bade mee go to the Constable to get lodging, now you have leisure to try if his wife will preferre you to a bed. You sir sawce, that made me stand in the cold, till my feet did freeze, and my teeth chatter, while you stood preaching of birds and beasts, telling me a tale of Spiders, Flies, and Frogs: goe trye now if any of them will bee so friendly to let thee have lodging. Why go you not man? feare not to speake with them; for I am sure you shall finde them at home: thinke not they are such ill husbands as you, to be abroad at this time of night.

With this *Johns* patience was greatly mooved, insomuch, that hee deepely swore, that if shee would not let him in, hee would breake downe the doore.

Why *John* (quoth shee) you neede not be so hote, your

cloathing is not so warme, and because I thinke this will be a warning for you against another time, how you shut mee out of my house, catch, there is the key, come in at thy pleasure, and looke thou goe to bed to thy fellowes, for with mee thou shalt not lye to night.

With that shee clapt to the casement, and got her to bedde, locking the chamber doore fast. Her husband that knew it was in vaine to seeke to come into her chamber, and being no longer able to indure the cold, got him a place among his prentises and there slept soundly. In the morning his wife rose betime, and merrily made him a Cawdle, and bringing it up to his bed side, asked him how he did?

(Quoth *John*) troubled with a shrew, who the longer shee lives, the worse shee is: and as the people of *Illyris* kill men with their lookes, so she kills her husbands heart with untoward conditions. But trust mee wife (quoth hee) seeing I finde you of such crooked qualities, that (like the Spider) ye turne the sweete flowers of good counsell into venemous poyson, from henceforth I will leave you to your owne wilfulnesse, and neither vexe my mind, nor trouble my selfe to restraine you: the which if I had wisely done last night, I had kept the house in quiet, and my selfe from cold.

Husband (quoth shee) thinke that women are like starlings, that will burst their gall before they will yeeld to the Fowler: or like the Fish *Scolopendra*, that cannot be toucht without danger. Notwithstanding, as the hard steele doth yeeld to the hammers stroke, being used to his kinde, so will women to their husbands, where they are not too much crost. And seeing ye have sworne to give me my will, I vow likewise that my wilfulnesse shall not offend you. I tell you husband, the noble nature of a woman is such, that for their loving friends they will not sticke (like the Pellican) to pierce their owne hearts to doe them good. And therefore forgiving each other all injuries past, having also tride one anothers patience, let us quench these burning coales of contention, with the sweete juyce of a faithfull kisse, and shaking hands, bequeath all our anger to the eating up of this Cawdle.

Her husband courteously consented: and after this time, they lived long together, in most godly, loving and kind sort, till in the end she dyed, leaving her husband wondrous wealthy.

CHAPTER II

Of *Jacke* of *Newberie* his great wealth, and number of servants: and also how hee brought the Queene *Katharine* two hundred and fifty men prepared for the warre at his owne cost against the king of Scots at *Floden field.*

Now *Jack* of *Newberie* being a widower, had the choice of many wives, mens daughters of good credit, and widowes of great wealth. Notwithstanding he bent his only like to one of his owne servants, whom he had tried in the guiding of his house a year or two: and knowing her carefulnesse in her businesse, faithfull in her dealing, an excellent good huswife, thought it better to have her with nothing, than some other with much treasure. And beside as her qualities were good, so was she of very comely personage, of a sweet favour, and faire complexion. In the end, hee opened his minde unto her, and craved her good will. The maid (though shee took this motion kindly) said, shee would do nothing without consent of her parents. Whereupon a Letter was writ to her father, being a poore man dwelling at *Alesburie* in *Buckingamshire*: who being joyfull of his daughters good fortune, speedily came to *Newberie*, where of her master he was friendly entertained: who after he had made him good cheare, shewed him all his servants at worke, and every office in his house.

Within one roome being large and long,
There stood two hundred Loomes full strong:
Two hundred men the truth is so,
Wrought in these Loomes all in a row.
By every one a pretty boy,
Sate making quils with mickle joy;
And in another place hard by,
An hundred women merily,
Were carding hard with joyfull cheere,
Who singing sate with voices cleere.
And in a chamber close beside,
Two hundred maidens did abide,
In petticoates of Stammell red,
And milke-white kerchers on their head:
Their smocke-sleeves like to winter snow,
That on the Westerne mountains flow,
And each sleeve with a silken band,
Was featly tied at the hand.
These pretty maids did never lin,
But in that place all day did spin:

24

And spinning so with voices meet,
Like Nightingals they sung full sweet.
Then to another roome came they,
Where children were in poore aray:
And every one sate picking wool,
The finest from the course to cull:
The number was seven score and ten,
The children of poore silly men:
And these their labours to requite,
Had every one a penny at night,
Beside their meat and drinke all day,
Which was to them a wondrous stay.
Within another place likewise,
Full fifty proper men he spies,
And these were Shearemen every one,
Whose skill and cunning there was showne:
And hard by them there did remaine,
Full fourscore Rowers taking paine.
A Dye-house likewise had he then,
Wherein he kept full forty men:
And likewise in his fulling Mill,
Full twenty persons kept he still.
Each weeke ten good fat oxen he
Spent in his house for certaintie:
Beside good butter, cheese, and fish,
And many another wholesome dish.
He kept a Butcher all the yeere,
A Brewer eke for Ale and Beere:
A Baker for to bake his Bread,
Which stood his hushold in good stead.
Five Cookes within his kitchin great,
Were all the yeare to dresse his meat.
Sixe scullian boyes unto their hands,
To make cleane dishes, pots, and pans,
Beside poore children that did stay,
To turne the broaches every day.
The old man that did see this sight,
Was much amaz'd, as well he might:
This was a gallant Cloathier sure,
Whose fame for ever shall endure.

When the old man had seene this great houshold and family,
then was he brought into the Ware-houses, some being fild
with wool, some with flockes, some with woad and madder,
and some with broadcloathes and kersies ready dyed and drest,
beside a great number of others, some strecht on the Tenters,
some hanging on poles, and a great many more lying wet in
other places. Sir (quoth the old man) I wis che zee you bee
bominable rich, and cham content you shall have my daughter
and Gods blessing and mine light on you both.

But Father (quoth *Jacke* of *Newberie*) what will you bestow
with her?

Marry heare you (quoth the old man) I vaith cham but a poore
man, but I thong God, cham of good exclamation among my

neighbours, and they will as zoone take my vice for any thing as a richer mans: thicke I will bestow, you shall have with a good will, because che heare very good condemnation of you in every place, therefore chil give you twenty Nobles and a weaning Calfe, and when I dye and my wife, you shall have the revelation of all my goods.

When *Jacke* heard his offer, he was straight content, making more reckoning of the womans modesty, than her Fathers money. So the marriage day being appointed, all things was prepared meete for the wedding, and royall cheere ordained, most of the Lords, Knights, and Gentlemen thereabout, were invited thereunto: the Bride being attyred in a gowne of sheepes russet, and a kertle of fine woosted, her head attyred with a billiment of gold, and her haire as yeallow as gold, hanging downe behinde her, which was curiously combed and pleated, according to the manner in those dayes: shee was led to Church betweene two sweete boyes, with Bride-laces and Rosemary tied about their silken sleeves: the one of them was sonne to Sir *Thomas Parry*, the other to Sir *Francis Hungerford*. Then was there a fair Bride-cup of silver and gilt carried before her, wherein was a goodly branch of Rosemary gilded very faire, hung about with silken Ribands of all colours: next was there a noyse of Musicians that played all the way before her: after her came all the chiefest maydens of the Country, some bearing great Bride Cakes, and some Garlands of wheate finely gilded, and so she past unto the Church.

It is needlesse for mee to make any mention here of the Bridegroome, who being a man so well beloved, wanted no company, and those of the best sort, beside divers Marchant strangers of the Stillyard, that came from *London* to the Wedding. The marriage being solemnized, home they came in order as before, and to dinner they went, where was no want of good cheare, no lacke of melody: Rennish Wine at this wedding was as plentifull as Beere or Ale: for the Marchants had sent thither ten Tunnes of the best in the Stillyard.

This wedding endured ten dayes, to the great reliefe of the poore that dwelt all about: and in the end, the Brides Father and Mother came to pay their Daughters portion: which when the Bridegroome had received, hee gave them great thankes: Notwithstanding he would not suffer them yet to depart, and against they should goe home, their sonne in law came unto them, saying; Father and Mother, all the thankes that my poore heart can yeeld, I give you for your good will, cost, and courtesie, and while I live make bold to use mee in any thing that I am able, and in requitall of the gift you gave me with your daughter, I give you here twenty pound to bestow as you finde occasion, and for your losse of time, and charges riding up and downe, I give you here as much broadcloath as shall make you a cloake, and my mother a holiday gowne, and when this is worne out, come to me and fetch more.

O my good zonne (quoth the old woman) Christs benizon bee with thee evermore: for to tell thee true, we had zold all our kine to make money for my daughters marriage, and this zeaven yeare we should not have been able to buy more: Notwithstanding we should have zold all that ever wee had, before my poore wench should have lost her marriage.

I (quoth the old man) chud have zold my coate from my backe, and my bed from under mee, before my gyrle should have gone without you.

I thanke you good father and mother (said the Bride) and I pray God long to keepe you in health: then the Bride kneeled downe and did her duty to her parents, who weeping for very joy, departed.

Not long after this, it chanced while our noble king was making warre in France, that *James* king of *Scotland*, falsly breaking his oath, invaded *England* with a great Army, and did much hurt upon the Borders: whereupon on the sudden, every man was appointed according to his ability, to bee ready with his men and furniture, at an houres warning, on paine of death. *Jacke* of *Newberie* was commanded by the Justices to set out sixe men, foure armed with Pikes, and two Calivers, and to meete the Queen in *Buckinghamshire*, who was there raising a great power to goe against the faithlesse king of Scots.

When *Jacke* had received this charge, hee came home in all hast, and cut out a whole broadcloath for horsemens coates, and so much more as would make up coates for the number of a hundred men: in short time hee had made ready fifty tall men well mounted in white coates, and red caps with yellow Feathers, Demilances in their hands, and fifty armed men on foote with Pikes, and fifty shotte in white coates also, every man so expert in the handling of his weapon, as few better were found in the field. Himselfe likewise in complet armour on a goodly Barbed Horse, rode foremost of the company, with a Lance in his hand, and a faire plume of yellow Feathers in his crest, and in this sort he came before the Justices: who at the first approach did not a little wonder what he should be.

At length when thee had discovered what hee was, the Justices and most of the Gentlemen gave him great commendations for this his good and forward minde shewed in this action: but some other envying hereat, gave out words that hee shewed himselfe more prodigall than prudent, and more vaine-glorious than well advised, seeing that the best Nobleman in the Country would scarce have done so much: and no marvell (quoth they) for such a one would call to his remembrance, that the King had often occasions to urge his subjects to such charges; and therefore would doe at one time as they might be able to doe at another: but *Jack* of *Newberie* like the Stork in the Spring-time, thinks the highest Sedar too lowe for him to build his nest in, and ere the yeare be halfe done may be glad to have his bed in a bush.

These disdainfull speeches being at last brought to *Jacke* of *Newberies* eare, though it grieved him much, yet patiently put them up till time convenient. Within a while after, all the souldiers of *Barkshire, Hampshire,* and *Wiltshire,* were commanded to shew themselves before the Queene at *Stonney Stratford,* where her Grace, with many Lords, Knights, and Gentlemen were assembled, with tenne thousand men. Against *Jacke* should goe to the Queene, he caused his face to bee smeared with bloud, and his white coate in like manner.

When they were come before her Highnesse, she demanded (above all the rest) what those white coats were? Whereupon, Sir *Henry Englefield* (who had the leading of the *Barkshire* men) made answer.

May it please your Majesty to understand, that hee which rideth formost there, is called *Jacke* of *Newbery,* and all those gallant men in white, are his owne servants, who are maintained all the yeare by him: whom hee at his owne cost hath set out in this time of extremity, to serve the King against his vaunting Foe: and I assure your Majesty, there is not, for the number, better souldiers in the field.

Good sir *Henry* (quoth the Queene) bring the man to mee, that I may see him: which was done accordingly. Then *Jacke* with all his men allighted, and humbly on their knees fell before the Queen.

Her Grace said, Gentleman arise; and putting forth her lilly white hand, gave it him to kisse.

Most gracious Queene (quoth hee) Gentleman I am none, nor the sonne of a Gentleman, but a poore Clothier, whose lands are his Loomes, having no other Rents but what I get from the backes of little sheepe: nor can I claime any cognisance but a wodden shuttle. Neverthelesse, most gratious Queene, these my poore servants and my selfe, with life and goods, are ready at your Majesties command, not onely to spend our blouds, but also to lose our lives in defence of our King and Country.

Welcome to mee *Jack* of *Newberie* (said the Queene) though a Clothier by trade, yet a Gentleman by condition, and a faith-full subject in heart: and if thou chance to have any sute in Court, make account the Queene will bee thy friend, and would to God the King had many such Clothiers. But tell mee, how came thy white coate besmeared with bloud, and thy face so bescratcht?

May it please your Grace (quoth hee) to understand, that it was my chance to meete with a monster, who like the people *Cynomolgy*, had the proportion of a man, but headed like a dogge, the biting of whose teeth was like the poisoned teeth of a Crocodile, his breath like the Basilisks, killing afarre off. I understand, his name was Envie, who assailed mee invisibly, like the wicked spirit of *Mogunce*, who flung stones at men, and could not bee seene: and so I come by my scratcht face, not knowing when it was done.

What was the cause this monster should afflict thee above the rest of thy company, or other men in the field?

Although, most Sovereigne Queen (quoth hee) this poysoned curre snarleth at many, and that few can escape the hurt of his wounding breath, yet at this time he bent his force against mee, not for any hurt I did him, but because I surpast him in hearty affection to my Sovereigne Lord, and with the poore Widow, offered all I had to serve my Prince and Country.

It were happy for *England* (said the Queene) if in everie market Towne there were a Jybbet to hang up curres of that kinde, who like *Æsops* dogge lying in the Manger, will doe no good himselfe, nor suffer such as would to doe any.

This speech being ended, the Queene caused her Army to be set in order, and in warlike manner to march toward *Flodden*, where King *James* had pitcht his field. But as they passed along with Drum and Trumpet, there came a Post from the valiant Earle of *Surrey*, with tydings to her Grace, that now she might dismisse her Army, for that it had pleased God to grant the noble Earle victory over the Scotts: whom he had by his wisedome and valiancy vanquished in fight, and slaine their King in battell. Upon which newes, her Majesty discharged her forces, and joyfully tooke her journey to *London*, with a pleasant countenance, praysing God for her famous victory, and yeelding thankes to all the noble Gentlemen and Souldiers for their readinesse in the action, giving many gifts to the Nobilitie, and great rewards to the Souldiers: among whom, she nothing forgot *Jacke* of *Newbery*, about whose necke she put a rich chaine of gold: at what time he with all the rest gave a great shout, saying, God save *Katherine* the noble Queen of *England*.

Many Noble men of *Scotland* were taken prisoners at this battell, and many more slaine: so that there never came a greater foile to *Scotland* than this: for you shall understand, that the Scottish King made full account to bee Lord of this Land, watching opportunity to bring to passe his faithlesse and trayterous practise: which was when our King was in *France*, at *Turney*, and *Turwin*: in regard of which warres the Scots vaunted there was none left in *England*, but shepheards and ploughmen who were not able to lead an Army, having no skill in martiall affaires. In consideration of which advantage, hee invaded the Countrey, boasting of victory before he had wonne: which was no small griefe to Queene *Margaret*, his wife, who was eldest sister to our noble King. Wherefore in disgrace of the Scots, and in remembrance of the famous atchieved victory, the Commons of *England* made this Song: which to this day is not forgotten of many.

THE SONG

King *Jamei* had made a vowe,
   keepe it well if he may:
That he will be at lovely *London*,
   upon Saint *James* his day.

Upon Saint *James* his day at noon,
   at faire *London* will I be;
And all the Lords in merry *Scotland*,
   they shall dine there with me.

Then bespake good Queene *Margaret*,
   the teares fell from her eyes:
Leave off these wars most noble King,
   keepe your fidelity.

The water runs swift and wondrous deep,
   from bottome unto the brimme:
My brother *Henry* hath men good enough,
   England is hard to winne.

Away (quoth he) with this silly foole,
   in prison fast let her lie:
For she is come of the English bloud,
   and for these words she shall dye.

With that bespake Lord *Thomas Howard*,
  the Queenes Chamberlaine that day:
If that you put Queen *Margaret* to death,
  Scotland shall rue it alway.

Then in a rage King *Jamie* did say,
  Away with this foolish Mome:
He shall be hanged, and the other be burned,
  so soone as I come home.

At *Flodden Field* the Scots came in,
  which made our Englishmen faine,
At *Bramstone-greene* this battell was seene:
  there was King *Jamie* slaine.

Then presently the Scots did flie,
  their Cannons they left behinde,
Their ensignes gay were won [1] all away,
  our Souldiers did beate them blinde.

To tell you plaine, twelve thousand were slaine,
  that to the fight did stand;
And many prisoners tooke that day,
  the best in all *Scotland*.

That day made many a fatherlesse childe,
  and many a widow poore;
And many a Scottish gay Lady
  sate weeping in her bowre.

Jacke with a feather was lapt all in leather,
  his boastings were all in vaine:
He had such a chance with a new morrice dance,
  he never went home againe.

---

[1] Won 1633; worne 1626.

CHAPTER III

ABOUT the tenth year of the kings reigne, his Grace made his progresse into *Barkshire*, against which time *Jack* of *Newbery* cloathed 30. tall fellowes, being his houshold servants, in blew coates, faced with Sarcenet, every one having a good sword and buckler on his shoulder, himselfe in a plaine russet coate, a paire of white kersie breeches without welt or guard, and stockens of the same peece sowed to his slops, which had a great codpeece, whereon he stucke his pinnes: who knowing the King would come over a certain meadow, neere adjoining to the Towne, got himselfe thither with all his men; and repairing to a certaine Ant-hill, which was in the field, tooke up his seat there, causing his men to stand round about the same with their swords drawne.

The King comming neer the place with the rest of his Nobility, and seeing them stand with their drawne weapons, sent to know the cause. *Garret* King at Armes was the Messenger, who spake in this sort. Good fellowes, the Kings Majesty would know to what end you stand here with your swords and bucklers prepared to fight.

With that, *Jacke* of *Newbery* started up, and made this answer. Harrold (quoth he) returne to his Highnesse, it is poore *Jacke* of *Newbery*, who being scant Marquesse of a Mole-hill, is chosen Prince of Ants: and here I stand with my weapons and Guard about mee, to defend and keep these my poore and painefull subjects, from the force of the idle Butterflies, their sworne enemies, lest they should disturbe this quiet Common-wealth, who this Summer season are making their Winters provision.

The messenger returning, told his Grace that it was one *Jacke* of *Newbery*, that stood there with his men about him, to guard (as they say) a company of Ants, from the furious wrath of the Prince of Butterflies. With this newes the King heartily laught, saying: Indeed it is no marvell he stands so well prepared, considering what a terrible tyrant he hath to deale withall. Certainly my Lords (quoth hee) this seemes to be a pleasant fellow: and therefore we will send to talke with him.

32

The messenger being sent, told *Jacke* he must come speak with the King. (Quoth he) his Grace hath a horse and I am on foote; therefore will him to come to mee: beside that, while I am away, our enemies might come and put my people in hazzard, as the Scots did *England*, while our King was in *France*.

How dares the Lambe be so bold with the Lyon (quoth the Herald)?

Why (quoth hee) if there be a Lyon in the field, here is never a cocke to feare him: and tell his Majestie, he might thinke me a very bad Governour, that would walke aside upon pleasure, and leave my people in perill. Herald (quoth hee) it is written, He that hath a charge must looke to it, and so tell thy Lord my King.

The Message being done, the King said: My Lords, seeing it will bee no other, wee will ride up to the Emperour of Ants, that is so carefull in his government.

At the Kings approach, *Jack* of *Newbery* and his servants put up all their weapons, and with a joyfull cry flung up their caps in token of victory. Why how now my masters (quoth the King) is your wars ended: Let mee see, where is the Lord Generall of this great Campe?

With that, *Jacke* of *Newbery* with all his servants fell on their knees, saying: God save the King of *England*, whose sight hath put our foes to flight, and brought great peace to the poore labouring people.

Trust mee (quoth our King) here bee pretty fellowes to fight against Butterflies: I must commend your courage, that dares withstand such mighty gyants.

Most dread Soveraigne (quoth *Jacke*) not long agoe, in my conceit, I saw the most provident Nation of the Ants, summoned their chiefe Peeres to a Parliament, which was held in the famous city *Dry Dusty*, the one and twentith day of September: whereas, by their wisedomes, I was chosen their King, at what time also many bills of complaint were brought in against divers il members in the common-wealth: among whom, the Moule was attainted of high treason to their State: and therefore was banished for ever from their quiet Kingdome: so was the Grashopper and the Catterpiller, because they were not onely idle, but also lived upon the labours of other men, amongst the rest, the Butterflie was very much misliked, but few durst say any thing to him, because of his golden apparell: who through sufferance grew so ambitious and malapert, that the poore Ant could no sooner get an egge into her nest, but he would have it

away, and especially against Easter, which at length was misliked. This painted asse tooke snuffe in the nose, and assembled
a great many other of his owne coate, by windie warres to roote
this painefull people out of the land, that hee himselfe might
bee seated above them all. (These were proud Butterflies, quoth
the King.) Whereupon I with my men (quoth *Jack*) prepared
our selves to withstand them, till such time as your Majesties
royall presence put them to flight.

Tush (said the King) thou must think that the force of flies
is not great.

Notwithstanding (quoth *Jacke*) their gay gownes make poore
men affraid.

I perceive (quoth Cardinall *Wolsie*) that you being a King of
Ants doe carry a great grudge to the Butterflies.

I (quoth *Jacke*) wee bee as great foes, as the Foxe and the
Snake are friends: for the one of them being subtle, loves the
other for his craft: but now I intend to be no longer a Prince,
because the majesty of a King hath eclipst my glory: so that
looking like the Peacocke on my blacke feet makes me abase
my vaine-glorious feathers, and humbly yeeld unto his Majesty
all my Sovereigne rule and dignity, both of life and goods,
casting my weapons at his feete, to doe any service wherein his
Grace shall command me.

God a mercy good *Jack* (quoth the King) I have often heard of
thee, and this morning, I mean to visite thy house.

Thus the King with great delight rode along untill hee came
to the Townes end, where a great multitude of people attended
to see his Majesty: where also Queen *Katharine* with all her
traine met him. Thus with great rejoycing of the Commons,
the King and Queen passed along to this jolly Clothiers house,
where the good wife of the house with threescore maidens
attending on her, presented the King with a Bee-hive, most
richly gilt with gold, and all the Bees therein were also made of
gold curiously by Art, and out of the top of the same Hive,
sprung a flourishing greene tree, which bore golden Apples,
and at the roote thereof lay divers Serpents, seeking to destroy
it, whom Prudence and Fortitude trode under their feete,
holding this inscription in their hands:

> Loe here presented to your Roiall sight,
> The figure of a flourishing Common-wealth:
> Where vertuous subjects labour with delight,
> And beate the drones to death which live by stealth:
> Ambition, Envie, Treason, loathsome serpents be,
> Which seeke the downefall of this fruitfull tree.

But Lady Prudence with deep searching eye,
Their ill intended purpose doth prevent,
And noble Fortitude standing alwaies nye,
Disperst their power prepar'd with bad intent.
Thus are they foild that mount with meanes unmeet,
And so like slaves are troden under feet.

The King favourably accepted this Embleme, and receiving
it at the womens hands, willed Cardinal *Wolsie* to look thereon,
commanding it should be sent to *Windsor Castle*. This Cardinall
was at that time Lord Chancellor of *England*, and a wonderfull
proud Prelate, by whose meanes great variance was set betwixt
the King of *England* and the French King, the Emperour of
Almaine, and divers other Princes of Christendome, whereby
the trafficke of those Merchants was utterly forbidden, which
bred a generall woe through *England*, especially among Clothiers:
insomuch, that having no sale for their cloath, they were faine
to put away many of their people which wrought for them, as
hereafter more at large shall be declared.

Then was his Majesty brought into a great Hall, where foure
long tables stood ready covered: and passing through that
place, the King and Queene came into a faire and large Parlour,
hung about with goodly Tapistry, where was a Table prepared
for his Highnesse and the Queenes Grace. All the floore where
the King sate was covered with broad cloathes in stead of greene
rushes: these were choice peeces of the finest wooll, of an Azure
colour, valued at an hundred pound a cloath, which afterward
was given to his Majesty. The King being set with the chiefest
of the Councell about him, after a delicate dinner, a sumptous
banquet was brought in, served all in glasse: the description
whereof were too long for mee to write, and you to read. The
great Hall was also filled with Lords, Knights, and Gentlemen,
who were attended by no other but the servants of the house.
The Ladies of Honour and Gentlewomen of the Court were all
seated in another Parlour by themselves: at whose table the
maidens of the house did waite in decent sort. The Serving-
men by themselves, and the Pages and footmen by themselves,
upon whom the prentices did attend most diligently. During
the Kings abiding in this place, there was no want of delicates:
Rhenish wine, Claret wine and Sacke, was as plentifull as small
Ale. Thus from the highest to the lowest, they were served
in such sort, as no discontent was found any way, so that great
commendations redownded unto the goodman of the house.

The Lord Cardinall that of late found himselfe galde by the
Allegory of the Ants, spake in this wise to the King. If it should

please your Highnesse (quoth he) but to note the vain-glory of these Artificers, you should finde no small cause of dislike in many of their actions.   For an instance, the fellow of this house, hee hath not stucke this day to undoe himselfe, onely to become famous by receiving of your Majesty: like *Herostratus* the Shoo-maker that burned the Temple of *Diana*, onely to get himself a name, more than for any affection he beares to your Grace, as may well be proved by this: Let there be but a simple Subsidie levied upon them for the assistance of your Highnesse Warres, or any other waightie affaires of the Common-wealth and state of the Realme, though it bee not the twentieth part of their substance, they will so grudge and repine, that it is wonderfull: and like people desperate cry out, they bee quite undone.

My Lord Cardinall (quoth the Queen) (under correction of my Lord the King) I durst lay an hundred pound *Jack* of *Newbery* was never of that minde, nor is not at this instant: if yee aske him, I warrant he will say so.   My selfe also had a proofe thereof at the Scottish invasion, at what time this man being seased but at sixe men, brought (at his owne cost) an hundred and fiftie into the field.

I would I had moe such subjects (said the King) and many of so good a minde.

Ho, ho, *Harry* (quoth *Will Sommers*) then had not *Empson* and *Dudley* been chronicled for knaves, nor sent to the Tower for treason.

But then they had not knowne the paine of imprisonment (quoth our King) who with their subtility grieved many others. But their subtilty was such that it broke their neckes (quoth *Will Sommers*).

Whereat the King and Queene laughing heartily, rose from the Table.   By which time *Jacke* of *Newbery* had caused all his folkes to goe to their worke, that his Grace and all the Nobility might see it: so indeed the Queen had requested.   Then came his Highnesse where hee saw an hundred Loomes, standing in one roome, and two men working in every one, who pleasantly sung on this sort.

THE WEAVERS SONG

When *Hercules* did use to spin,
    and *Pallas* wrought upon the Loome,
Our trade to flourish did begin,
    while Conscience went not selling Broome.[1]
    Then love and friendship did agree,
    To keep the band of amitie.

---

[1] Broomes, 1626.

When Princes sons kept sheepe in field,
  and Queenes made cakes of wheaten flowre,
Then men to lucre did not yeeld,
  which brought good cheere in every bower.
    Then love and friendship did agree,
    To hold the bands of amitie.

But when that Giants huge and hie,
  did fight with speares like Weavers beames,
Then they in iron beds did lie,
  and brought poore men to hard extreames.
    Yet love and friendship did agree,
    To hold the bands of amitie.

Then *David* tooke his sling and stone,
  not fearing great *Goliahs* strength,
He pierst his braine, and broke the bone,
  though he were fifty foote of length.
    For love and friendship, etc.

But while the Greekes besieged *Troy*,
  Penelope apace did spin,
And Weavers wrought with mickle joy,
  though little gaines were comming in.
    For love and friendship, etc.

Had *Helen* then sate carding wooll,
  (whose beauteous face did breed such strife)
She had not been sir *Paris* trull,
  nor caus'd so many lose their life.
    Yet we by love did still agree, etc.

Or had King *Priams* wanton sonne
  beene making quills with sweet content,
He had not then his friends undone,
  when he to *Greece* a gadding went.
    For love and friendship did agree, etc.

The Cedar tree indures more stormes,
  than little shrubs that sprout not hie:
The Weaver lives more void of harmes,
  than Princes of great dignitie.
    While love and friendship doth agree, etc.

The Shepheard sitting in the field,
  doth tune his pipe with hearts delight:
When Princes march with speare and shield,
  the poore man soundly sleepes all night.
    While love and friendship doth agree, etc.

Yet this by proofe is daily tride,
  For Gods good gifts we are ingrate:
And no man through the world so wide,
  lives well contented with his state.
    No love nor friendship we can see,
    to hold the bands of amitie.

Well sung good fellowes (said our King): Light hearts and
merry mindes live long without gray haires.

But (quoth *Will Sommers*) seldome without red noses.

Well (said the King) there is a hundred angells to make cheere withall: and looke that every yeare once you make a feast among your selves, and frankely (every yeare) I give you leave to fetch foure Buckes out of *Dunington* Parke, without any mans let or controulement.

O I beseech your Grace (quoth *Will Sommers*) let it be with a condition.

What is that (said our King)?

My Liege (quoth hee) that although the Keeper will have the skins, that they may give their wives the hornes.

Goe to (said the Queene) thy head is fuller of knavery, than thy purse is of crownes.

The poore workemen humbly thanked his Majesty for his bountifull liberality: and ever since, it hath beene a custome among the Weavers, every yeare presently after *Bartholmew-tide*, in a remembrance of the Kings favour, to meet together, and make a merry feast.

His Majesty came next among the spinsters and carders, who were merrily a working: whereat *Will Sommers* fell into a great laughter.

What ailes the foole to laugh (said the King)?

Marry (quoth *Will Sommers*) to see these maidens get their living as Buls doe eate their meate.

How is that (said the Queen)?

By going still backward (quoth *Will Sommers*): and I will lay a wager, that they that practise so well being maides to goe backward, will quickly learne ere long to fall backward.

But sirra (said the Cardinall) thou didst fall forward when thou brokest thy face in master *Kingsmills* seller.

But you my Lord sate forward (quoth *Will Sommers*) when you sate in the stockes at Sir *Amie Paulets*. Whereat there was greater laughing than before.

The King and Queene, and all the Nobility heedfully beheld these women, who for the most part were very faire and comely creatures, and were all attired alike from top to toe. Then (after due reverence) the maidens in dulcet manner chaunted out this Song, two of them singing the Ditty, and all the rest bearing the burden.

THE MAIDENS SONG

It was a Knight in *Scotland* borne,
　　follow my love, leap over the strand:
Was taken prisoner and left forlorne,
　　even by the good Earle of *Northumberland*.

Then was he cast in prison strong,
 follow my love, leap over the strand:
Where he could not walke nor lye along,
 even by the good Earle of *Northumberland*.

And as in sorrow thus he lay,
 follow my love, come over the strand:
The Earles sweet Daughter walkt that way,
 and she the faire flower of *Northumberland*.

And passing by, like an Angell bright,
 follow my love, come over the strand:
This prisoner had of her a sight,
 and she the faire flower of *Northumberland*.

And lowd to her this knight did cry,
 follow my love, come over the strand:
The salt teares standing in his eie,
 and she the faire flower of *Northumberland*.

Faire Lady (he said) take pitt yon me,
 follow my love, come over the strand;
And let me not in prison dye,
 and you the faire flower of *Northumberland*.

Faire Sir, how should I take pitty on thee,
 follow my love, come over the strand:
Thou being a foe to our Country,
 and I the faire flower of *Northumberland*.

Faire Lady, I am no foe (he said)
 follow my love, come over the strand:
Through thy sweete love here was I staid,
 for thee the faire flower of *Northumberland*.

Why shouldst thou come here for love of me,
 follow my love, come over the strand:
Having wife and children in thy Countrie,
 and I the faire flower of *Northumberland*.

I sweare by the blessed Trinitie,
 follow my love, come over the strand:
I have no wife nor children I,
 nor dwelling at home in merry *Scotland*.

If courteously you will set me free,
 follow my love, come over the strand:
I vow that I will marry thee,
 so soone as I come in merry *Scotland*.

Thou shalt be Lady of Castles and Towres,
 follow my love, come over the strand:
And sit like a Queen in princely bowers,
 when I am at home in faire *Scotland*.

Then parted hence this Lady gay,
 follow my love, come over the strand:
And got her fathers ring away,
 to help this sad knight into faire *Scotland*.

Likewise much gold she got by sleight,
  follow my love, come over the strand:
And all to help this forlorne knight,
  to wend from her father to faire *Scotland.*

Two gallant steeds both good and able,
  follow my love, come over the strand:
She likewise tooke out of the stable,
  to ride with this knight into fair *Scotland.*

And to the Jaylor she sent this ring,
  follow my love, come over the strand:
The knight from prison forth to bring,
  to wend with her into faire *Scotland.*

This token set this prisoner free,
  follow my love, come over the strand:
Who straight went to this faire Lady,
  to wend with her into faire *Scotland.*

A gallant steed he did bestride,
  follow my love, come over the strand:
And with the Lady away did ride,
  and she the faire flower of *Northumberland.*

They rode till they came to a water cleere,
  follow my love, come over the strand:
Good sir how should I follow you here,
  and I the faire flower of *Northumberland.*

The water is rough and wonderfull deep,
  follow my love, come over the strand:
And on my saddle I shall not keep,
  and I the faire flower of *Northumberland.*

Feare not the foord, faire Lady (quoth he)
  follow my love, come over the strand:
For long I cannot stay for thee,
  and thou the faire flower of *Northumberland.*

The Lady prickt her wanton steed,
  follow my love, come over the strand:
And over the river swom with speed,
  and she the faire flower of *Northumberland.*

From top to toe all wet was she,
  follow my love, come over the strand:
This have I done for love of thee,
  and I the faire flower of *Northumberland.*

Thus rode she all one winters night,
  follow my love, come over the strand:
Till *Edenborow* they saw in sight,
  the chiefest towne in all *Scotland.*

Now chuse (quoth he) thou wanton flower,
  follow my love, come over the strand:
Whether thou wilt be my Paramour,
  or get thee home to *Northumberland.*

For I have wife and children fine,
  follow my love, come over the strand:
In *Edenborow* they be alive,
  then get thee home to faire *England*.

This favour shalt thou have to boote,
  follow my love, come over the strand:
Ile have thy horse, goe thou a foote,
  goe get thee home to *Northumberland*.

O false and faithlesse knight (quoth she)
  follow my love, come over the strand:
And canst thou deale so bad with me,
  and I the faire flower of *Northumberland*?

Dishonour not a Ladies name,
  follow my love, come over the strand:
But draw thy sword, and end my shame,
  and I the faire flower of *Northumberland*.

He tooke her from her stately Steed,
  follow my love, come over the strand:
And left her there in extreme need,
  and she the faire flower of *Northumberland*.

Then sat she downe full heavily,
  follow my love, come over the strand:
At length two knights came riding by,
  two gallant knights of faire *England*.

She fell downe humbly on her knee,
  follow my love, come over the strand:
Saying, courteous Knights take pitty on me,
  and I the faire flower of *Northumberland*.

I have offended my father deere,
  follow my love, come over the strand:
And by a false knight that brought me here,
  from the good Earle of *Northumberland*.

They tooke her up behinde him then,
  follow my love, come over the strand:
And brought her to her fathers againe,
  And he the good Earle of *Northumberland*.

All you faire maidens be warned by me,
  follow my love, come over the strand:
Scots were never true, nor never will be,
  to Lord, nor Lady, nor faire *England*.

FINIS

After the Kings Majesty and the Queene had heard this song sweetely sung by them, hee cast them a great reward: and so departing thence, went to the Fulling-mils, and Dye-house, where a great many were also hard at worke: and his Majesty perceiving what a great number of people were by this one

man set on worke, both admired, and commended him, saying
further, that no Trade in all the Land was so much to bee
cherished and maintained as this, which (quoth hee) may well
be called, The life of the poore. And as the King returned from
this place with intent to take horse and depart, there met him a
great many of children in garments of white silke, frienged with
gold, their heads crowned with golden Bayes, and about their
armes each one had a scarfe of green sarcenet fast tied, in their
hands they bore silver bowes, and under their girdles golden
arrowes.

The foremost of them represented *Diana*, Goddesse of Chastity,
who was attended on by a traine of beautifull Nymphes, and
they presented to the King foure prisoners:

The first was a sterne and grisly woman, carrying a frowning
countenance, and her forehead full of wrinkles, her hayre as
black as pitch, and her garments all bloudy, a great sword shee
had in her hand all stained with purple gore: they called her
name *Bellona*, Goddesse of warres, who had three daughters:
the first of them was a tall woman, so leane and ill-favoured,
that her cheeke bones were ready to start out of the skinne, of a
pale and deadly colour: her eyes sunke into her head: her
legges so feeble, that they could scantly carry the body; all
along her armes and hands through the skinne you might tell
the sinews, joints and bones: her teeth were very strong and
sharpe withall: she was so greedy, that shee was ready with
her teeth to teare the skinne from her owne armes: her attyre
was blacke, and all torne and ragged, she went barefooted,
and her name was *Famine*.

The second was a strong and lusty woman, with a looke
pittilesse, and unmercifull countenance: her garments were all
made of Iron and Steele, and she carried in her hand a naked
weapon, and she was called the *Sword*.

The third was also a cruell creature, her eyes did sparkle like
burning coales: her hayre was like a flame, and her garments
like burning brasse: she was so hote, that none could stand
neere her, and they called her name *Fire*.

After this they retyred againe, and brought unto his Highnesse two other Personages, their countenance was Princely
and amiable, their attyre most rich and sumptuous: the one
carried in his hand a golden Trumpet, and the other a Palme
tree: and these were called *Fame* and *Victorie*, whom the Goddesse of Chastity charged to waite upon this famous Prince for
ever. This done, each childe after other with due reverence,

gave unto his Majesty a sweete smelling Gilliflower, after the manner of the Persians, offering something in token of loyalty and obedience.

The King and Queene beholding the sweete favour and countenance of these children, demanded of *Jacke* of *Newberie* whose children they were?

Who answered: It shall please your Highnesse to understand, that these are the children of poore people, that doe get their living by picking of wooll, having scant a good meale once in a weeke.

With that the King began to tell his Gilliflowers, whereby he found that there was 96. children.

Certainely (said the Queene) I perceive God gives as faire children to the poore as to the rich, and fairer many times: and though their dyet and keeping bee but simple, the blessing of God doth cherish them. Therefore (said the Queene) I will request to have two of them to waite in my Chamber.

Faire *Katharine* (said the King) thou and I have jumpt in one opinion, in thinking these children fitter for the Court than the Countrey: whereupon he made choise of a dozen more, foure he ordained to be Pages to his royall Person, and the rest he sent to the Universities, allotting to every one a Gentlemans living. Divers of the Noble-men did in like sort entertaine some of those children into their services, so that (in the end) not one was left to picke wooll, but were all so provided for, that their Parents never needed to care for them: and God so blessed them, that each of them came to bee men of great account and authority in the Land, whose posterities remaine to this day worshipfull and famous.

The King, Queene, and Nobles, being ready to depart, after great thanke and gifts given to *Jacke* of *Newbery* his Majesty would have made him Knight, but he meekely refused it, saying, I beseech your Grace let mee live a poore Clothier among my people, in whose maintenance I take more felicity, than in all the vaine titles of Gentillity: for these are the labouring Ants whom I seeke to defend, and these be the Bees which I keepe: who labour in this life, nor for ourselves, but for the glory of GOD, and to do service to our dread Sovereigne.

Thy Knighthood need be no hinderance of thy Faculty (quoth the King).

O my dread Soveraigne (said *Jacke*) honour and worship may bee compared to the Lake of *Lœthe*, which makes men forget themselves that taste thereof: and to the end I may still keepe in minde from whence I came, and what I am, I beseech your Grace let mee rest in my russet coate, a poore Clothier to my dying day.

Seeing then (said the King) that a mans minde is a Kingdome to himselfe, I will leave thee to the riches of thy owne content, and so farewell.

The Queenes Majesty taking her leave of the good wife with a Princely kisse, gave her in token of remembrance a most precious and rich Diamond set in gold, about the which was also curiously set sixe Rubies and sixe Emeralds in one peece, valued at nine hundred Markes: and so her Grace departed.

But in this meane space, *Will Sommers* kept company among the maides, and betooke himselfe to spinning as they did, which among them was held as a forfeit of a gallon of wine, but *William* by no meanes would pay it, except they would take it out in kisses, rating every kisse at a farthing.

This paiment wee refuse for two causes (quoth the maides): the one for that we esteeme not kisses at so base a rate; and the other, because in so doing we should give as much as you.

CHAPTER IV

How the maidens served *Will Sommers* for his sawcinesse.

THE madens consented together, seeing *Will Sommers* was so busie both with their worke and in his words, and would not pay his forfeiture, to serve him as he deserved: first therefore they bound him hands and feet, and set him upright against a post, tying him there to: which hee tooke in ill part, notwithstanding he could not resist them. And because he let his tongue run at randome, they set a fair gagge in his mouth, such a one as he could not for his life put away: so that hee stood as one gaping for winde. Then one of them got a couple of dogs droppings, and putting them in a bagge, laid them in soke in a bason of water, while the rest turned downe the coller of his Jerkin, and put an house-cloath about his necke in stead of a fine towell: then came the other maide with a bason and water in the same, and with the perfume in the pudding-bagge, flapt him about the face and lips, till he looked like a tawnie Moore, and with her hand washt him very orderly: the smell being somewhat strong, Will could by no meanes abide it, and for want of other language, cryed, *Ah ha ha ha*. Faine hee would have spet, and could not, so that hee was faine to swallow downe such licour as hee never tasted the like. When hee had a pretty while been washed in this sort, at the length he croucht downe upon his knees, yeelding himselfe to their favour: which the maidens perceiving, pulled the gag out of his mouth.

Hee had no sooner the liberty of his tongue, but that he curst and swore like a divell: the maids that could scant stand for laughing, at last askt how hee liked his washing?

Gods ounds (quoth hee) I was never thus washt, nor ever met with such Barbers since I was borne: let mee goe (quoth he) and I will give you whatsoever you will demand, wherewith hee cast them an English Crowne.

Nay (quoth one of the Maides) you are yet but washt, but wee will shave you ere yee goe.

Sweete Maides (quoth hee) pardon my shaving, let it suffice that you have washt mee: if I have done a trespasse to your Trade, forgive it mee, and I will never hereafter offend you.

45

Tush (said the Maides) you have made our wheeles cast their bands, and bruised the teeth of our cardes in such sort, as the offence may not bee remitted without great pennance. As for your gold, wee regard it not: therefore as you are perfumed fit for the dogs, so wee enjoine you this night to serve all our hogs, which pennance, if you will sweare with all speede to performe, wee will let you loose.

O (quoth *Will*) the huge Elephant was never more fearefull of the silly sheep, than I am of your displeasures: therefore let mee loose, and I will doe it with all diligence.

Then they unbound him, and brought him among a great company of Swine, which when *Will* had wel viewed over, he drave out of the yard all the Sowes:

Why how now (quoth the Maides) what meane you by this?

Mary (quoth *Will*) these be all sowes, and my pennance is but to serve the hogs.

Is it true (quoth they) have you overtaken us in this sort? Well, looke there be not one hog unserved wee would advise you.

William Sommers stript up his sleeves very orderly, and clapt an apron about his motly hosen, and taking a paile served the hogs handsomely. When he had given them all meat, he said thus:

> My taske is duely done,
> My liberty is wonne,
> The hogs have eate their crabs,
> Therefore farewell you drabs.

Nay soft friend (quoth they) the veriest hog of all hath yet had nothing.

Where the divell is he (said *Will*) that I see him not?

Wrapt in a motley Jerken (quoth they) take thy selfe by the nose, and thou shalt catch him by the snout.

I was never so very a hog (quoth he) but I would alway spare from my own belly to give a woman.

If thou doe not (say they) eate (like the prodigall Childe) with thy fellow hogs, we will so shave thee, as thou shalt deerly repent thy disobedience.

Hee seeing no remedy, committed himselfe to their mercy: and so they let him goe. When he came to the Court, he shewed to the King all his adventure among the weavers maidens, wherat the King and Queene laughed heartily.

CHAPTER V

In a faire large Parlour which was wainscotted round about, *Jacke* of *Newbery* had fifteene faire Pictures hanging, which were covered with Curtaines of greene silke, fringed with gold, which he would often shew to his friends and servants.

In the first was the Picture of a shepheard, before whom kneeled a great King named *Viriat*, who sometime governed the people of *Portugall*.

See here (quoth *Jacke*) the father a shepheard, the sonne a Soveraigne. This man ruled in *Portugall*, and made great warres against the Romanes, and after that invaded *Spaine*, yet in the end was traiterously slaine.

The next was the Portraiture of *Agathocles*, which for his surpassing wisedome and manhood, was created King of *Sicilia*, and maintained battell against the people of *Carthage*. His father was a poore Potter, before whom he also kneeled. And it was the use of this King, that whensoever he made a banquet, he would have as well vessels of earth as of gold set upon the Table, to the intent he might alwayes beare in minde the place of his beginning, his Fathers house and family.

The third was the picture of *Iphicrates* an *Athenian* born, who vanquished the Lacedemonians in plaine and open battaile. This man was Captaine Generall to *Artaxerxes*, King of *Persia*, whose father was notwithstanding a Cobler, and there likewise pictured. *Eumenes* was also a famous Captaine to *Alexander* the great, whose father was no other than a Carter.

The fourth was the similitude of *Aelius Pertinax*, sometime Emperour of *Rome*, yet was his father but a Weaver: and afterward, to give example to others of low condition to beare mindes of worthy men, he caused the shop to be beautified with Marble curiously cut, wherein his father before him was wont to get his living.

The fifth was the picture of *Dioclesian*, that so much adorned *Rome* with his magnificall and triumphant victories. This was a famous Emperour, although no other than the sonne of a Book-binder.

Valentinian stood the next, painted most artificially, who was also crowned Emperour, and was but the sonne of a poore Rope-maker: as in the same picture was expressed; where his father was painted by him, using his trade.

The seventh was the Emperour *Probus,* whose father being a Gardener, was pictured by him holding a spade.

The eighth picture was of *Marcus Aurelius,* whom every age honoureth, he was so wise and prudent an Emperour; yet was he but a Cloth-weavers son.

The ninth was the Portraiture of the valiant Emperour *Maximinus,* the son of a Blacksmith, who was there painted as he was wont to worke at the Anvill.

In the tenth table was painted the Emperour *Gabianus,* who at the first was but a poore shepheard.

Next to this picture, was placed the pictures of two Popes of *Rome,* whose wisedome and learning advanced them to that dignitie. The first was the lively Counterfeit of Pope *John* the 22 whose father was a Shoomaker: hee being elected Pope, encreased their rents and patrimonie greatly.

The other was the Picture of Pope *Sixtus* the fourth of that name, being a poore Marriners son.

The thirteenth Picture was of *Lamusius* King of *Lombardie,* who was no better than the son of a common Strumpet: being painted like a naked childe walking in the water, and taking hold of the poynt of a Launce, by the which hee held fast, and saved himselfe. The reason whereof, was this: After his lewde mother was delivered of him, shee unnaturally threw him into a deepe stinking Ditch, wherein was some water. By hap king *Agilmond* passed that way, and found this childe almost drowned; who moving him softly with the point of his Launce, the better to perceive what hee was, the childe (though then newely borne) tooke hold thereof with one of his pretty hands, not suffering it to slide or slip away againe: which thing the King considering, being amazed at the strange force of this yongue little Infant, caused it to be taken up, and carefully to be fostered. And because the place where hee found him was called *Lama,* hee named the childe *Lamusius:* who afterward grew to be so brave a man, and so much favoured of Fortune, that in the end hee was crowned King of the *Lombards,* who lived there in honour, and in his succession after him, even untill the time of the unfortunate King *Albovina,* when all came to ruine, subversion and destruction.

In the fourteenth picture *Primislas* King of *Bohemia* was

most artificially drawne; before whom there stood an Horse without Bridle or Saddle, in a field where Husband-men were at plough. The cause why this King was thus painted (quoth *Jacke*) was this. At that time the King of the *Bohemians* died without issue, and great strife being amongst the Nobility for a new king, at length they all consented that a horse should bee let into the field, without bridle or saddle, having all determined with most assured purpose to make him their king, before whom this horse rested: At what time it came to passe, that the horse first stayed himselfe before this *Primislas*, being a simple creature, who was then busie driving the plough, they presently made him their Sovereigne, who ordered himselfe and his king-dome very wisely. Hee ordained many good lawes, hee com-passed the Citie of *Prague* with strong walles, besides many other things, meriting perpetuall laud and commendations.

The fifteenth was the Picture of *Theophrastus*, a Philosopher, a counsellor of Kings, and companion of Nobles, who was but sonne of a Taylor.

Seeing then my good servants, that these men have been advanced to high estate and Princely dignities, by wisedome, learning and diligence, I would wish you to imitate the like vertues, that you might attaine the like honours: for which of you doth know what good fortune God hath in store for you? there is none of you so poorely borne, but that men of baser birth have come to great honours. The idle hand shall ever goe in a ragged garment, and the sloathfull live in reproach: but such as doe lead a vertuous life, and governe themselves dis-creetly, shall of the best be esteemed, and spend their daies in credit.

CHAPTER VI

How all the Clothiers in *England* joined together, and with one consent
complained to the King of their great hindrance sustained for want
of Traffique into other Countries, whereupon they could get no sale
for their Cloath.

By meanes of the warres which our King had with other
countries, many Merchant strangers were prohibited for comming to *England*, as also our owne Merchants (in like sort) were
forbidden to have dealings with *France* or the Low-countries:
by meanes whereof the Clothiers had most of their cloath lying
on their hands, and that which they sold was at so low a rate
that the money scantly paid for the wooll and workemanship.
Whereupon they sought to ease themselves by abating the poore
workemens wages. And when that did not prevaile, they turnd
away many of their people, Weavers, Shearmen, Spinsters and
Carders, so that where there was a hundred Looms kept in one
towne, there was scant fifty: and hee that kept twenty put downe
tenne. Many a poore man (for want of worke) was hereby
undone, with his wife and children, and it made many a poore
widow to sit with a hungry belly. This bred great woe in most
places in *England*. In the end *Jack* of *Newberie* intended (in
the behalfe of the poore) to make a Supplication to the King:
and to the end hee might do it the more effectually, hee sent
Letters to all the chiefe cloathing townes in *England* to this
effect.

The Letter

Welbeloved friends and brethren, having a taste of the generall
griefe, and feeling (in some measure) the extremitie of these
times, I fell into consideration by what meanes we might best
expell these sorrowes, and recover our former commodity.

When I had well thought hereon, I found that nothing was
more needefull herein, than a faithfull unity among our selves.
This sore of necessity can no way be cured but by concord: for
like as the flame consumes the candle, so men through discord
waste themselves. The poore hate the rich, because they will
not set them on worke: and the rich hate the poore, because
they seeme burdenous: so both are offended for want of gaine.

50

When *Belinus* and *Brennus* were at strife, the Queen their
mother in their greatest fury perswaded them to peace, by
urging her conception of them in one wombe, and mutuall
cherishing of them from their tender yeares: so let our Art of
Cloathing, which like a kinde mother hath cherished us with
the excellency of her secrets, perswade us to an unity. Though
our Occupation be decaied, let us not deale with it as men doe
by their old shooes, which after they have long borne them out
of the myre, doe in the end fling them on the dunghill: or as
the Husband-man doth by his Bees, who for their Honey burnes
them. Deare friends, consider that our Trade will maintaine
us, if wee will uphold it: and there is nothing base, but that
which is basely used.

Assemble therefore your selves together, and in every towne
tell the number of those that have their living by meanes of this
Trade, note it in a Bill, and send it to mee. And because sutes
in Courts are like Winter nights, long and wearisome, let there
be in each place a weekely collection made to defray charges:
for I tell you, Noble mens Secretaries and cunning Lawyers
have slow tongues and deafe eares, which must bee daily noynted
with the sweete oyle of Angells. Then let two honest discreet
men bee chosen and sent out of every towne to meete mee at
Blackwell Hall in *London* on *All Saints Eeve,* and then we will
present our humble petition to the King. Thus I bid you
heartily farewell.

Copies of this Letter being sealed, they were sent to all the
cloathing Townes of *England,* and the Weavers both of linnen
and woollen gladly received them: so that when all the Bills
were brought together, there were found of the Clothiers, and
those they maintained, threescore thousand and sixe hundred
persons. Moreover, every cloathing Towne sending up two
men to *London,* they were found to bee an hundred and twelve
persons, who in very humble sort fell downe before his Majesty
walking in S. *James* his *Parke,* and delivered to him their Petition.

The King presently perusing it, asked if they were all Clothiers?

Who answered (as it were one man) in this sort: Wee are (most
gracious king) all poore Clothiers, and your Majesties faithfull
subjects.

My Lords (quoth the King) let these mens complaint bee
thoroughly lookt into, and their griefs redressed: for I account
them in the number of my best Common-wealths men. As the
Clergy for the soule, the Souldier for defence of his countrey

the Lawyer to execute justice, the Husband-man to feede the belly: so is the skilfull Clothier no lesse necessary for the cloathing of the backe, whom we may reckon among the chiefe Yeomen of our Land: and as the christall sight of the eye is tenderly to be kept from harmes because it gives the whole body light: so is the Clothiers whose cunning hand provides garments to defend our naked parts from the Winters nipping frost. Many more reasons there are, which may move us to redresse their griefes: but let it suffice that I command to have it done.

With that, his Grace delivered the Petition to the Lord Chauncellor, and all the Clothiers cryed, God save the King.

But as the King was ready to depart, hee suddenly turned about, saying: I remember there is one *Jacke* of *Newberie*, I muse hee had not his hand in this businesse, who profest himselfe to bee a defender of true Labourers.

Then said the Duke of *Sommerset*: It may bee his purse is answerable for his person.

Nay (quoth the Lord Cardinall) all his treasure is little enough to maintaine warres against the butterflies.

With that *Jack* shewed himselfe unto the King, and privately told his Grace of their griefe anew.

To whom his Majesty said: Give thy attendance at the Councell Chamber, where thou shalt receive an answer to thy content. And so his Highnes departed.

Finally, it was agreed that the Marchants should freely traffique one with another, and that Proclamation thereof should bee made as well on the other side the Sea, as in our Land: but it was long before this was effected, by reason the Cardinall being Lord Chancellor, put off the matter from time to time.

And because the Clothiers thought it not best to depart before it was ended, they gave their daily attendance at the Cardinalls house: but spent many dayes to no purpose: sometime they were answered, My Lord was busie, and could not be spoke withall; or else he was asleepe, and they durst not wake him: or at his study, and they would not disturbe him: or at his prayers, and they durst not displease him: and still one thing or other stood in the way to hinder them. At last, *Patch* the Cardinalls foole, being (by their often repaire thither) well acquainted with the Clothiers, came unto them and said: What, have you not spoken with my Lord yet?

No truly (quoth they) we heare say he is busie, and we stay till his grace bee at leasure.

Is it true (said *Patch*)? and with that in all haste he went out of the hall, and at last came in againe with a great bundle of straw on his backe.

Why how now *Patch* (quoth the Gentlemen) what wilt thou doe with that straw?

Mary (quoth he) I will put it under these honest mens feete, lest they should freeze ere they finde my Lord at leasure.

This made them all to laugh, and caused *Patch* to beare away his straw againe. Well, well, (quoth hee) if it cost you a groates worth of faggets at night, blame not me.

Trust me (said *Jacke* of *Newbery*) if my Lord Cardinalls father had beene no hastier in killing of Calves, than hee is in dispatching of poor mens sutes, I doubt he had never worne a Myter.

This he spake betwixt themselves softly, but yet not so softly, but that he was over-heard by a flattering Fellow that stood by, who made it knowne to some of the Gentlemen, and they straight certified the Cardinall thereof.

The Cardinall (who was of a very high spirit, and a loftie aspiring minde) was marvellously displeased at *Jacke* of *Newbery*: wherefore in his rage hee commanded and sent the Clothiers all to prison, because the one of them should not sue for the others releasement. Foure dayes lay these men in the *Marshalsey*, till at last they made their humble Petition to the King for their release: but some of the Cardinals friends kept it from the kings sight. Notwithstanding, the Duke of *Sommerset*, knowing thereof, spake with the Lord Cardinall about the matter, wishing hee would speedily release them, lest it breed him some displeasure: for you may perceive (quoth the Duke) how highly the King esteemes men of that Faculty.

Sir (quoth the Cardinall) I doubt not but to answer their imprisonment well enough, being perswaded that none would have given me such a quip but an Heretike: and I dare warrant you were this *Jacke* of *Newbery* well examined, hee would bee found to bee infected with *Luthers* spirit, against whom our King hath of late written a most learned Booke, in respect whereof, the Popes holinesse hath intitled his Majesty *Defender of the Faith*: therefore I tell you such fellowes are fitter to be faggots for fire, than Fathers of Families: notwithstanding (at your Graces request) I will release them.

Accordingly the Cardinall sent for the Clothiers afore him to *White hall*, his new built house by *Westminster*, and there bestowing his blessing upon them, said: Though you have offended mee I pardon you; for as *Steven* forgave his enemies that stoned him, and our Saviour those sinfull men that crucified him, so do I forgive you that high trespasse committed in disgrace of my birth: for herein doe men come neerest unto God, in shewing mercy and compassion. But see hereafter you offend no more. Touching your sute it is granted, and to morrow shall be published through *London*.

This being said they departed: and according to the Cardinalls words, their businesse was ended. The Stillyard Marchants joyfull hereof, made the Clothiers a great banquet. After which, each man departed home, carrying tydings of their good successe; so that within short space, Clothing was againe very good, and poore men as well set on worke as before.

CHAPTER VII

How a yongue Italian Marchant comming to _Jack_ of _Newberies_ house, was greatly inamoured of one of his maidens, and how he was served.

AMONG other servants which _Jacke_ of _Newbery_ kept, there was in his house threescore maidens, which every Sunday waited on his wife to Church and home againe, who had divers offices. Among other, two were appointed to keepe the beames and waights, to waigh out wooll to the Carders and Spinsters, and to receive it in againe by waight. One of them was a comely maiden, faire and lovely, borne of wealthy Parents, and brought up in good qualities, her name was _Jone_: so it was, that a yongue wealthy Italian Marchant, comming oft from _London_ thither to bargaine for cloath (for at that time Clothiers most commonly had their cloath bespoken, and halfe paid for afore hand). This Master _Benedicke_ fell greatly inamoured of this maiden: and therefore offered much courtesie to her, bestowing many gifts on her, which she received thankefully: and albeit his outward countenance shewed his inward affection, yet _Jone_ would take no knowledge thereof. Halfe the day sometime would hee sit by her, as shee was waighing wooll, often sighing and sobbing to himselfe, yet saying nothing, as if he had been tonguelesse, like the men of _Coromandæ_; and the loather to speake, for that hee could speak but bad English. _Jone_ on the other side that well perceived his passions, did as it were triumph over him, as one that were bondslave to her beauty, and although shee knew well enough before that shee was faire, yet did shee never so highly esteeme of her selfe as at this present: so that when she heard him either sigh, or sob, or groane, shee would turne her face in a carelesse sort, as if she had been borne (like the woman of _Taprobana_) without eares.

When Master _Bennedicke_ saw shee made no reckoning of his sorrowes, at length hee blabored out this broken English, and spake to her in this sort. Metressa _Jone_, be me tra and fa, mee love you wod all mine hart, and if you no shall love me again, me know mee shall die, sweet Mistresse love a me, and be me fa and tra you sal lack noting. First; me wil give you de silke

55

for make you a Frog: Second, de fin fin Camree for make you
ruffes; and the turd shal be for make fin handkercher, for wipe
your nose.

Shee mistaking his speech, began to be collericke, wishing
him to keepe that bodkin to picke his teeth.

Ho ho Metresse *Jone* (quoth hee) be Got, you be angry. Oh
Metresse *Jone*, bee no chafe with you friene for noting.

Good sir (quoth she) keepe your friendship for them that cares
for it, and fixe your love on those that can like you, as for mee
I tell you plain, I am not minded to marry.

Oh tis no matter for marrye, if you will come in my chamber,
beshit my bed, and let mee kisse you.

The Maide though she were very much displeased, yet at these
words, shee could not forbeare laughing for her life.

Ah ah Metresse *Jone*: mee is very glad to see you merrie,
holde your hand I say, and there is foure Crowne because you
laugh on mee.

I pray you Sir keepe your Crownes, for I need them not.

Yes be Got you shal have them Metresse *Jone*, to keepe in a
pox for you.

Shee that could not well understand his broken language,
mistooke his meaning in many things: and therfore wild him
not to trouble her any more. Notwithstanding such was his
love toward her, that he could not forbeare her company, but
made many journies thither for her sake. And as a certaine
spring in *Arcadia* makes men to starve that drinke of it: so
did poore *Bennedicke*, feeding his fancy on her beauty: for when
he was in *London*, he did nothing but sorrow, wishing he had
wings like the monsters of *Tartaria*, that he might fly to and fro
at his pleasure. When any of his friends did tell her of his ardent
affection toward her, shee wisht them to rub him with the sweat
of a Mule, to asswage his amorous passion, or to fetch him some
of the water in *Boetia*, to coole and extinguish the heate of his
affection: for (quoth she) let him never hope to be helpt by me.

Well (quoth they) before he saw thy alluring face, he was a
man reasonable and wise, but is now a starke foole, being by
thy beauty bereft of wit, as if hee had drunk of the river *Cea*,
and like bewitching *Circes* thou hast certainely transformed him
from a man to an Asse. There are stones in *Pontus* (quoth they)
that the deeper they be laid in the water, the fiercer they burn:
unto the which fond Lovers may fitly be compared, who the
more they are denyed, the hotter is their desire: but seeing it
is so, that he can find no favour at your hand, wee will shew

him what you have said, and eyther draw him from his dumpes, or leave him to his owne will.

Then spake one of the Weavers that dwelt in the Towne, and was a kinsman to this maide, I muse (quoth he) that master *Bennedicke* will not bee perswaded, but like the Moath, will play with the flame that will scortch his wings. Mee thinkes, hee should forbeare to love, or learne to speake, or else woo such as can answer him in his language: for I tell you, that *Jone* my kinswoman, is no taste for an Italian.

These speeches were told to *Bennedicke* with no small addition. When our yongue marchant heard the matter so plaine, he vowed to be revenged of the Weaver, and to see if hee could finde any more friendship of his wife: therefore dissembling his sorrow and covering his griefe, with speede hee tooke his journey to *Newberie*, and pleasantly saluted Mistresse *Jone*: and having his purse full of crownes, he was very liberall to the workefolkes, especially to *Jones* kinsman, insomuch that hee got his favour many times to goe forth with him, promising him very largely to doe great matters, and to lend him a hundred pound, wishing him to bee a servant no longer, beside he liberally bestowed on his wife many gifts, and if she washt him but a band, he would give her an Angell: if hee did but send her childe for a quart of Wine, hee would give him a shilling for his paines. The which his courtesie changed the Weavers minde, saying he was a very honest Gentleman, and worthy to have one farre better than his kinswoman.

This pleased master *Bennedick* well to heare him say so, notwithstanding he made light of the matter, and many times when the Weaver was at his Masters at worke, the Merchant would be at home with his wife, drinking and making merry. At length time bringing acquaintance, and often conference breeding familiarity, master *Bennedick* began somewhat boldly to jest with *Gillian*, saying that her sight and sweet countenance, had quite reclaymed his love from *Jone*, and that she onely was the mistresse of his heart: and if she would lend him her love, he would give her golde from *Arabia*, orient pearles from *India*, and make her bracelets of most precious Diamonds. Thy garments shall be of the finest silke that is made in *Venice*, and thy purse shall still be stuft with Angels. Tell me thy minde my love, and kill mee not with unkindnesse, as did thy scornefull kinswoman, whose disdaine had almost cost me my life.

O master *Bennedicke*, thinke not the wives of *England* can be

won by rewards, or enticed with fayre words, as children are
with Plums: it may be that you being merrily disposed, do speak
this to try my constancy. Know then, that I esteeme more
the honour of my good name, than the slyding wealth of the
world.

Master *Bennedick* hearing her say so, desired her, that considering it was love that forced his tongue to bewray his hearts
ardent affection, that yet she would be secret: and so for that
time tooke his leave.

When hee was gone, the woman began to call her wits together,
and to consider of her poore estate, and withall the better to
note the comelinesse of her person, and the sweet favour of her
face: which when shee had well thought upon, shee began to
harbour new thoughts, and to entertain contrary affections,
saying, Shall I content myselfe to be wrapt in sheepes russet
that may swim in silks, and sit all day carding for a groat, that
can have crownes at my command? No (quoth she) I will
no more beare so base a minde, but take Fortunes favours while
they are to be had. The sweet Rose doth flourish but one
moneth, nor Womens beauties but in yongue yeares. As the
Winters frost consumes the Summer flowers, so doth old age
banish pleasant delight. O glorious gold (quoth shee) how
sweet is thy smell? how pleasing is thy sight? Thou subduest
Princes, and overthrowest kingdomes, then how should a silly
woman withstand thy strength? Thus she rested meditating
on preferment, purposing to hazzard her honesty to maintaine
her selfe in braverie: even as occupiers corrupt their consciences
to gather riches.

Within a day or two master *Bennedicke* came to her againe,
on whom she cast a smiling countenance: which hee perceiving
(according to his old custome) sent for Wine, and very merry
they were. At last, in the middest of their cups, he cast out
his former question: and after farther conference, she yeelded,
and appointed a time when he should come to her: for which
favour, he gave her halfe a dozen portigues.

Within an houre or two after, entring into her owne conscience,
bethinking how sinnefully she had sold her selfe to folly, began
thus to expostulate. Good Lord (quoth shee) shall I breake
that holy vowe which I made in marriage, and pollute this body
of mine which the Lord hath sanctified? Can I breake the
commandement of my God, and not rest accursed? or be a
traytor to my husband, and suffer no shame? I heard once
my brother read in a book, that *Bucephalus*, *Alexanders* Steed,

being a beast, would not be backt by any but the Emperour, and shall I consent to any but my husband? *Artemisa* being a Heathen Lady, loved her husband so well, that shee drunke up his ashes, and buried him in her owne bowels, and should I, being a Christian, cast my Husband out of my heart? The Women of *Rome* were wont to crowne their Husbands heads with Bayes, in token of victorie, and shall I give my husband hornes in token of infamie? An Harlot is hated of all vertuous minded people, and shall I make my selfe a Whore? O my God forgive my sin (quoth shee) and cleanse my heart from these wicked imaginations.

And as she was thus lamenting, her husband came home: at whose sight her teares were doubled, like unto a river whose streame is encreased by showers of raine. Her husband seeing this, would needes know the cause of her sorrow: but a great while she would not shew him, casting manie a piteous looke upon him, and shaking her head, at last she said, O my deare husband, I have offended against God and thee, and made such a trespasse by my tongue, as hath cut a deepe scarre in my conscience, and wounded my heart with griefe like a Sword: like *Penelope* so have I been wooed, but like *Penelope* I have not answered.

Why woman (quoth he) what is the matter? If it be but the bare offence of thy tongue, why shouldest thou so grieve? considering that womens tongues are like Lambs tayles, which seldome stand still: And the Wise man saith, Where much talke is, must needes be some offence. Womens beauties are fayre markes for wandring eyes to shoote at: but as every Archer hits not the white, so every Wooer winnes not his mistresse favour. All Cities that are besiged are not sackt, nor all women to be mislikt that are loved. Why wife, I am perswaded thy faith is more firme, and thy constancie greater to withstand Lovers alarums, than that any other but my selfe should obtaine the fortresse of thy heart.

O sweet husband (quoth she) we see the strongest Tower, at length falleth downe by the Canons force, though the Bullets be but Iron: then how can the weake Bulwarke of a Womans breast make resistance, when the hot Canons of deepe perswading wordes are shotte off with golden Bullets, and every one as big as a Portigue?

If it be so wife, I may think my selfe in a good case, and you to be a very honest woman. As *Mars* and *Venus* danc't naked together in a Net, so I doubt, you and some knave have played naked together in a bed: but in faith thou queane, I will send thee to salute thy friends without a Nose: and as thou hast sold thy honesty, so will I sell thy company.

Sweete Husband, though I have promised, I have performed nothing: every bargain is not effected, and therefore as *Judas* brought again the thirty silver plates, for the which he betrayed his Master: so repenting my folly, Ile cast him againe his gold, for which I should have wronged my Husband.

Tell me (quoth her husband) what he is.

It is master *Bennedicke* (quoth shee) which for my love have left the love of our kinswoman, and hath vowed himselfe for ever to live my servant.

O dissembling Italian (quoth hee) I will be revenged on him for this wrong. I know that any favour from *Jone* our kinswoman, will make him runne like unto a man bitten with a mad dogge: therefore be ruled by mee, and thou shalt see me dresse him in his kinde.

The woman was very well pleased, saying, hee would be there that night.

All this works well with me (quoth her husband) and to supper will I invite *Jone* my kinswoman, and in the mean space make up the bed in the Parlour very decently.

So the goodman went forth, and got a sleepy drench from the Poticaries, the which he gave to a yongue Sow, which hee had in his yard, and in the evening layde her downe in the bed in the Parlour, drawing the Curtaines round about.

Supper time beeing come, master *Bennedicke* gave his attendance, looking for no other company but the good wife: Notwithstanding at the last mistresse *Jone* came in with her kinsman, and sate downe to supper with him.

Master *Bennedicke* musing at their sudden approach, yet neverthelesse glad of mistresse *Jones* company, past the supper time with many pleasant conceits, *Jone* shewing her selfe that night more pleasant in his company than at any time before: wherefore he gave the good man great thankes.

Good master *Bennedicke*, little doe you think how I have travelled in your behalfe to my kinswoman, and very much adoe I had to bring the peevish Wench into any good liking of your love: notwithstanding by my very great diligence and perswasions, I have at length won her good will to come hither, little thinking to finde you here, or any such good cheere to entertain her: all which I see is fallen out for your profite. But trust me, all the world cannot now alter her minde, nor turne her love from you: In regard whereof, shee hath promised me to lye this night in my house, for the great desire she hath of your good company: and in requitall of all your great courtesies shewed to me, I am very well content to bring you to her bed.   Marry this you must consider, and so she bad me tell you, that you should come to bed with as little noyse as you could, and tumble nothing that you find, for feare of her best gowne and her hat, which she will lay hard by the bed side, next her best partlet, and in so doing, you may have company with her all night, but say nothing in any case till you be a bed:

O (quoth he) Mater *Jan*, be Got Mater *Jan*, me wil not spoile her clothes for a towsand pound, ah me love mietres *Jone* more than my wife.

Well, supper being done, they rose from the table.   Master *Bennedick* imbracing mistresse *Jone*, thankt her for her great curtesie and company, and then the good man and he walkt into the Towne, and *Jone* hyed her home to her masters, knowing nothing of the intended jest.   Master *Bennedicke* thought every houre twaine, till the Sun was downe, and that he were a bed with his beloved.   At last he had his wish, and home hee came to his friends house.

Then said *John*, master *Bennedick* you must not in any case have a candle when you go into the chamber, for then my kinswoman will be angry, and darke places fits best Lovers desires.

O Mater *Jan* (quoth he) its no such matter for light, mee shall fine Metres *Jone* well enough in the darke.

And entring in the parlour, groping about, hee felt a gowne and hat.   O Metres *Jone* (quoth hee) heere is your gowne and hat, me shal no hurt for a tousand poun.

Then kneeling downe by the bed side, insteade of mistresse *Jone*, he saluted the sow in this sort.   O my love and my delight, it is thy faire face that hath wounded my heart, thy gray sparkling eyes, and thy Lilly white hands, with the comely proportion of thy pretty body, that made mee in seeking thee to forget my selfe, and to find thy favour, lose my owne freedom: but now is the time come wherein I shall reape the fruits of a plentifull harvest.   Now my deare, from thy sweet mouth let mee sucke the hony balme of thy breath, and with my hand stroke those Rosie cheekes of thine, wherein I have tooke such pleasure. Com with thy pretty lips and entertaine me into thy bed with one gentle kisse: Why speakest thou not my sweete heart, and stretch out thy Alabaster armes to infold thy faithfull friend? Why should ill pleasing sleepe close up the chrystall windowes

of thy body so fast, and bereave thee of thy five Lordly attendants wherewith thou wast wont to salute thy friends? let it
not offend thy gentle eares that I thus talk to thee. If thou
hast vowed not to speake, I will not break it: and if thou wilt
command me to bee silent, I will be dumbe: but thou needest
not feare to speak thy minde, seeing the cloudy night concealeth
every thing.

By this time master *Bennedicke* was unready, and slipt into
bed, where the Sowe lay swathed in a sheete, and her head bound
in a great linnen cloth: As soone as he was laid, he began to
embrace his new bedfellow, and laying his lips somewhat neer
her snout, hee felt her draw her breath very short.

Why how now love (quoth he) be you sick, be Got mistris
Jone your breat be very strong: have you no cacke a bed?

The Sow feeling her selfe disturbed, began to grunt and keep
a great stirre: whereat master *Benedick* (like a mad man) ran
out of the bed, crying, de devil de devil. The good man of the
house (being purposely provided) came rushing in with halfe a
dozen of his neighbours, asking what was the matter.

Got ound (quoth *Benedicke*) here be de great devil cry hoh,
hoh, hoh, bee Gossen I tinke you play the knave wid me, and
me wil be revenge be Got.

Sir (quoth hee) I knowing you loved mutton, thought porke
nothing unfit: and therefore provided you a whole Sow, and as
you like this entertainment, spend Portegues. Walke, walk,
Barkeshire maides will be no Italians strumpets, nor the wives
of *Newbery* their bauds.

Barkeshire dog (quoth *Benedick*) owle face shack hang dou
and dy veife, have it not be for me love to sweete Metresse *Jone*,
I will no come in your houz: but farewell tell I cash you, be Goz
bode, I make your hog nose bud.

The good man and his neighbours laught aloud, away went
master *Benedick*, and for very shame departed from *Newbery*
before day.

CHAPTER VIII

How *Jacke* of *Newberie* keeping a very good house, both for his servants and reliefe of the poore, won great credite thereby: and how one of his wives gossips found fault therewith.

GOOD morrow good Gossip: now by my truly I am glad to see you in health. I pray you how doth master *Winchcombe?* What never a great belly yet? now fie: by my fa your husband is waxt idle.

Trust mee Gossip (saith mistresse *Winchcombe*) a great belly comes sooner than a new coate: but you must consider we have not beene long married: But truely gossip you are welcome: I pray you to sit downe, and we will have a morsell of something by and by.

Nay truely gossip, I cannot stay (quoth shee) in troth I must be gone: for I did but even step in to see how you did.

You shall not chuse but stay a while (quoth mistresse *Winchcomb*): and with that a faire napkin was laide upon the little table in the Parlour, hard by the fire side, whereon was set a good cold Capon, with a great deale of other good cheere, with ale and wine plentie.

I pray you good Gossip eate, and I beshrew you if you spare (quoth the one).

I thanke you hartily good Gossip (saith the other). But good gossip I pray you tell me: doth your husband love you well, and make much of you?

Yes truly, I thanke God (quoth shee).

Now by my troth (said the other) it were a shame for him if he should not: for though I say it before your face, though he had little with you, you were worthy to be as good a mans wife as his.

Trust me, I would not change my *John* for my lord Marquesse (quoth shee) a woman can be but well, for I live at hearts ease, and have all things at will, and truly he will not see me lack any thing.

Mary Gods blessing on his hart (quoth her Gossip) it is a good hearing: but I pray you tell me, I heard say, your husband is chosen for our Burgesse in the Parliament house, is it true?

Yes verily (quoth his wife): I wis it is against his will: for it will be no small charges unto him.

Tush woman, what talke you of that? thankes be to God, there is never a Gentleman in all *Barkshire* that is better able to beare it. But heare you, gossip, shall I bee so bold to aske you one question more?

Yes, with all my heart (quoth she).

I heard say that your husband would now put you in your hood and silke gowne, I pray you is it true?

Yes in truth (quoth mistresse *Winchcombe*) but far against my minde Gossip: my french-hood is bought already, and my silke gowne is a making: likewise the Goldsmith hath brought home my chaine and bracelets: but I assure you gossip, if you will beleeve me, I had rather goe an hundred miles, than weare them: for I shall bee so ashamed that I shall not looke upon any of my neighbours for blushing.

And why, I pray you? (quoth her Gossip) I tell you deare woman, you neede not bee any thing abashed or blush at the matter, especially seeing your husbands estate is able to maintaine it: now trust mee truly, I am of opinion you will become it singular well.

Alas (quoth mistresse *Winchcombe*) having never beene used to such attyre, I shall not know where I am, nor how to behave my selfe in it: and beside, my complexion is so blacke, that I shall carry but an ill favoured countenance under a hood.

Now, without doubt (quoth her Gossip) you are to blame to say so: beshrew my heart if I speak it to flatter, you are a very faire and well favoured yongue woman, as any is in *Newberie.* And never feare your behaviour in your hood: for I tell you true, as old and withred as I am my selfe, I could become a hood well enough, and behave my selfe as well in such attyre, as any other whatsoever, and I would not learne of never a one of them all: what woman, I have been a pretty wench in my dayes, and seene some fashions. Therefore you neede not to feare, seeing both your beauty and comely personage deserves no lesse than a french-hood: and be of good comfort. At the first (possible) folkes will gaze something at you: but bee not you abashed for that, it is better they should wonder at your good fortune, than lament at your misery: but when they have seene you two or three times in that attyre, they will afterward little respect it: for every new thing at the first seemes rare, but being once a little used, it growes common.

Surely Gossip you say true, (quoth shee) and I am but a foole

to bee so bashfull: it is no shame to use Gods gifts for our credits,
and well might my husband thinke me unworthy to have them,
if I would not weare them: and though I say it, my hoode is a
faire one, as any woman weares in this Country, and my gold
chaine and bracelets are none of the worst sort, and I will shew
them you, because you shall give your opinion upon them:
and therewithall shee stept into her chamber and fetcht them
forth.

When her Gossip saw them, shee said, now beshrew my fingers
but these are faire ones indeede. And when doe you meane to
weare them Gossip?

At Whitsontide (quoth shee) if God spare mee life.

I wish that well you may weare them (said her Gossip) and I
would I were worthy to bee with you when you dresse your
selfe, it should bee never the worse for you. I would order the
matter so, that you should set every thing about you in such
sort, as never a Gentlewoman of them all should staine you.

Mistris *Winchcombe* gave her great thanks for her favour,
saying, that if she needed her helpe, she would be bold to send
for her.

Then began her Gossip to turne her tongue to another tune,
and now to blame her for her great house keeping. And thus
shee began: Gossip, you are but a yongue woman, and one that
hath had no great experience of the World, in my opinion you
are something too lavish in expences: pardon mee good Gossip,
I speake but for good will; and because I love you, I am the
more bold to admonish you: I tell you plaine, were I the mistresse
of such a house, having such large allowance as you have, I
would save 20. pound a yeare that you spend to no purpose.

Which way might that bee (quoth Mistris *Winchcombe*)?
indeed I confesse I am but a greene huswife, and one that hath
had but small triall in the World, therefore I would bee very
glad to learne any thing that were for my husbands profit and
my commoditie.

Then listen to mee (quoth shee): You feede your folkes with
the best of the beefe, and the finest of the wheate, which in my
opinion is a great oversight: neither doe I heare of any Knight
in this countrie that doth it. And to say the truth, how were
they able to beare that port which they doe, if they saved it
not by some meanes? Come thither, and I warrant you that
you shall see but browne bread on the boord: if it bee wheate
and rye mingled together, it is a great matter, and the bread
highly commended: but most commonly they eate eyther barly

bread, or rye mingled with pease, and such like course graine: which is doubtlesse but of small price, and there is no other bread allowed, except at their owne boord. And in like manner for their meate: it is well knowne, that neckes and points of beefe is their ordinarie fare: which because it is commonly leane, they seeth therewith now and then a peece of bacon or porke, whereby they make their pottage fat, and therewith drives out the rest with more content. And thus must you learne to doe. And beside that, the midriffes of the Oxen, and the cheekes, the sheepes heads, and the gathers, which you give away at your gate, might serve them wel enough: which would bee a great sparing to your other meate, and by this meanes you would save in the yeare much money, whereby you might the better maintaine your hoode and silke gowne. Againe, you serve your folkes with such superfluities, that they spoile in a manner as much as they eate: beleeve mee were I their Dame, they should have things more sparingly, and then they would thinke it more dainty.

Trust mee Gossip (quoth Mistresse *Winchcombe*) I know your wordes in many things to bee true: for my folkes are so corne fed, that wee have much adoo to please them in their dyet: one doth say this is too salt, and another saith this is too grosse, this is too fresh, and that too fat, and twenty faults they will finde at their meales: I warrant you they make such parings of their cheese, and keepe such chipping of their bread, that their very ortes would serve two or three honest folkes to their dinner.

And from whence I pray you proceedes that (quoth her Gossip) but of too much plentie? but yfaith were they my servants, I would make them glad of the worst crummes they cast away, and thereupon I drink to you, and I thank you for my good cheere with all my heart.

Much good may it do you good gossip (said mistresse *Winchcomb*): and I pray you when you come this way, let us see you.

That you shall verily (quoth she) and so away she went.

After this, mistresse *Winchcombe* tooke occasion to give her folks shorter commons, and courser meate than they were wont to have: which at length being come to the good mans eare, hee was very much offended therewith, saying: I will not have my people thus pincht of their victualls. Empty platters makes greedy stomackes, and where scarcity is kept, hunger is nourished: and therefore wife as you love mee, let mee have no more of this doings.

Husband (quoth shee) I would they should have enough: but

it is sinne to suffer, and a shame to see the spoile they make: I
could bee very well content to give them their bellies full, and
that which is sufficient, but it grieves mee, to tell you true, to
see how coy they are, and the small care they have in wasting
of things: and I assure you, the whole Towne cries shame of it,
and it hath bred mee no small discredit for looking no better to
it. Trust mee no more, if I was not chekt in my owne house
about this matter, when my eares did burne to heare what
was spoken.

Who was it that chekt thee, I pray thee tell mee? was it not
your old gossip, dame dainty, mistresse trip and goe? I beleeve
it was.

Why man if it were she, you know shee hath beene an old
house-keeper, and one that hath known the World, and that
shee told mee was for good will.

Wife (quoth hee) I would not have thee to meddle with such
light braind huswives, and so I have told thee a good many
times, and yet I cannot get you to leave her company.

Leave her company? why husband, so long as she is an honest
woman, why should I leave her company? She never gave me
hurtfull counsell in all her life, but hath alwaies been ready to
tell mee things for my profit, though you take it not so. Leave
her company? I am no gyrle I would you should well know, to
bee taught what company I should keepe: I keepe none but
honest company, I warrant you. Leave her company ketha?
Alas poore soule, this reward shee hath for her good will. I wis,
I wis, she is more your friend, than you are your owne.

Well, let her bee what shee will (said her husband): but if shee
come any more in my house, she were as good no. And therefore take this for a warning I would advise you: and so away
he went.

CHAPTER IX

How a Draper in *London*, who owed *Jacke* of *Newbery* much mony, became
  bankrout, whom *Jack* of *Newbery* found carrying a porters basket
  on his neck, and how he set him up againe at his owne cost, which
  Draper afterward became an Alderman of *London*.

THERE was one *Randoll Pert* a Draper, dwelling in *Watling-
streete*, that owed *Jacke* of *Newbery* five hundred pounds at one
time, who in the end fell greatly to decay, in so much that hee
was cast in prison, and his wife with her poore children turned
out of doores. All his creditors except *Winchcombe* had a share
of his goods, never releasing him out of prison, so long as he had
one peny to satisfie them. But when this tidings was brought
to *Jack* of *Newberies* eare, his friends counselled him to lay
his action against him.

Nay (quoth he) if hee be not able to pay me when he is at
liberty, he will never be able to pay mee in prison: and therefore
it were as good for me to forbear my mony without troubling
him, as to adde more sorrow to his grieved heart, and be never
the neerer. Misery is troden down by many, and once brought
low, they are seldome or never relieved: therefore he shall rest
for me untoucht, and I would to God he were cleare of all other
mens debts, so that I gave him mine to begin the world againe.

Thus lay the poore Draper a long time in prison, in which
space, his Wife which before for daintinesse would not foule
her fingers, nor turne her head aside, for feare of hurting the
set of her neckenger, was glad to goe about and wash buckes
at the Thames side, and to be a chare-woman in rich mens
houses, her soft hand was now hardened with scouring, and in
steade of gold rings upon her lilly fingers, they were now fild
with chaps, provoked by the sharpe, lee, and other drudgeries.

At last, Master *Winchcombe* being (as you heard) chosen
against the Parliament a Burgesse for the towne of *Newberie*,
and comming up to *London* for the same purpose, when hee was
alighted at his Inne, hee left one of his men there, to get a Porter
to bring his trunke up to the place of his lodging. Poore
Randoll Pert, which lately before was come out of prison, having
no other meanes of maintenance, became a Porter to carry
burthens from one place to another, having an old ragged

doublet, and a torne paire of breeches, with his hose out at the
heeles, and a paire of old broken slip shooes on his feete, a rope
about his middle in stead of a girdle, and on his head an old
greasie cap, which had so many holes in it, that his haire started
through it: who assoone as hee heard one call for a Porter,
made answer straight: heere master, what is it that you would
have carried?

Mary (quoth hee) I would have this Trunke borne to the
spread Eagle at *Iviebridge*.

You shall Master (quoth hee) but what will you give mee for
my paines?

I will give thee two pence.

A penny more and I will carry it (said the Porter): and so
being agreed, away he went with his burthen, till he came to
the *spread Eagle* doore, where on a sudden espying Master
Winchcombe standing, he cast downe the Trunke, and ran away
as hard as ever hee could.

Master *Winchcombe* wondring what hee meant thereby, caused
his man to runne after him, and so fetch him againe: but when
hee saw one pursue him, hee ranne then the faster; and in
running, here hee lost one of his slip shooes, and then another:
ever looking behinde him, like a man pursued with a deadly
weapon, fearing every twinkling of an eye to bee thrust thorow.
At last his breech, being tide but with one point, what with the
haste hee made, and the weakenesse of the thong, fell about his
heeles: which so shackled him, that downe hee fell in the streete
all along, sweating and blowing, being quite worne out of
breath: and so by this meanes the Serving-man overtooke him,
and taking him by the sleeve, being as windlesse as the other,
stood blowing and puffing a great while ere they could speake
one to another.

Sirrah (quoth the Serving man) you must come to my Master,
you have broken his Trunke all to peeces, by letting it fall.

O for Gods sake (quoth hee) let me goe, for Christs sake let
mee goe, or else Master *Winchcombe* of *Newbery* will arrest mee,
and then I am undone for ever.

Now by this time *Jacke* of *Newbery* had caused his Trunke to
bee carried into the house, and then he walked along to know
what the matter was: and when he heard the Porter say that he
would arrest him, hee wondred greatly, and having quite forgot
Perts favour, being so greatly changed by imprisonment and
poverty, hee said, Wherefore should I arrest thee? tell me good
fellow: for my owne part I know no reason for it.

O Sir (quoth hee) I would to God I knew none neyther.

Then asking him what his name was: the poore man falling downe on his knees, said: Good Master *Winchcombe* beare with me and caste mee not into prison: my name is *Pert*, and I do not deny but that I owe you five hundred pound: yet for the love of God take pitty upon mee.

When Master *Winchcombe* heard this, hee wondred greatly at the man, and did as much pitty his misery, though as yet hee made it not known, saying: Passion of my heart man, thou wilt never pay mee thus: never thinke being a Porter to pay five hundred pound debt. But this hath your prodigality brought you to, your thriftlesse neglecting of your businesse, that set more by your pleasure than your profit. Then looking better upon him, he said: What, never a shooe to thy foote, hose to thy legge, band to thy necke, nor cap to thy head? O *Pert*, this is strange: but wilt thou be an honest man, and give me a bil of thy hand for my money?

Yes sir, with all my hart (quoth *Pert*).

Then come to the Scriveners (quoth he) and dispatch it, and I will not trouble thee.

Now when they were come thither, with a great many following them at their heeles, master *Winchcombe* said: Hearest thou Scrivener? this fellow must give me a bill of his hand for five hundred pounds, I pray thee make it as it should bee.

The Scrivener looking upon the poore man, and seeing him in that case, said to master *Winchcombe*: Sir, you were better to let it bee a Bond, and have some sureties bound with him.

Why Scrivener (quoth hee) doest thou thinke this is not a sufficient man of himselfe for five hundred pound?

Truely Sir (said the Scrivener) if you thinke him so, you and I are of two mindes:

Ile tell thee what (quoth Master *Winchcombe*) were it not that wee are all mortall, I would take his word assoone as his Bill or Bond; the honesty of a man is all.

And wee in *London* (quoth the Scrivener) doe trust Bonds farre better than honesty. But Sir, when must this money bee paid?

Marry Scrivener, when this man is Sherifte ot *London*.

At that word the Scrivener and the people standing by laughed heartily, saying: In truth Sir, make no more adoo but forgive it him: as good to doe the one as the other.

Nay, beleeve mee (quoth hee) not so: therefore doe as I bid you.

Whereupon the Scrivener made the Bill to be paid when *Randoll Pert* was Sheriffe of *London*, and thereunto set his owne hand for a witnesse, and twenty persons more that stood by, set to their hands likewise.

Then hee asked *Pert* what he should have for carrying his trunk.

Sir (quoth hee) I should have three pence, but seeing I finde you so kinde, I will take but two pence at this time.

Thankes good *Pert* (quoth he) but for thy three pence, there is three shillings: and looke thou come to mee to morrow morning betimes.

The poore man did so, at what time master *Winchcombe* had provided him out of *Burchin-lane*, a faire sute of apparell, Marchant like, with a faire blacke cloak, and all other things fit to the same: then hee tooke him a shop in *Canweek streete*, and furnisht the same shop with a thousand pounds worth of cloath: by which meanes, and other favours that master *Winchcombe* did him, hee grew againe into great credit, and in the end became so wealthy, that while master *Winchcombe* lived hee was chosen Sheriffe, at what time he payed five hundred pounds every penny, and after dyed an Alderman of the Citie.

CHAPTER X

UPON a time it came to passe, when master *Winchcombe* was
farre from home, and his wife gone abroad: That mistris many
better, dame tittle, tattle, Gossip pintpot, according to her
old custome, came to mistris *Winchcombes* house, perfectly
knowing of the good mans absence, and little thinking the good
wife was from home: where knocking at the gate, *Tweedle* stept
out and askt who was there? where hastily opening the wicket,
he suddainely discovered the full proportion of this foule beast,
who demanded if their mistris were within.

What mistres *Franke* (quoth hee) in faith welcome: how have
you done a great while? I pray you come in.

Nay, I cannot stay (quoth shee). Notwithstanding, I did
call to speake a word or two with your mistris, I pray you tell
her that I am here.

So I will (quoth hee) so soone as she comes in.

Then said the woman, What is she abroad? why then farewell
good *Tweedle*.

Why what haste, what haste, mistris *Franke*, (quoth he) I
pray you stay and drink ere you goe. I hope a cuppe of new
Sacke will do your old belly no hurt:

What (quoth shee) have you new Sacke already? Now by
my honesty I drunke none this yeare, and therefore I doe not
greatly care if I take a taste before I goe: and with that shee
went into the wine-cellar with *Tweedle*, where first hee set before
her a peece of powdred beefe as greene as a leeke: And then
going into the kitchen, he brought her a peece of rosted beefe
hote from the spit.

Now certaine of the maidens of the house, and some of the
yongue men, who had long before determined to bee revenged
of this pratling huswife: came into the Cellar one after another,
one of them bringing a great peece of a gammon of Bacon in his
hand: and every one bad mistris *Franke* welcome: and first
one drunke to her, and then another, and so the third, the
fourth, and the fift: so that mistresse *Frankes* braines waxt

72

as mellow as a Pippin at Michaelmas, and so light, that sitting
in the Cellar, she thought the world ran round. They seeing
her to fall into merry humours, whetted her on in merriment
as much as they could, saying, Mistresse *Franke*, spare not I
pray you, but thinke your selfe as welcome as any woman in
all *Newberie*, for we have cause to love you, because you love
our Mistresse so well.

Now by my troth (quoth shee) lisping in her speech (her
tongue waxing somewhat too big for her mouth) I love your
Mistresse well indeed, as if shee were mine owne daughter.

Nay but heare you (quoth they) she begins not to deale well
with us now

No my Lambs (quoth shee) why so?

Because (quoth they) she seeks to barre us of our allowance,
telling our Master, that hee spends too much in house-keeping.

Nay then (quoth shee) your Mistresse is both an Asse, and
a Foole: and though shee go in her Hood, what care I? she is
but a girle to mee: Twittle twattle, I know what I know: Go
too, drinke to mee. Well *Tweedle*, I drinke to thee with all
my heart: why thou horeson, when wilt thou bee married?
O that I were a yongue wench for thy sake: but tis no matter,
though I be but a poore woman, I am a true woman. Hang
dogs, I have dwelt in this towne these thirty winters.

Why then (quoth they) you have dwelt heere longer than
our Master.

Your Master (quoth shee)? I knew your Master a boy, when
he was calld *Jacke* of *Newberie*, I *Jacke*, I knew him calld plaine
Jacke: and your Mistresse, now shee is rich, and I am poore,
but its no matter, I knew her a draggle tayle girle, marke yee?

But now (quoth they) shee takes upon her lustily, and hath
quite forgot what shee was.

Tush, what will you have of a greene thing (quoth shee)?
Heere I drinke to you, so long as she goes where she list a
gossiping: and its no matter, little said is soone amended:
But heare you my masters, though mistresse *Winchcombe* goe
in her Hood, I am as good as shee, I care not who tell it her:
I spend not my husbands money in Cherries and Codlings, go
too, go too, I know what I say well enough: I thanke God I am
not drunke: Mistresse *Winchcomb*, mistresse? No, *Nan Winchcombe*, I will call her name, plaine *Nan*: what, I was a woman
when she was sirreverence a paltry girle, though now shee goes
in her Hood and Chaine of Gold: what care I for her? I am her
elder, and I know more of her trickes: nay I warrant you, I

know what I say, tis no matter, laugh at me and spare not, I am not drunke I warrant: and with that being scant able to holde open her eyes, she beganne to nodde, and to spill the Wine out of the Glasse: which they perceyving, let her alone, going out of the Cellar till shee was sound asleepe, and in the meane space they devised how to finish this peece of knavery.

At last they all consented to lay her forth at the backe side of the house, halfe a mile off, even at the foote of a Style, that whosoever came next over, might finde her: notwithstanding, *Tweedle* stayed hard by to see the end of this Action.   At last comes a notable Clowne from *Greeneham*, taking his way to *Newbery*: who comming hastily over the Style, stumbled at the woman, and fell down cleane over her.   But in his starting up, seeing it was a woman, cryed out, Alas, alas.

How now, what is the matter (quoth *Tweedle*)?

O (quoth hee) here lies a dead woman.

A dead woman (quoth *Tweedle*) thats not so I trow, and with that hee tumbled her about:

Bones of me (quoth *Tweedle*) tis a drunken woman, and one of the Towne undoubtedly: in troth it is a great pitty she should lye here.

Why doe you know her (quoth the Clowne)?

No not I (quoth *Tweedle*) neverthelesse, I will give thee halfe a groate, and take her in thy Basket, and carry her throughout the Towne, and see if any body know her.

Then said the other, let me see the money, and I will: For by the Masse, che earnd not halfe a groat this great while.

There it is (quoth *Tweedle*): then the fellow put her in his Basket, and so lifted her upon his back.

Now by the Masse shee stinkes vilely of Drinke, or Wine, or some thing.   But tell me, What shall I say when I come into the Towne (quoth he)?

First (quoth *Tweedle*) I would have thee so soone as ever thou canst get to the Townes end, with a lusty voyce to cry, O yes, and then say, Who knowes this woman, who?   And though possible some will say, I know her, and I know her; yet doe not thou set her downe till thou commest to the Market Crosse, and there use the like wordes: and if any be so friendly, to tell thee where shee dwels, then just before her doore cry so againe: and if thou performe this bravely, I will give thee halfe a groat more.

Master *Tweedle* (quoth he) I knowe you well enough, you dwell with Master *Winchcombe*, doe you not?   Ifaith if I doe it not in the nicke, give mee never a penny:

And so away hee went, till hee came to the Townes end, and there he cryes out as boldly as any Bayliffes man, O yes, who knowes this woman, who?

Then said the drunken woman in the Basket, her head falling first on one side, and then on the other side, Who co mee, who?

Then said he againe, Who knowes this woman, who?

Who co mee, who? (quoth shee) and looke how oft he spoke the one, shee spoke the other: saying still, Who co me, who co me, who? Whereat all the people in the streete fell into such a laughter, that the teares ranne downe againe.

At last one made answere, saying: Good fellow, shee dwels in the *North brooke street*, a little beyond Master *Winchcombes*.

The fellow hearing that, goes downe thither in all haste, and there in the hearing of a hundred people, cryes, Who knowes this woman, who?

Whereat her husband comes out, saying: Marry that doe I too well, God helpe mee.

Then said the Clowne, If you know her, take her: for I knowe her not but for a drunken beast.

And as her husband tooke her out of the Basket, she gave him a sound boxe on the eare, saying, What you Queanes, do you mocke mee? and so was carried in.

But the next day, when her braine was quiet, and her head cleered of these foggy vapours, she was so ashamed of her selfe, that shee went not forth of her doores a long time after: and if any body did say unto her, Who co me, who? shee would be so mad and furious, that shee would be ready to draw her knife and sticke them, and scold, as if she strove for the best game at the cucking stoole. Moreover, her pratling to mistresse *Winchcombes* folks of their mistresse, made her on the other side to fall out with her, in such sort, that shee troubled them no more, eyther with her company or her counsell.

CHAPTER XI

At the winning of *Morlesse* in *France*, the noble Earle of *Surrey* being at that time Lord High Admirall of *England*, made many Knights: among the rest was Sir *George Rigley*, brother to Sir *Edward Rigley*, and sundry other, whose valours farre surpassed their wealth: so that when peace bred a scarcitie in their purse, and that their credits grew weake in the Citie, they were enforced to ride into the Country, where at their friends houses they might have favourable welcome, without coyne or grudging.

Among the rest, *Jacke* of *Newberie* that kept a table for all commers, was never lightly without many such guestes: where they were sure to have both welcome and good cheare, and their mirth no lesse pleasing than their meate was plenty. Sir *George* having lyen long at boord in this brave Yeomans house, at length fell in liking of one of his maidens, who was as fair as she was fond. This lusty wench hee so allured with hope of marriage, that at length she yeelded him her love, and therewithall bent her whole study to worke his content: but in the end, shee so much contented him, that it wrought altogether her owne discontent: to become high, she laid her selfe so low, that the Knight suddenly fell over her, which fall became the rising of her belley. But when this wanton perceived her selfe to be with childe, she made her moane unto the Knight in this manner.

Ah Sir *George*, now is the time to performe your promise, or to make me a spectacle of infamy to the whole world for ever: in the one you shal discharge the duety of a true knight, but in the other shew your selfe a most perjured person. Small honour will it bee to boast in the spoyle of poore maydens, whose innocencie all good Knights ought much rather to defend.

Why thou lewd paltry thing (quoth he) commest thou to father thy bastard upon me? Away ye dunghill carrion, away: Heare you good huswife, get you among your companions, and lay your litter where you list: for if you trouble mee any more, by heaven I sweare, thou shalt dearely abide it: and so bending his browes like the angry god of war, he went his wayes, leaving the childe-breeding wench to the hazzard of her fortune, eyther good or bad.

This poore mayden seeing her selfe for her kindnesse thus cast off, shedde many teares of sorrow for her sinne, inveighing, with many bitter groanes, against the unconstancie of love alluring men. But in the end, when shee saw no other remedy, shee made her case knowne unto her mistresse: who after she had given her many bitter checks and tants, threatning to turne her out of doores, shee opened the matter to her husband.

So soone as he heard thereof, hee made no more to doe, but presently poasted to *London* after Sir *George*, and found him at my Lord Admirals. What, master *Winchcombe* (quoth he) you are heartily welcome to *London*, and I thanke you for my good cheere. I pray you how doth your good wife, and all our friends in *Barkshire?*

All well and merry, I thanke you good Sir *George* (quoth hee): I left them in health, and I hope they doe so continue. And trust me sir (quoth he) having earnest occasion to come up to talke with a bad debtor, in my journey it was my chance to light in company of a gallant widow: a Gentlewoman shee is, of wondrous good wealth, whom griesely death hath bereft of a kinde husband, making her a widow, ere she had been halfe a yeare a wife: her land, Sir *George*, is as well worth a hundred pound a yeare as one penny, being as faire and comely a creature, as any of her degree in our whole countrey: Now sir, this is the worst, by the reason that she doubts her selfe to be with childe, she hath vowed not to marry these twelve moneths: but because I wish you well, and the Gentlewoman no hurt, I came of purpose from my businesse to tell you thereof: Now Sir *George*, if you thinke her a fit wife for you, ride to her, wooe her, winne her, and wedde her.

I thanke you good master *Winchcombe* (quoth he) for your favour ever toward me, and gladly would I see this yongue widow if I wist where.

She dwelleth not halfe a mile from my house (quoth master *Winchcombe*) and I can send for her at any time if you please.

Sir *George* hearing this, thought it was not best to come there, fearing *Joane* would father a childe upon him, and therefore answered, hee had no leisure to come from my Lord: But (quoth he) would I might see her in *London*, on the condition it cost me twenty nobles.

Tush Sir *George* (quoth Master *Winchcombe*) delayes in love are dangerous, and he that will wooe a widow, must take time by the forelocke, and suffer none other to steppe before him, lest hee leape without the widowes love. Notwithstanding, seeing now I have told you of it, I will take my Gelding and get me home: if I heare of her comming to *London*, I will send you word, or perhaps come my selfe: till when, adiew good Sir *George*.

Thus parted master *Winchcombe* from the Knight: and being come home, in short time he got a fair Taffety gowne, and a French hood for his mayde, saying: Come ye drabbe, I must be fayne to cover a foule fault with a fayre garment, yet all will not hide your great belly: but if I finde meanes to make you a Lady. what will you say then?

O Master (quoth shee) I shall be bound while I live to pray for you.

Come then minion (quoth her mistresse) and put you on this gowne and french hood: for seeing you have lien with a Knight, you must needs be a Gentlewoman.

The mayde did so: and being thus attyred, shee was set on a fayre Gelding, and a couple of men sent with her up to *London*: and being well instructed by her master and dame what she should doe, she tooke her journy to the Citie in the Tearme time, and lodged at the *Bell* in the *Strand*: and mistresse *Lovelesse* must be her name, for so her Master had warned her to call her selfe: Neyther did the men that wayted on her, know the contrary; for master *Winchcombe* had borrowed them of their Maister, to wayte upon a friend of his to *London*, because hee could not spare any of his owne servants at that time: notwithstanding, they were appointed for the Gentlewomans credite, to say they were her owne men. This being done, master *Winchcombe* sent Sir *George* a letter, that the Gentlewoman which he told him of, was now in *London*, lying at the *Bell* in the *Strand*, having great businesse at the Tearme.

With which newes Sir *Georges* heart was on fire, till such time as he might speake with her: three or foure times went he thither, and still she would not be spoken withall, the which close keeping of her selfe, made him the more earnest in his suite.

At length hee watcht her so narrowly, that finding her going forth in an evening, shee followed her, shee having one man before, and another behinde: carrying a verie stately gate in the streete, it drove him into the greater liking of her, being the more urged to utter his minde. And suddenly stepping before her, hee thus saluted her, Gentlewoman, God save you, I have often beene at your lodging, and could never finde you at leasure.

Why sir (quoth shee) (counterfeiting her naturall speech)
have you any businesse with me?

Yes faire Widow (quoth hee) as you are a clyent to the law,
so am I a sutor for your love: and may I finde you so favourable
to let mee pleade my owne case at the barre of your beauty,
I doubt not but to unfold so true a tale, as I trust will cause
you to give sentence on my side.

You are a merry Gentleman (quoth shee): but for my owne
part, I know you not; neverthelesse, in a case of love, I will bee
no let to your sute, though perhaps I helpe you little therein.
And therefore Sir, if it please you to give attendance at my
lodging, upon my returne from the *Temple*, you shall know more
of my minde, and so they parted.

Sir *George* receiving hereby some hope of good happe, stayed
for his deare at her lodging doore: whom at her comming shee
friendly greeted, saying, Surely Sir, your diligence is more than
the profit you shall get thereby: but I pray you how shall I
call your name?

George Rigley (quoth hee) I am called, and for some small
deserts I was knighted in *France*.

Why then Sir *George* (quoth shee) I have done you too much
wrong to make you thus dance attendance on my worthlesse
person.   But let mee bee so bold to request you to tell mee, how
you came to know mee: for my owne part I cannot remember
that ever I saw you before.

Mistris *Lovelesse* (said Sir *George*) I am well acquainted with
a good neighbour of yours, called Master *Winchcombe*, who is my
very good friend, and to say the truth, you were commended
unto mee by him.

Truly Sir *George* (said shee) you are so much the better welcome: Neverthelesse, I have made a vowe not to love any man
for this twelve moneths space.   And therefore Sir, till then I
would wish you to trouble your selfe no further in this matter
till that time be expired: and then if I finde you bee not intangled
to any other, and that by triall I finde out the truth of your love,
for Master *Winchcombe* sake your welcome shall be as good as
any other Gentlemans whatsoever.

Sir *George* having received this answer, was wonderous woe,
cursing the day that ever he meddled with *Joane*, whose time of
deliverance would come long before a twelve Moneth were
expired, to his utter shame, and overthrow of his good fortune:
for by that meanes should hee have Master *Winchcombe* his
enemy, and therewithall the losse of this faire Gentlewoman.

Wherefore to prevent this mischiefe, hee sent a Letter in all haste to Master *Winchcombe,* requesting him most earnestly to come up to *London,* by whose perswasion hee hoped straight to finish the marriage. Master *Winchcombe* fulfilled his request, and then presently was the marriage solemnized at the Tower of *London,* in presence of many Gentlemen of Sir *Georges* friends. But when hee found it was *Joane* whom he had gotten with childe, hee fretted and fumed, stampt, and star'd like a divell.

Why (quoth M. *Winchcombe*) what needs all this? Came you to my table to make my maide your strumpet? had you no mans house to dishonour but mine? Sir, I would you should well know, that I account the poorest wench in my house too good to bee your whore, were you ten knights: and seeing you tooke pleasure to make her your wanton, take it no scorne to make her your wife: and use her well too, or you shall heare of it. And hold thee *Joane* (quoth hee) there is a hundred pounds for thee: And let him not say thou camest to him a begger.

Sir *George* seeing this, and withall casting in his minde what friend Master *Winchcombe* might bee to him, taking his wife by the hand, gave her a loving kisse, and Master *Winchcombe* great thankes. Whereupon hee willed him for two yeares space to take his dyet and his Ladies at his house: which the Knight accepting, rode straight with his wife to *Newberie.*

Then did the Mistris make curtsie to the Maide, saying: You are welcome Madam, giving her the upper hand in all places. And thus they lived afterward in great joy: and our King hearing how *Jacke* had matcht Sir *George,* laughing heartily thereat, gave him a living for ever, the better to maintaine my Lady his Wife.

THOMAS

OF

READING.

OR,

The ſixe worthie Yeomen
of the Weſt.

Now the fift time corrected and enlarged
By *T. D.*

LONDON,
Printed by W. I. for T. P.
1 6 2 3.

THE PLEASANT HISTORIE OF THE SIXE WORTHY YEOMEN OF THE WEST

IN the dayes of King *Henry* the first, who was the first King that instituted the high Court of Parliament, there lived nine men, which for the trade of Clothing, were famous through-out all England. Which Art in those daies was held in high reputation, both in respect of the great riches that thereby was gotten, as also of the benefite it brought to the whole Common-wealth: the yonger sons of Knights and Gentlemen, to whom their Fathers would leave no lands, were most commonly pre-ferred to learn this trade, to the end that therby they might live in good estate, and drive forth their daies in prosperity.

Among all Crafts this was the onely chiefe, for that it was the greatest merchandize, by the which our Countrey became famous through all Nations. And it was verily thought, that the one halfe of the people in the land lived in those daies therby, and in such good sort, that in the Common-wealth there were few or no beggers at all: poore people, whom God lightly blesseth with most children, did by meanes of this occupation so order them, that by the time that they were come to be sixe or seven yeares of age, they were able to get their owne bread: Idlenesse was then banished our coast, so that it was a rare thing to heare of a thiefe in those daies. Therefore it was not without cause that Clothiers were then both honoured and loved, among whom these nine persons in this Kings daies were of great credit, viz. *Tho. Cole* of *Reading*, *Gray* of *Glocester*, *Sutton* of *Salisburie*, *Fitzallen* of *Worcester*, (commonly called *William* of *Worcester*) *Tom Dove* of *Excester*, and *Simon* of *South-hampton*, alias *Sup-broath*: who were by the King called, The sixe worthy Husbands of the West. Then were there three living in the North, that is to say, *Cutbert* of *Kendall*, *Hogekins* of *Hallifax*, and *Martin Byram* of *Manchester*. Every one of these kept a great number of servants at worke, spinners, carders, weavers, fullers, dyers, sheeremen, and rowers, to the great admiration of all those that came into their houses to behold them.

Now you shall understand, these gallant Clothiers, by reason of their dwelling places, separated themselves in three severall companies: *Gray* of *Glocester*, *William* of *Worcester*, and *Thomas* of *Reading*, because their journey to *London* was all one way, they conversed commonly together. And *Dove* of *Excester*, *Sutton* of *Salisburie*, and *Simon* of *South-hampton*, they in like sort kept company the one with the other, meeting ever all together at *Basingstoke*: and the three Northerne Clothiers did the like, who commonly did not meet till they came to Bosome Inne in *London*.

Moreover, for the love and delight that these Westerne men had each in others companie, they did so provide, that their Waines and themselves would ever meet upon one day in *London* at *Jarrats* Hall, surnamed the Gyant, for that hee surpassed all other men of that age, both in stature and strength: whose merriments and memorable deedes, I will set downe unto you in this following discourse.

CHAPTER I

This King *Henry*, who for his great learning and wisdome was called *Beauclarke*, beeing the third Son to the renowned Conquerour: after the death of his brother *William Rufus*, tooke upon him the gouvernement of this Land, in the absence of his second brother *Robert* Duke of *Normandie*, who at this time was at wars amongst the Infidels, and was chosen King of *Jerusalem*, the which he, for the love he bare to his owne countrey, refused, and with great honour returned from the holy Land; of whose comming when King *Henrie* understood, knowing hee would make claime to the crowne, sought by all meanes possible to winne the good will of his Nobilitie, and to get the favor of the Commons by curtesie: for the obtaining whereof hee did them many favours, thereby the better to strengthen himselfe against his brother.

It chanced on a time, as he, with one of his sonnes, and divers of his Nobilitie, rode from *London* towards *Wales*, to appease the fury of the Welshmen, which then began to raise themselves in armes against his authority, that he met with a great number of Waines loaden with cloath, comming to *London*, and seeing them still drive one after another so many together, demaunded whose they were:

The Waine-men answered in this sort: *Coles* of *Reading* (quoth they.)

Then by and by the King asked another, saying: Whose cloth is all this?

Old *Coles* (quoth he):

And againe anone after he asked the same question to others, and stil they answered, Old *Coles*.

And it is to be remembred, that the King met them in such a place, so narrow and streight, that he with the rest of his traine, were faine to stand as close to the hedge, whilest the carts passed by, the which at that time being in number above two hundred, was neere hand an houre ere the King could get roome to be gone: so that by his long stay, he began to be displeased, although the admiration of that sight did much qualifie his furie; but breaking out in discontent, by reason of his stay, he said, he thought Old *Cole* had got a Commission for all the carts in the country to cary his cloth.

And how if he have (quoth one of the Wain men) doth that grieve you good sir?

Yes, good sir (said our King) what say you to that?

The fellow seeing the King (in asking that question) to bend his browes, though he knew not what he was, yet being abasht, he answered thus: Why sir, if you be angry, no body can hinder you; for possible sir, you have anger at commaundement.

The king seeing him in uttering of his wordes to quiver and quake, laughed heartily at him, as well in respect of his simple answere, as at his feare: and so soone after the last Wain went by, which gave present passage unto him and his Nobles: and thereupon entring into communication of the commoditie of cloathing, the King gave order at his home returne, to have Old *Cole* brought before his Majestie, to the intent he might have conference with him, noting him to be a subject of great abilitie: but by that time he came within a mile of *Stanes*, he met another company of waines in like sort laden with cloth, whereby the King was driven into a further admiration: and demanding whose they were, answere was made in this sort:

They be goodman *Suttons* of *Salisbury*, good sir: and by that time a score of them were past, he asked againe, saying: whose are these;

Suttons of *Salisburie* (qd. they) and so still, as often as the King asked that question, they answered, *Suttons* of *Salisburie*.

God send me many such *Suttons* (said the King).

And thus the farther he travelled Westward, more Waines and more he met continually: upon which occasion he said to his Nobles, That it would never grieve a King to die for the defence of a fertile Countrie and faithfull subjects. I alwaies thought (quoth he) that *Englands* valor was more than her wealth, yet now I see her wealth sufficient to maintaine her valour, which I will seeke to cherish in all I may, and with my sword keepe my selfe in possession of that I have, Kings and Lovers can brooke no partners: and therefore let my Brother *Robert* thinke, that although hee was Heire to *England* by birth, yet I am King by possession. All his favourers I must account my foes, and will serve them as I did the ungratefull Earle of *Shrewsbury*, whose lands I have seized, and banisht his body.

But now we will leave the King to his journey into *Wales*, and waiting his home returne, in the meane time tell you the meeting of these jolly Clothiers at *London*.

CHAPTER II

How *William* of *Worcester*, *Gray* of *Gloucester*, and old *Cole* of *Reading*,
met altogether at *Reading*, and of their communication by the way
as they rode to *London*

WHEN *Gray* of *Glocester*, and *William* of *Worcester* were come
to *Reading*, according to their custome, they alwaies called olde
Cole to have his companie to *London*, who also duely attended
their comming, having provided a good breakfast for them:
and when they had well refreshed themselves, they tooke their
horses and rode on towards the Cittie: and in their journey
William of *Worcester* asked them if they had not heard of the
earle of *Moraigne* his escape out of the land:

What is he fled (qd. *Gray*)?

I muse much at this matter, being in such great regard with
the King as he was: but I pray you, do you not know the cause
of his going (qd. *Cole*)?

The common report (quoth *Gray*) is this, that the covetous
earle, who through a greedy desire, never left begging of the
King for one thing or other, and his request being now denied
him, of meere obstinacie and wilfull frowardnesse, hath banished
himselfe out of the land, and quite forsaken the Countrey of
Cornwall, having made a vow never to set foote within *England*
againe, and as report goeth, he with the late banisht Earle of
Shrewsbury, have joyned themselves with *Robert* duke of *Normandie*, against the King, the which action of theirs hath inflamed the Kings wrath, that their Ladies with their Children
are quite turned out of doores succorlesse and friendlesse, so
that as it is told me, they wander up and downe the countrie
like forlorne people, and although many doe pittie them, yet
few doe releeve them.

A lamentable hearing (qd. *William* of *Worcester*) and with
that casting their eies aside, they aspied *Tom Dove* with the
rest of his companions come riding to meete them, who as soone
as they were come thither, fell into such pleasant discourses,
as did shorten the long way they had to *Colebroke*, where alwaies
at their comming towards *London* they dined: and being once
entred into their Inne, according to olde custome, good cheere
was provided for them: for these Clothiers were the chiefest

guests that travailed along the way: and this was as sure as an act of Parliament, that *Tom Dove* could not digest his meat without musicke, nor drinke wine without women, so that his hostesse being a merrie wench, would oftentimes call in two or three of her neighbours wives to keepe him company: where, ere they parted, they were made as pleasant as Pies.

And this being a continuall custome amongst them when they came thither, at length the womens husbands beganne to take exceptions at their wives going thither: whereupon great controversie grew betweene them, in such sort, that when they were most restrayned, then they had most desire to worke their willes:

Now gip (quoth they) must we be so tied to our taske, that we may not drinke with our friends? fie, fie, upon these yellowe hose, will no other die serve your turne? have wee thus long bin your wives, and doe you now mistrust us? verily you eate too much salt, and that makes you grow cholericke, badde livers judge all others the like, but in faith you shall not bridle us so like asses, but wee will goe to our friends, when we are sent for, and doe you what you can.

Well (quoth their husbands) if you be so head-strong, we will tame you: it is the duty of honest women to obey their husbands sayings.

And of honest men (quoth they) to thinke well of their wives; but who doe sooner empeach their credite, then their husbands, charging them, if they doe but smile, that they are subtile; and if they doe but winke, they account them wiley, if sad of countenance, then sullen: if they bee froward, then they are counted shrewes: and sheepish if they bee gentle: if a woman keepe her house, then you will say shee is melancholy, if shee walke abroad, then you call her a gadder; a Puritane, if shee be precise: and a wanton, if she be pleasant: so there is no woman in the world that knowes how to please you: that we thinke our selves accurst to be married wives, living with so many woes. These men, of whose company you forewarne us, are (for ought that ever we saw) both honest and courteous, and in wealth farre beyond your selves: then what reason is there, why we should restraine to visit them? is their good will so much to be requited with scorne, that their cost may not be countervailed with our company? if a woman be disposed to play light of love, alas, alas doe you thinke that you can prevent her? Nay wee shall abide by it, that the restraint of libertie inforceth women to be lewd: for where a woman cannot be trusted, she cannot thinke her selfe beloved, and if not beloved, what cause hath she to care for such a one? therefore husbands, reforme your opinions, and doe not worke your owne woes, with our discredit. The Clothiers, we tell you, are jolly fellowes, and but in respect of our curtesie, they would scorne our company.

The men hearing their wives so well to plead for themselves, knew not how to answere, but said, they would put the burden on their consciences, if they deale unjustly with them, and so left them to their owne wills. The women having thus conquered their husbands conceits, would not leave the favour of their friends for frownes, and as above the rest *Tom Dove* was the most pleasantest, so was he had in most reputation with the women, who for his sake made this Song:

> Welcome to towne, *Tom Dove, Tom Dove*
> The merriest man alive,
> Thy company still we love, we love,
> God grant thee well to thrive,
> And never will depart from thee,
> For better or worse, my joy,
> For thou shalt still have our good will,
> Gods blessing on my sweet Boy.

This song went up and downe through the whole country, and at length became a dance among the common sort, so that *Tom Dove*, for his mirth and good fellowship, was famous in every place.

Now when they came to *London*, they were welcome to the host *Jarrat* the Gyant, and assoone as they were alighted, they were saluted by the Merchants, who waited their comming thither, and alwaies prepared for them a costly supper, where they commonly made their bargaine, and upon every bargaine made, they still used to send some tokens to the Clothiers wives. The next morning they went to the hall, where they met the Northern Clothiers, who greeted one another in this sort.

What, my Masters of the West, well met: what cheere? what cheere?

Even the best cheere our Merchants could make us: (quoth *Gray*.)

Then you could not chuse but fare well (quoth *Hogekins*):

And you be weary of our company, adieu (quoth *Sutton*):

Not so, said *Martin*, but shall wee not have a game ere wee goe?

Yes faith for an hundred pounds.

Well said, old *Cole* (said they): and with that *Cole* and *Gray* went to the dice with *Martin* and *Hogekins*; and the dice running on *Hogekins* side, *Coles* money beganne to waste.

Now by the Masse (quoth *Cole*) my mony shrinks as bad as Northerne cloth.

When they had played long, *Gray* stept to it, and recovered againe the money that *Cole* had lost. But while they were thus playing, the rest being delighted in contrarie matters, every man satisfied his owne humour.

Tom Dove called for musicke, *William* of *Worcester* for wine, *Sutton* set his delight in hearing merry tales, *Simon* of *Southhampton* got him into the kitchin, and to the pottage pot hee goes, for he esteemed more a messe of pottage, then of a vension pastie. Now sir, *Cutbert* of *Kendall* was of another minde, for no meat pleased him so well as mutton, such as was laced in a red petticoate. And you shall understand, that alwaies when they went to dice, they got into *Bosomes* Inne; which was so called of his name that kept it, who being a foule sloven, went alwaies with his nose in his bosome, and one hand in his pocket, the other on his staffe, figuring forth a description of cold winter, for he alwaies wore two coates, two caps, two or three paire of stockings, and a high paire of shooes, over the which he drew on a great paire of lined slippers, and yet would oft complaine of cold, wherfore of all men generally he was called Old Bosome, and his house *Bosomes* Inne.

This lump of cold ice had lately married a yong wife, who was as wily as she was wanton, and in her company did *Cutbert* onely delight, and the better to make passage to his love, he would often thus commune with her: I muse good wife (quoth he).

Good wife (quoth she)? Verily, sir, in mine opinion, there is none good but God, and therefore call me Mistresse.

Then said *Cutbert*, Faire Mistris, I have often mused, that you being a proper woman, could find in your heart for to match with such a greazie Carle as this, an evill mannered mate, a foule lump of kitchin stuffe, and such a one as is indeede, a scorne of men; how can you like him that all women mislikes? or love such a loathsome creature? me thinks verily it should grieve you to lend him a kisse, much more to lie with him.

Indeed sir (quoth she) I had but hard fortune in this respect, but my friends would have it so, and truly my liking and my love toward him are alike, he never had the one, nor never shall get the other: yet I may say to you before I married him, there were divers proper young men that were sutors unto me, who loved mee as their lives, and glad was he that could get my company, those were my golden dayes, wherein my pleasure abounded, but these are my yeres of care and griefe, wherein

my sorrowes exceede. Now no man regards mee, no man cares
for me, and albeit in secret they might beare mee good will,
yet who dares shew it? and this is a double griefe, he carries
over me so jealous a minde, that I cannot looke at a man, but
presently hee accuseth me of inconstancie, although (I protest)
without cause.

And in troth (qd. *Cutb.*) he should have cause to complaine
for somewhat, were I as you.

As sure as I live, and so he shall (quoth she) if he doe not
change his byas.

Cutb. hearing her say so, beganne to grow further in requesting
her favour, wishing he might be her servant and secret friend,
and the better to obtain his desire, he gave her divers gifts,
insomuch that she began something to listen unto him: and
albeit she liked well of his speeches, yet would she blame him,
and take him up very short sometimes for the same, till in the
end, *Cutbert* shewed himselfe to be desperate, saying hee would
drowne himselfe rather than live in her disdaine.

O my sweet heart not so (qd. shee) God forbid I should be the
death of any man: Comfort thy selfe, kind *Cutbert*, and take
this kisse in token of further kindnesse, and if thou wilt have
my favour, thou must be wise and circumspect, and in my
husbands sight I would alwaies have thee to find fault with my
doings, blame my bad huswifries, dispraise my person, and take
exceptions at every thing, whereby he will be as well pleased,
as *Simon* of *South-hampton* with a messe of pottage.

Deere Mistresse (quoth he) I will fulfill your charge to the
uttermost, so that you will not take my jest in earnest.

Shee answered, Thy foulest speeches I will esteeme the fairest,
and take every dispraise to be a praise from thee, turning each
word to the contrarie: and so for this time adieu, good *Cutb.* for
supper time drawes nere, and it is meet for me to looke for
my meat.

With that down comes old Bosome, calling his wife, saying,
Ho *Winifred*, is supper readie? they have done playing above:
therefore let the Chamberlaine cover the Table.

By and by husband (qd. she) it shall be done straight way.

How now my Masters who wins (qd. *Cutb.*).

Our mony walkes to the West (qd. *Martin*): *Cole* hath woone
of me, and *Gray* hath gotten well:

The best is (qd. *Hogekins*) they will pay for our supper:

Then let us have good store of Sacke (qd. *Sutton*).

Content (said *Cole*) for I promise you, I strive not to grow rich by dice-playing, therefore call for what you wil, I will pay for all.

Yea (said *Simon*)! Chamberlaine, I pray thee bring a whole bottle of pottage for me.

Now *Tom Dove* had all the fidlers at a becke of his finger, which follow him up and down the citie, as diligent as little chickens after a hen, and made a vow, that there should want no musicke. And at that time there lived in London a musician of great reputation, named *Reior*, who kept his servants in such costly garments, that they might seeme to come before any Prince. Their coates were all of one colour; and it is said, that afterward the Nobilitie of this Land, noting it for a seemely sight, used in like maner to keepe their men all in one liverie. This *Reior* was the most skilfullest musician that lived at that time, whose wealth was very great, so that all the Instruments whereon his servants plaid, were richly garnished with studdes of silver, and some gold: the bowes belonging to their Violines were all likewise of pure silver. He was also for his wisdome called to great office in the cittie, who also builded (at his owne cost) the Priory and Hospitall of Saint *Bartholomew* in *Smithfield*. His servants being the best consorts in the Citie, were by *Tom Dove* appointed to play before the young Princes.

Then supper being brought to the bord, they all sat down, and by and by after comes up their host, who tooke his place among them: and anone after, the good-wife in a red peticote and a wastcoate, comes among them as white as a Lilly, saying, My Masters, you are welcome, I pray you be merry.

Thus falling close to their meate, when they had well fed, they found leysure to talke one with another: at what time *Cutb.* began thus to finde fault, Ywis, my hoast (quoth he) you have a wise huswife to your wife, heere is meate drest of a new fashion: God sends meate, and the divell sends cookes.

Why what ails the meate (quoth she) serves it not your turne? better men then your selfe are content withall, but a paultrie companion is ever worst to please.

Away, you sluttish thing (qd. *Cutb.*) your husband hath a sweet jewell of you: I marvell such a grave ancient man would match himselfe with such a young giglot, that hath as much hand-somenes in her, as good huswifry, which is just nothing at all.

Well sir (saide shee) in regard of my husbands presence I am loth to aggravate anger, otherwise I would tell thee thy owne.

Goe to, what neede all this (quoth the company)? in good faith, *Cutbert*, you are too blame, you find fault where none is.

Tush, I must speake my mind (quoth *Cutbert*) I cannot dissemble, I trust the good man thinkes never the worse of me: so I have his good will, what the foule evill care I for his wifes.

Enough (quoth *Tom Dove*) let us with musicke remove these brabbles, we meane to be merry, and not melancholy.

Then said olde *Cole*, Now trust me, *Cutbert*, we will have your hostesse and you friends ere we part: here woman I drinke to you, and regard not his words, for he is babbling wheresoever he comes.

(Quoth the woman) nothing grieves me so much, as that hee should thus openly checke mee, if he had found any thing amisse, he might have spied a better time to tell me of it then nowe, ywis hee neede not thrust my bad huswifrie into my husbands head, I live not so quietly with him, God wot: and with that she wept.

Come *Cutb.* (quoth they) drinke to her, and shake handes and be friendes.

Come on, you puling baggage (quoth he) I drinke to you, here will you pledge mee and shake hands?

No, (quoth shee) I will see thee choakt first, shake hands with thee? I will shake hands with the divell assoone.

Goe to (said her husband) you shall shake hands with him then: If you will not shake hands, ile shake you: what, you young huswife?

Well husband (said she) it becomes a woman to obey her husband, in regard whereof, I drink to him.

Thats well said (quoth the company): and so she tooke her leave and went downe.

And within a while after, they paid the shot, and departed thence to *Jarrats* Hall, where they went to their lodging; and the next day they tooke their way homeward all together: and comming to *Colebrooke,* they tooke up their lodging, and it was *Coles* custome to deliver his money to the goodwife of the house to keepe it till morning, which in the end turned to his utter destruction, as hereafter shall be shewed.

CHAPTER III

How *Grayes* wife of *Glouester*, with one or two more of her neighbours went to the Faire, where servants came to be hired, and how she tooke the Earle of *Shrewesburies* Daughter into her service

It was wont to be an old custome in *Gloustershire*, that at a certaine time in the yeare, all such young men and Maidens as were out of service, resorted to a faire that was kept neere *Gloucester*, there to be readie for any that would come to hire them, the yong men stood all on a row on the one side, and the Maidens on the other. It came to passe, that the Earle of *Shrewsburies* daughter, whose Father was lately banished, being driven into great distresse, and weary with travaile, as one whose delicate life was never used to such toyle, sate her downe upon the high way side, making this lamentation.

O false and deceitfull world (quoth she)! who is in thee that wishes not to be rid of thee, for thy extremities are great? Thou art deceitfull to all, and trustie to none. Fortune is thy treasurer, who is like thy selfe, wavering and unconstant, she setteth up tyrants, beateth downe Kings: giveth shame to some, and renowne to others: Fortune giveth these evils, and we see it not: with her hands she toucheth us, and we feele it not, she treades us under foote, and we know it not: she speakes in our eares, and we heare her not: she cries aloud, and we understand her not: And why? because we know her not, untill miserie doth make her manifest.

Ah my deare father, well maist thou do. Of all misfortunes it is most unhappy to be fortunate: and by this misfortune came my fall. Was ever good Lady brought to this extremity? What is become of my rare Jewels, my rich aray, my sumptuous fare, my waiting servants, my many friends, and all my vaine pleasures? my pleasure is banisht by displeasure, my friends fled like foes, my servants gone, my feasting turned to fasting, my rich array consumed to ragges, and my jewells deckes out my chiefest enemies: therefore of all things the meanest state is best, poverty with suretie, is better than honour mixed with faree: seeing God hath allotted me to this misery of life, I will frame my heart to embrace humility, and carry a mind answerable to my misfortunes, fie on this vaine title of Ladiship, how little doth it availe the distressed? No, no, I must therefore forget my birth and parentage, and think no more on my fathers house, where I was wont to bee served, now will I learne to serve, and plaine *Meg* shall be my name, good Lord grant I may get a good service, nay any service shall serve, where I may have meate, drinke, and apparel.

She had no sooner spoke these words, but she spied a couple of Maidens more comming towards her; who were going to the faire: and bidding her good morrow, asked her if she went to the faire.

Yea mary (qd. she) I am a poore mans child that is out of service, and I heare that at the Statute, folkes do come of purpose to hire servants.

True it is (said the Maidens) and thither go we for the same purpose, and would be glad of your company.

With a good will, and I am right glad of yours (said she) beseeching you good Maidens, you will doe me the favour, to tell me what service were best for me: for the more too blame my parents, they would never put me forth to know any thing.

Why what can you doe (quoth the maidens) can you brew and bake, make butter and cheese, and reape corne well?

No verily (said *Margaret*) but I would be right glad to learne to doe any thing whatsoever it be:

If you could spin or card (said another) you might do excellent well with a clother, for they are the best services that I know, there you shall bee sure to fare well, and so live merrily.

Then *Margaret* wept saying alas, what shall I do? I was never brought up to these things.

What can you doe nothing (quoth they)?

No truly (quoth she) that is good for any thing, but I can read and write, and sowe, some skill I have in my needle, and a little on my Lute: but this, I see will profit me nothing.

Good Lord (quoth they) are you bookish? wee did never heare of a Maide before that could reade and write. And although you can doe no other thing, yet possible you may get a service, if you can behave your selfe manerly.

I pray you (qd. another) seeing you are bookish, will you doe so much as to reade a love-letter that is sent me, for I was at a friends of mine with it, and he was not at home, and so I know not what is in it.

I pray you let me see it (quoth *Margaret*) and I will shew you.

Whereupon she readeth as followeth.

> O *Jenny* my joy, I die for thy love,
> And now I heare say that thou dost remove:
> And therefore, *Jenny*, I pray thee recite,
> Where shall I meete thee soone at night.
>
> For why, with my Master no more will I stay,
> But for thy love I will runne away:
> O *Jenny, Jenny*, thou puttest me to paine,
> That thou no longer wilt here remaine.
>
> I will weare out my shooes of Neats Leather,
> But thou and I will meete together,
> And in spight of Fortune, Rat, or Mouse,
> Wee will dwell together in one house.
>
> For who doth not esteeme of thee,
> Shall have no service done of me:
> Therefore good *Jenny* have a care,
> To meete poore *Fragment* at the faire.

Now alas, good soule (quoth *Jenny*) I think he be the kindest young man in the world.

The rest answered, that he seemed no lesse.

And surely it appeareth that he is a pretty wittie fellow (quoth one of them) how finely he hath written his letter in rime, trust me, I will give you a good thing, and let me have a copy of it to send to my sweet heart:

That you shall with all my heart: and so comming to the faire, they tooke up their standing.

Within a while after, goodwife *Gray* of *Gloucester* came thither to store herselfe of divers commodities: and when shee had bought what she wold, she told her neighbor she had great need of a Maid servant or twaine: therefore (qd. she) good neighbour goe with me, and let me have your opinion.

With a good wil (said her neighbor) and together they went, and looking and viewing the Maidens over, she tooke speciall notice of *Margaret*.

Beleeve me (quoth she) there stands a very proper Maiden, and one of a modest and comely countenance.

Verily (said her neighbor) so she is, as ever I looked upon.

The Maiden seeing them to view her so well, was so abashed, that a scarlet colour overspred her lilly cheeks, which the woman perceiving came unto her, and asked if she were willing to serve.

The Maid with a low curtesie, and a most gentle speech, answered it was the onely cause of her comming.

Can you spinne or card (said good-wife *Gray*)?

Truly Dame (said she) though my cunning therein be but

small, my goodwill to learne is great, and I trust, my dilligence shall content you.

What wages will you take (quoth goodwife *Gray*)?

I will referre that (said *Margaret*) to your conscience and courtesie, desiring no more then what I shall deserve. Then asking what country woman she was, the Maiden wept, saying, Ah good Dame, I was untimely borne in Shropshire, of poore parents, and yet not so needie as unfortunate, but death having ended their sorrowes, hath left me to the crueltie of these envious times, to finish my Parents Tragedie with my troubles.

What Maiden! (qd. her dame) have you a care to doe your busines, and to live in Gods feare, and you shall have no care to regard fortunes frownes, and so they went home together.

Now, so soone as the goodman saw her, hee asked his wife where she had that Maiden. She said, at the Faire.

Why then (quoth he) thou hast brought al the Faire away, and I doubt it were better for us, to send the Faire to another Towne, then to keepe the Faire here.

Why man (quoth she) what meane you by that?

Woman, I meane this, that she will prove a Loadstone, to draw the hearts of all my men after her, and so we shal have wise service done of all sides.

Then said his wife, I hope, husband, *Margaret* will have a better care both to her owne credit, and our commodity then so, and so let her alone to looke to such matters.

Is thy name *Margaret* (quoth her Master)? proper is thy name to thy person, for thou art a pearle indeed, orient, and rich in beautie.

His wife hearing him say so, began to change her opinion: What husband (quoth she) is the winde at that doore? Begin you to like your maid so well? I doubt I had most need to looke to your selfe: before God, I had rather then an angell I had chosen some other: but heare you maid; you shall packe hence, I will not nourish a snake in my bosome, and therefore get you gone, I will none of you, provide a service where you may.

The Maiden hearing her say so, fell downe one her knees, and besought her, saying, O sweet dame, be not so cruel to me, to turne me out of doores, now: alas, I know not where to go, or what to do, if you forsake me. O let not the fading beauty of my face dispoyle me of your favour: for rather then that shall hinder my service, this my knife shall soone disfigure my face, and I will banish beautie as my greatest enemy. And with that, her aboundant teares stopped her speech, that shee could not utter one word more.

The woman seeing this, could not harbour any longer, nor could her Master stay in the roome for weeping.

Well, *Margaret* (said her dame) (little knowing that a Lady kneeled before her) using thy selfe wel I will keepe thee, and thou shalt have my good will, if thou governe thyselfe with wisedome; and so she sent her about her businesse.

Her husband comming to supper, said. How now wife, art thou so doubtfull of mee, that thou hast put away thy Maiden?

I wis (qd. she) you are a wise man, to stand praising of a Maidens beauty before her face:

And you a wise woman (qd. he) to grow jealous without a cause.

So to supper they went, and because *Margaret* shewed her selfe of finest behaviour above the rest, she was appointed to waite on the table. And it is to be understood, that *Gray* did never eate his meat alone, but still had some of his neighbors with him, before whom he called his maid, saying, *Margaret*, come hither. Now because there was another of the same name in the house, she made answere.

I call not you Maiden (qd. he) but *Margaret* with the lilly white hand.

After which time she was ever called so.

CHAPTER IV

How the Kings Majestie sent for the Clothiers, and of the sundry favours which he did them

KING *Henry* providing for his voyage into *Fraunce*, against King *Lewis* and *Robert* Duke of *Normandie* his owne brother, committed the government of the Realme in his absence, to the Bishop of *Salisbury*, a man of great wisdome and learning, whom the King esteemed highly, and afterward he thought good to send for the chiefe Clothiers of *England*, who according to the Kings appointment came to the Court, and having licence to come before his Majestie, he spake to this effect.

The strength of a King is the love and friendship of his people, and he governes over his Realme most surely, that ruleth justice with mercy: for he ought to feare many, whom many do feare: therfore the governors of the Common-wealth ought to observe two speciall precepts: the one is, that they so maintain the profit of the Commons, that whatsoever in their calling they doe, they referre it thereunto: the other, that they be alwaies as well carefull over the whole Common-wealth, as over any part thereof; lest while they uphold the one, the other be brought to utter decay.

And forasmuch as I doe understand, and have partly seene, that you the Clothiers of *England* are no small benefit to the wealth publike, I thought it good to know from your owne mouthes, if there be any thing not yet graunted that may benefit you, or any other thing to be removed that doth hurt you.

The great desire I have to maintaine you in your trades, hath moved me hereunto. Therefore boldly say what you would have in the one thing or the other, and I will grant it you.

With that, they all fell downe upon their knees, and desired God to save his Majestie, and withall, requested three daies respite to put in their answere: which was graunted. And thereupon they departed.

When the Clothiers had well considered of these matters, at length they thought meete to request of his Majestie for their first benefite, that all the Cloth-measures through the Land might be of one length, whereas to their great disadvantage before, every good towne had a severall measure, the difficulty thereof was such, that they could not keepe them in memory, nor know how to keepe their reckonings.

The second thing whereof they found themselves grieved, was this, that the people would not take crackt money, though it were never so good silver: whereupon it came to passe, that the Clothiers and divers others receiving great summes of money, do take among it much crackt money, it served them to no use, because it would not goe currant, but lay upon their hands without profit or benefit, whereof they prayed reformation.

The third was a griefe, whereof *Hodgekins* of *Halifax* com-playned, and that was, That whereas the towne of *Halyfax* lived altogether upon Cloathing, and by the reason of false borderers, and other evill minded persons, they were oft robbed, and had their Clothes carried out of their fieldes, where they were drying, That it would please his Majestie to graunt the towne this privilege, That whatsoever he was that was taken stealing their Cloth, might presently without any further tryall be hanged up.

When the day of their appearance approached, the Clothiers came before the King, and delivered up their Petition in writing, which his Majestie most graciously perusing, saide, hee was ready to fulfill their request: and therefore for the first point of their Petition, he called for a staffe to be brought him, and measuring thereupon the just length of his owne arme, delivered it to the Clothiers, saying. This measure shall bee called a yard, and no other measure throughout all the Realme of *England* shall be used for the same, and by this shall men buy and sell, and we will so provide, that whosoever he be that abuseth our subjects by any false measure, that he shall not onely pay a fine for the same to the King, but also have his body punished by imprisonment.

And as concerning the second point of your Petition, because of my sudden departure out of the Land, I know not better how to ease you of this griefe (of crackt money) this decree I make, because they account crackt money not currant, I say, none shal be currant but crackt money. And therefore I will give present charge, that all the money thorow the Land shall be slit, and so you shall suffer no losse.

But now for your last request for the towne of *Halifax*, where by theeves your Clothes are so often stolne from you, seeing the lawes already provided in that case, are not sufficient to keepe men in awe, it is indeed high time to have sharper punishment for them.

With that *Hodgekins* unmannerly interrupted the King, saying in broad Northerne speech, Yea gude faith, mai Liedge, the faule eule of mai saule, giff any thing will keepe them whiat, till the karles be hanged by the cragge. What the dule care they for boaring their eyne, sea lang as they mae gae groping up and downe the Country like fause lizar lownes, begging and craking?

The King smiling to heare this rough-hewen fellow made this reply: Content thee *Hodgekins*, for we will have redresse for all: and albeit that hanging of men was never seene in *England*, yet seeing the corrupt world is growne more bold in all wickednesse, I thinke it not amisse to ordain this death for such malefactors: and peculiarly to the towne of *Hallifax* I give this priviledge, That whosoever they finde stealing their Cloth, being taken with the goods, that without further judgment, they shall be hanged up.

Thus (said our King) have I granted what you request, and if hereafter you find any other thing that may be good for you, it shall be granted; for no longer would I desire to live among you, then I have care for the good of the Common-wealth, at which word ended, the King rose from his royall throne, while the Clothiers on their knees prayed for both his health, and happy successe, and shewed themselves most thankefull for his highnesse favour. His majestie bending his body towards them, said that at his home returne, he would (by the grace of God) visit them.

CHAPTER V

How the Clothiers had provided a sumptuous feast for the Kings sonnes
Prince *William* and Prince *Richard*, at *Gerrards* Hall, shewing also
what chaunce befell *Cutbert* of *Kendall* at that same instant

THE Clothiers departing from the Court in a merry mind,
joyfull of their good successe, each one to other praised and
magnified the Kings great wisedome and vertue, commending
also his affability and gentle disposition, so that *Hodgekins*
affirmed on his faith, that hee had rather speake to his Kings
Majestie, then to many Justices of peace.

Indeed (said *Cole*) he is a most mild and mercifull Prince, and
I pray God he may long raigne over us.

Amen said the rest.

Then said *Cole*, My Masters, shall we forget the great curtesie
of the Kings sonnes, those sweet and gentle Princes, that still
shewed us favour in our suite? in my opinion, it were reason
to gratifie them in some sort, that we may not utterly bee condemned of ingratitude: wherefore (if you thinke good) wee will
prepare a banquet for them at our hoast *Garrats*, who as you
know, hath a faire house, and goodly roomes: Besides, the man
himselfe is a most couragious mind and good behaviour, sufficient
to entertain a Prince: his wife also is a dainty fine Cooke: all
which considered, I know not a fitter place in *London*.

Tis true (quoth *Sutton*) and if the rest be content, I am pleased
it shal be so.

At this they all answered, Yea, for (quoth they) it will not be
passing forty shillings a peece, and that we shall recover in our
crackt money.

Being thus agreed, the feast was prepared.

Tom Dove (quoth they) we will commit the providing of
musicke to thee:

And I (said *Cole*) will invite divers of our Merchants and their
wives to the same.

That is well remembred (said *Gray*).

Upon this they called to the hoast and hostis, shewing their
determination, who most willingly said, all things should be
made ready, but I would have two daies liberty (said the good
wife) to prepare my house and other things.

Content (said the Clothiers) in the meane space we will bid our guests, and dispatch our other affaires.

But *Simon* of *Southampton* charged his hostise, that in any case she should not forget to make good store of pottage.

It shall be done (quoth she).

It is to be remembred, that while this preparation was in hand, that *Cutb.* of *Kendall* had not forgot his kindnes to his hostisse of *Bosomes* Inne. Therefore finding time convenient when her husband was overseeing his haymakers, he greeted her in this sort, Sweet hostesse, though I were the last time I was in towne, over bold with you, yet I hope it was not so offensive to you, as you made shew for.

Bold, my *Cutb.* (quoth she)? thou hast vowed thy selfe my servant: and so being, you are not to be blamed for doing what I wild you. By my honestie, I could not chuse but smile to my selfe, so soone as I was out of their sight, to thinke how prettily you began to brabble.

But now (quoth he) we will change our chidings to kissings, and it vexeth mee that these cherry lippes should be subject to such a Lobcocke as thy husband.

Subject to him (quoth she)! In faith sir, no, I will have my lips at as much liberty as my tongue, the one to say what I list, and the other to touch whom I like: In troth, shall I tell thee, *Cutb.* the churles breath smels so strong, that I care as much for kissing of him, as for looking on him: 'tis such a mis-shapen mizer, and such a bundle of beastlinesse, that I can never thinke on him without spitting. Fie upon him, I would my friends had carried me to my grave, when they went with me to the Church, to make him my husband. And so shedding a few dissembling teares, she stopt.

What my sweet Mistrisse (quoth he) weepe you? Nay sit downe by my side, and I will sing thee one of my country Jigges to make thee merry.

Wilt thou in faith (quoth shee)?

Yes verily (said *Cutbert*):

And in troth (quoth she) if you fall a singing I will sing with you.

That is well, you can so suddenly change your notes (quoth *Cutbert*) then have at it.

> *Man.* Long have I lov'd this bonny Lasse,
>   Yet durst not shew the same.
> *Wom.* There in you prove your selfe an Asse,
> *Man.* I was the more to blame.

	Yet still will I remaine to thee,
	Trang dilly do, trang dilly:
	Thy friend and lover secretly,
Wom.	Thou art my owne sweet bully.

Man.	But when shall I enjoy thee,
	delight of thy faire love?
Wom.	Even when thou seest that fortune doth,
	all manner lets remove.
Man.	O, I will fold thee in my armes,
	Trang dilly do, trang dilly,
	And keepe thee so from sudden harmes,
Wom.	Thou art my owne sweet bully.

Wom.	My husband he is gone from home,
	you know it very well.
Man.	But when will he returne againe?
Wom.	In truth I cannot tell.
	If long he keepe him out of sight,
	Trang dilly do, trang dilly,
	Be sure thou shalt have thy delight.
Man.	Thou art my bonny lassie.

While they were singing this song, her husband being on a sudden come home, stood secretly in a corner and heard all, and blessing himselfe with both his hands, said, O abhominable dissimulation, monstrous hypocrisie, and are you in this humour? can you braule together and sing together? Well (quoth he) I will let them alone, to see a little more of their knavery. Never did Cat watch Mouse so narrowly, as I will watch them: And so going into the Kitchen, hee asked his wife if it were not dinner time.

Even by and by, husband (quoth she) the meat will be ready.

Presently after comes in *Hodgekings* and *Martin*, who straight asked for *Cutbert* of *Kendall*. Answere was made, that he was in his Chamber. So when they had called him, they went to dinner: then they requested that their host and hostesse would sit with them.

Husband (said she) you may goe if you please: but as for me, I will desire pardon.

Nay, good wife, goe up (said her husband). What woman, you must beare with your guests.

Why husband (qd. she) do you thinke that any can beare the flirts and frumps, which that Northerne tike gave me the last time he was in towne; now God forgive me, I had as liefe see the divell as to see him: therefore good husband goe up your selfe, and let me alone, for in faith, I shall never abide that Jacke while I live.

Upon these words away went her husband, and though he said

little, hee thought more. Now when he came up, his guests bade him welcome.

I pray you sit downe, good mine hoast (quoth they) where is your wife? what will she sit with us?

No verily (said he) the foolish woman hath taken such a displeasure against *Cutbert*, that she sweares she will never come in his company.

Is it so (said the other)? then trust mee we are well agreed: and I sweare by my fathers sale (qd. hee) that were it not meere for good will to you, then love to her, I would never come to your house meere.

I beleeve it well (said old *Bosome*). And so with other communication they drove out the time, till dinner was ended.

After they were risen, *Martin* and *Hodgekins* got them forth about their affaires, but *Cut.* tooke his host by the hand, saying, My host, ile go talk with your wife; for my part I thought we had bin friends: but seeing her stomack is so big, and her heart so great, I will see what she will say to me; and with that hee stept into the kitchin, saying, God speed you hostise.

It must be when you are away then (said she).

What is your reason (said the other)?

Because God never comes where knaves are present.

Gip goodly draggletaile (qd. he) had I such a wife, I would present her tallow-face to the devell for a candle.

With that she bent her browes, and like a fury of hell began to flie at him, saying, Why you gag-tooth jacke, you blinking companion, get thee out of my kitchin quickly, or with my powdred beefe broth, I will make your pate as bald as a friers.

Get me gon (quoth hee)? thou shalt not bid me twice: out you durty heeles, you will make your husbands haire growe through his hood I doubt:

And with that he got him into the Hall, and sat him downe on the bench by his hoast, to whom he said: Tis pittie, my Oast, that your aged yeeres that loves quietnesse, should be troubled with such a scolding queane.

I, God helpe me, God helpe me (quoth the old man) and so went towards the Stable: which his wife watching, suddenly stept out and gave *Cutbert* a kisse.

Within an houre after, the old man craftily called for his Nag to ride to field: but as soone as he was gone, *Cutbert* and his Hostesse were such good friends, that they got into one of the Warehouses, and lockt the doore to them: but her husband having set a spie for the purpose, suddenly turned backe, and called for a capcase which lay in the Warehouse. The servant could not find the key by any meanes. Whereupon hee caled to have the locke broke open. Which they within hearing, opened the doore of their owne accord.

So soone as her husband spied her in that place, with admiration he said: O the passion of my hart, what do you here? what you two that cannot abide one another? what make you so close together? is your chiding and rayling, brabling, and brauling, come to this? O what dissemblers are these!

Why, my host (qd. *Cutbert*) what need you take the matter so hotte? I gave a Cheese to my country man *Hodgekins*, to lay up, and delivered it to your wife to be kept; and then is it not reason, that she should come and seeke me my Cheese?

O (quoth the old man) belike the dore was lockt, because the cheese should not run away.

The doore (said his wife) unknown to us clapt to it selfe, and having a spring locke, was presently fast.

Well huswife (qd. he) I will give you as much credit as a Crocadile, but as for your companion, I will teach him to come hither to looke cheeses.

And with that he caused his men to take him presently, and to bind him hand and foote. Which being done, they drew him up in a basket into the smoky lover of the hall, and there they did let him hang all that night, even till the next day dinner time, when he should have beene at the banquet with the princes: for neither *Hodgekins* nor *Martin* could intreat their inflamed hoast to let him downe.

And in such a heate was he driven with drawing him up, that he was faine to cast off his gownes, his cotes, and two paire of his stockings, to coole himselfe, making a vow he shold hang there 7. yeares, except the kings sonnes came in person to beg his pardon, which most of all grieved *Cutbert*. When *Cole* and the rest of the Westerne Yeomen heard hereof, they could not chuse but laugh, to thinke that he was so taken tardy.

The yong princes having given promise to be with the clothiers, kept their houre, but when all the rest went to give them entertainment, *Simon* was so busie in supping his pottage, that he could not spare so much time. Which when the princes saw with a smiling countenance they said, Sup *Simon*, theres good broath,

Or else beshrew our hostesse: (quoth he) never looking behind him to see who spake, till the Prince clapt him on the shoulder. But good Lord, how blank he was when he spied them, knowing not how to excuse the matter.

Well, the princes having ended their banket, *Garrat* comes and with one of his hands tooke the table of sixteene foote long quite from the ground over their heads, from before the princes, and set it on the other side of the hall, to the great admiration of all them that beheld it.

The princes being then ready to depart, the Clothiers moved them in pleasant maner, to be good to one of their company, that did neither sit, lie, nor stand.

Then he must needes hang (qd. the Princes).

And so he doth, most excellent princes (qd. they); and there-withall told them the whole matter.

When they heard the storie, downe to *Bosomes* Inne they go, where looking up into the roofe, spied poore *Cutbert* pinned up in a basket, and almost smoaked to death, who although he were greatly ashamed, yet most pitifully desired that they would get his release.[1]

What is his trespasse (said the Prince)?

Nothing if it shall like your Grace (qd. he) but for looking for a cheese:

But he could not find it without my wife (said the goodman) the villaine had lately dined with mutton, and could not digest his meate without cheese, for which cause I have made him to fast these twenty houres, to the end he may have a better stomacke to eate his dinner, then to use dalliance.

Let me intreate you (quoth the Prince) to release him: and if ever hereafter you catch him in the corne, clappe him in the pownd.

Your Grace shall request or command any thing at my hand (said the old man) and so *Cutbert* was let downe unbound, but when he was loose, he vowed never to come within that house more.

And it is said, the old man *Bosome* ordained, that in remembrance of this deed, every yeare once all such as came thither to aske for cheeses, should be so served: which thing is to this day kept.

---

[1] His release, released 1623.

E 824

CHAPTER VI

How *Simons* wife of *South-hampton*, being wholy bent to pride and pleasure,
requested her husband to see *London*, which being granted, how she
got good wife *Sutton* of *Salisburie* to go with her, who tooke *Crab* to
go along with them, and how he prophecied of many things

THE Clothiers being all come from *London*, *Simons*[1] wife of
South-hampton, who was with her husband very mery and
pleasant, brake her mind unto him in this sort:

Good Lord husband, will you never be so kind as let me goe
to *London* with you? shall I be pend up in *South-hampton*, like
a parret in a cage, or a Capon in a coope? I would request no
more of you in lieu of all my paines, carke and care, but to have
one weeks time to see that faire Citie: what is this life, if it be
not mixt with some delight? and what delight is more pleasing
then to see the fashions and maners of unknowne places?
Therefore good husband, if thou lovest me, deny not this simple
request. You know I am no common gadder, nor have oft
troubled you with travell. God knowes, this may be the last
thing that ever I shall request at your hands.

Woman (quoth he) I would willingly satisfie your desire, but
you know it is not convenient for both of us to be abroad, our
charge is so great, and therefore our care ought not to bee small.
If you will goe your selfe, one of my men shall goe with you, and
money enough you shall have in your purse: but to go with you
my selfe, you see my businesse will not permit me.

Husband (said she) I accept your gentle offer, and it may be
I shal intreat my gossip *Sutton* to go along with me.

I shall be glad (qd. her husband) prepare your selfe when
you will.

When she had obtained this license, she sent her man *Weasell*[2]
to *Salisbury*, to know of good wife *Sutton* if she would keepe her
company to *London*. *Suttons* wife being as willing to go, as
she was to request, never resting till shee had gotten leave of
her husband; the which when she had obtained, casting in her
minde their pleasure would be small, being but they twaine:
thereupon the wily woman sent letters by collericke *Crabbe*[3] her

---

[1] Simons, Suttons 1623, 1632. [2] Welsell 1623, 1632.
[3] Crabbe 1632· Cracke 1623.

man, both to *Grayes* wife, and *Fitzallens* wife, that they would meet them at *Reading*, who liking well of the match, consented, and did so provide, that they met according to promise at *Reading*, and from thence with *Coles* wife they went altogether, with each of them a man to *London*, each one taking up their lodging with a severall friend.

When the Merchants of *London* understood they were in towne, they invited them every day home to their owne houses, where they had dilicate good cheere: and when they went abroade to see the commodities of the Cittie, the Merchants wives ever bore them companie, being attired most daintie and fine: which when the Clothiers wives did see, it grieved their hearts they had not the like.

Now when they were brought into *Cheap-side*, there with great wonder they beheld the shops of the Goldsmithes; and on the other side, the wealthy Mercers, whose shoppes shined with all sorts of coloured silkes: in *Watlingstreet* they viewed the great number of Drapers: in *Saint Martins* Shoomakers: at *Saint Nicholas Church*, the flesh shambles: at the end of the old *Change*, the fishmongers: in *Candleweeke streete* the Weavers: then came into the *Jewes street*, where all the Jewes did inhabite: then came they to *Blackwell hall*, where the country Clothiers did use to meete.

Afterwards they proceeded, and came to *S. Pauls Church*, whose steeple was so hie, that it seemed to pierce the cloudes, on the top whereof, was a great and mightie Wether-cocke, of cleane silver, the which notwithstanding seemed as small as a sparrow to mens eyes, it stood so exceeding high, the which goodly weather-cocke was afterwards stolen away, by a cunning cripple, who found meanes one night to clime up to the top of the steeple, and tooke it downe: with the which, and a great summe of money which he had got together by begging in his life time, he builded a gate on the North-side of the Citty, which to this day is called *Criple-gate*.

From thence they went to the Tower of *London*, which was builded by *Julius Cæsar*, who was Emperour of *Rome*. And there they beheld salt and wine, which had lien there ever since the Romaines invaded this land, which was many yeares before our Saviour Christ was borne, the wine was growne so thicke, that it might have beene cut like a jelly. And in that place also they saw the money that was made of leather, which in ancient time went currant amongst the people.

When they had to their great contentation beheld all this,

they repaired to their lodgings, having also a sumptuous supper ordained for them, with all delight that might bee. And you shall understand, that when the country weavers, which came up with their dames, saw the weavers of *Candlewike-street*, they had great desire presently to have some conference with them; and thus one began to challenge the other for workemanship,

(Quoth *Weasell*) ile worke with any of you all for a crowne, take if you dare, and he that makes his yard of cloth soonest, shall have it.

You shall be wrought withall (said the other) and if it were for ten crownes: but we will make this bargaine, that each of us shall winde their owne quilles.

Content (quoth *Weasell*): and so to worke they went, but *Weasell* lost.

Whereupon another of them tooke the matter in hand, who lost likewise: so that the *London* weavers triumphed against the country, casting forth divers frumps.

Alas poore fellowes (quoth they) your hearts are good, but your hands are ill.

Tush, the fault was in their legges (quoth another) pray you friend, were you not borne at home?

Why doe you aske (quoth *Weasell*)?

Because (said hee) the biggest place of your legge is next to your shooe.

Crab [1] hearing this, beeing cholericke of nature, chafed like a man of law at the Bar, and he wagers with them four crownes to twaine: the others agreed, to worke they goe: but *Crab* conquered them all. Whereupon, the *London* weavers were nipt in the head like birds, and had not a word to say.

Now (saith *Crab*) as we have lost nothing, so you have wonne nothing, and because I know you cannot be right weavers, except you be good fellowes, therefore if you will go with us, we will bestow the Ale upon you.

That is spoken like a good-fellow and like a weaver (quoth the other).

So along [2] they went as it were to the signe of the red Crosse.

When they were set downe, and had drunke well, they began merrily to prattle, and to extoll *Crab* to the skies. Whereupon *Crab* protested, that he would come and dwell among them.

Nay, that must not be (said a *London* weaver): the King hath given us priviledge, that none should live among us, but such as serve seven yeeres in *London*.

[1] Crab, Cutbert 1623, 1632.   [2] along 1632: long 1623.

With that *Crab,* according to his old maner of prophesying, said thus:

The day is very neere at hand,
When as the King of this faire land,
Shal priviledge you more then so:
Then weavers shall in skarlet goe.

And to one brotherhood be brought,
The first is in *London* wrought,
When other trades-men by your fame,
Shall covet all to doe the same.

Then shall you all live wondrous well,
But this one thing I shall you tell:
The day will come before the doome,
In *Candleweeke street* shall stand no loome.

Nor any weaver dwelling there,
But men that shall more credit beare:
For Clothing shall be sore decayed,
And men undone that use that trade.

And yet the day some men shall see,
This trade againe shall raised be.
When as Bayliffe of *Sarum* towne;
Shall by and purchase *Bishops downe.*

When there never man did sow,
Great store of goodly corne shall grow;
And woad, that makes all colours sound,
Shall spring upon that barren ground.

At that same day I tell you plaine,
Who so alive doth then remaine,
A proper Maiden they shall see,
Within the towne of *Salisburie.*

Of favour sweet, and nature kind,
With goodly eies, and yet starke blind,
This poore blind Maiden I do say,
In age shall goe in rich array.

And he that takes her to his wife,
Shall lead a joyfull happy life,
The wealthiest Clothier shall he be,
That ever was in that country.

But clothing kept as it hath beene,
In *London* never shall be seene:
For weavers then the most shall win,
That worke for cloathing next the skin.

Till pride the Common-wealth doth peele,
And causeth huswives leave their wheele.
Then poverty upon each side,
Unto those workemen shall betide.

At that time, from an Eagles neast,
That proudly builded in the West,
A sort shall come with cunning hand,
To bring strange weaving in this land,

And by their gaines that great will fall,
They shall maintaine the weavers Hall:
But long they shall not flourish so,
But folly will them overthrow.

And men shall count it mickle shame,
To beare that kind of Weavers name,
And this as sure shall come to passe,
As here is ale within this glasse.

When the silly soules that sate about him heard him speake
in this sort, they admired, and honoured *Crabbe* for the same.

Why my masters (said *Weasell*) doe you wonder at these
words? he will tell you twenty of these tales, for which cause
we call him our canvas Prophet: his attire fits his title, said
they and we never heard the like in our lives: and if this shold
be true, it would be strange.

Doubt not but it will be true (qd. *Weasel*): for ile tell you what,
he did but once see our *Nicke* kisse *Nel*, and presently he powred
out this rime:

That kisse, O *Nel*, God give thee joy,
Will nine months hence breed thee a boy.

And ile tell you what, you shall heare: we kept reckoning, and
it fell out just as *Jones* buttockes on a close stoole, for which
cause, our maids durst never kisse a man in his sight:

Upon this they broke company, and went every one about his
busines, the *London* weavers to their frames, and the countrey
fellowes to their dames, who after their great banquetting and
merriment, went every one home to their owne houses, though
with lesse money than they brought out, yet with more pride.

Especially *Simons* wife of *South-hampton*, who told the rest
of her gossips, that she saw no reason, but that their husbands
should maintaine them, aswell as the Merchants did their
wives: for I tell you what (quoth she) we are as proper women
(in my conceit,) as the proudest of them all, as handsome of
body, as faire of face, our legs as well made, and our feet as fine:
then what reason is there (seeing our husbands are of as good
wealth,) but we should be as well maintained.

You say true gossip (said *Suttons* wife): trust me, it made me
blush, to see them brave it out so gallantly, and wee to goe so
homely:

But before God (said the other) I will have my husband to buy me a *London* gowne, or in faith he shall have little quiet:

So shall mine (said another):

And mine too (qd. the third): and all of them sung the same note: so that when they came home, their husbands had no little to doe: Especially *Simon*, whose wife dayly lay at him for *London* apparell, to whome he said, Good woman, be content, let us goe according to our place and abilitie: what will the Bailiffes thinke, if I should pranke thee up like a Peacocke, and thou in thy attire surpasse their wives? they would either thinke I were madde, or else that I had more mony then I could well use, consider, I pray thee good wife, that such as are in their youth masters, doe prove in their age starke beggars.

Besides that, it is enough to raise me up in the Kings booke, for many times, mens coffers are judged by their garments: why, we are country folks, and must keepe our selves in good compasse: gray russet, and good hempe-spun cloath doth best become us; I tell thee wife, it were as undecent for us to goe like Londoners as it is for Londoners to goe like courtiers.

What a coyle keepe you (quoth she)? are not we Gods creatures as well as Londoners? and the Kings subjects, aswell as they? then finding our wealth to be as good as theirs, why should we not goe as gay as Londoners? No husband, no, here is the fault, wee are kept without it, onely because our husbands be not so kind as Londoners: why man, a Cobler there keepes his wife better than the best Clothier in this countrey: nay, I will affirme it, that the *London* Oyster-wives, and the very kitchin-stuffe cryers, doe exceed us in their Sundaies attire: nay, more then that, I did see the Water-bearers wife which belongs to one of our Merchants, come in with a Tankerd of water on her shoulder, and yet halfe a dozen gold rings on her fingers.

You may then thinke, wife (quoth he) she got them not with idlenesse.

But wife you must consider what *London* is, the chiefe and capitall Cittie of all the land, a place on the which all strangers cast their eies, it is (wife) the Kings chamber and his Majesties royall seate: to that Cittie repaires all nations under heaven. Therefore it is most meete and convenient, that the Citizens of such a Citie should not goe in their apparell like Peasents, but for the credit of our countrey, weare such seemely habits, as do carrie gravity and comelinesse in the eyes of all beholders.

But if we of the countrey went so (quoth she) were it not as great credit for the land as the other?

Woman (qd. her husband) it is altogether needlesse, and in divers respects it may not be.

Why then, I pray you (quoth she) let us goe dwell at London.

A word soone spoken (said her husband) but not so easie to be performed: therefore wife, I pray thee hold thy prating, for thy talke is foolish:

Yea, yea husband, your old churlish conditions will never be left, you keepe me here like a drudge and a droile, and so you may keepe your money in your purse, you care not for your credit, but before I will goe so like a shepheardesse, I will first goe naked: and I tell you plain, I scorne it greatly, that you should clap a gray gowne on my backe, as if I had not brought you two pence: before I was married you swore I should have any thing that I requested, but now all is forgotten.

And in saying this, she went in, and soone after she was so sicke, that needes she must go to bed: and when she was laid, she drave out that night with many grievous groanes, sighing and sobbing, and no rest she could take God wot. And in the morning when she should rise, the good soule fell downe in a swowne, which put her maidens in a great flight, who running downe to their master, cryed out; Alas, alas, our Dame is dead, our Dame is dead.

The goodman heareing this, ran up in all hast and there fell to rubbing and chafing of her temples, sending for *aqua vitæ*, and saying, Ah my sweet heart, speake to me, good wife, alacke, alacke, call in the neighbours, you queanes (quoth he).

With that shee lift up her head, fetching a great groane, and presently swouned againe, and much a doe ywis, he had to keepe life in her: but when she was come to her selfe, How dost thou wife (qd. he)?

What wilt thou have? for Gods sake tel me if thou hast a mind to any thing, thou shalt have it.

Away dissembler (qd. she) how can I beleeve thee? thou hast said to me as much a hundred times, and deceived me, it is thy churlishnesse that hath killed my heart, never was woman matcht to so unkind a man.

Nay good wife, blame me not without cause; God knoweth how dearely I love thee.

Love me! no, no, thou didst never carry my love but on the tip of thy tongue (quoth she) I dare sweare thou desirest nothing so much as my death, and for my part, I would to God thou hadst thy desire: but be content, I shall not trouble thee long:

and with that fetching a sigh, she swouned and gave a great groane.

The man seeing her in this case was wondrous woe: but so soone as they had recovered her, he said, O my deare wife, if any bad conceit hath ingendered this sicknesse, let me know it; or if thou knowest any thing that may procure thy health, let me understand thereof, and I protest thou shalt have it, if it cost me all that ever I have.

O husband (quoth she) how may I credite your wordes, when for a paltrie sute of apparell you denied mee?

Well wife (quoth he) thou shalt have apparell or any thing else thou wilt request, if God send thee once health.

O husband, if I may find you so kind, I shall thinke my selfe the happiest woman in the world, thy words have greatly comforted my heart, mee thinketh if I had it, I could drinke a good draught of renish wine.

Well, wine was sent for: O Lord (said she) that I had a peece of chicken, I feele my stomacke desirous of some meate:

Glad am I of that (said her husband) and so the woman within a few daies after was very well.

But you shall understand, that her husband was faine to dresse her London-like, ere he could get her quiet, neither wold it please her except the stuffe was bought in *Cheapside*: for out of *Cheapside* nothing would content her, were it never so good: insomuch, that if she thought a taylor of *Cheapside* made not her gowne, she would sweare it were quite spoiled.

And having thus wonne her husband to her will, when the rest of the Clothiers wives heard thereof, they would be suted in the like sort too; so that ever since, the wives of *South-hampton*, *Salisbury*, of *Glocester*, *Worcester*, and *Reading*, went all as gallant and as brave as any Londoners wives.

CHAPTER VII

How the Clothiers sent the King aide into *France*, and how he overcame
his brother *Robert*, and brought him into *England*, and how the
Clothiers feasted his Majestie and his sonne at *Reading*

THE Kings Majestie being at the warres in *Fraunce*, against
Lewis the French King, and Duke *Robert* of *Normandie*, sending
for divers supplies of souldiers out of *England*, the Clothiers at
their owne proper cost set out a great number, and sent them
over to the King.

Which *Roger* Bishop of *Salisburie*, who governed the Realme
in the Kings absence, did certifie the King thereof, with his
letters written in their commendations.

And afterwards it came to passe, that God sent his Highnes
victory over his enemies, and having taken his brother prisoner,
brought him most joyfully with him into *England*, and appointed
him to be kept in *Cardife* castle prisoner, yet with this favour,
that he might hunt and hawke where he would, up and downe
the countrey, and in this sorte hee lived a good while, of whom
we will speake more at large hereafter.

The King being thus come home, after his winters rest, he
made his summers progresse into the west countrey, to take
a view of all the chiefe townes: whereof the Clothiers being
advertised, they made great preparation against his comming,
because he had promised to visite them all.

And when his Grace came to *Reading*, he was entertained and
received with great joy and triumph: *Thomas Cole* being the
chiefe man of regard in all the towne, the King honored his
house with his princely presence, where during the Kings abode,
he, and his son, and Nobles were highly feasted.

There the King beheld the great number of people, that was
by that one man maintained in worke, whose hearty affection
and love toward his Majestie did well appeare, aswell by their
outward countenances, as their gifts presented unto him. But
of *Cole* himselfe the King was so well perswaded, that he committed such trust in him, and put him in great authoritie in the
towne. Furthermore the King said, That for the love which
those people bore him living, that he would lay his bones among

116

them when he was dead. For I know not (said he) where they may be better bestowed, till the blessed day of resurrection, then among these my friends which are like to be happy partakers of the same.

Whereupon his Majestie caused there to be builded a most goodly and famous Abbey: in which he might shew his devotion to God, by increasing his service, and leave example to other his successors to doe the like. Likewise within the towne he after builded a faire and goodly castle, in the which he often kept his Court, which was a place of his chiefe residence during his life, saying to the Clothiers, that seeing he found them such faithfull subjects, he would be their neighbor, and dwell among them.

After his Majesties royal feasting at *Reading*, he proceeded in progresse, till he had visited the whole west countries, being wondrously delighted, to see those people so diligent to apply their busines: and comming to *Salisburie*, the Bishop received his Majestie with great joy, and with triumph attended on his Grace to his palace, where his Highnesse lodged.

There *Sutton* the Clothier presented his Highnesse with a broad cloth, of so fine a threed, and exceeding good workmanship, and therewithall of so faire a colour, as his Grace gave commendation thereof, and as it is said, he held it in such high estimation, that thereof he made his parliament robes, and the first parliament that was ever in *England*, was graced with the Kings person in those robes, in requitall whereof his Highnes afterward yeelded *Sutton* many princely favours.

And it is to be remembred, that *Simon* of *South-hampton* (seeing the King had overpast the place where he dwelt) came with his wife and servants to *Salisburie*, and against the K. going forth of that Citty, he caused a most pleasant arbour to be made upon the toppe of the hill leading to *Salisburie*, beset all with red and white roses, in such sort, that not any part of the timber could be seene, within the which sat a maiden attired like a Queen, attended on by a faire traine of maidens, who at the Kings approach presented him with a Garland of sweet flouers, yeelding him such honour as the Ladies of *Rome* were wont to doe to their Princes after their victories: which the King tooke in gracious part, and for his farewell from that country, they bore him company over part of the Plaine, with the sound of divers sweet instruments of musicke. All which when his Grace understood was done at the cost of a Clothier, he said hee was the most honoured by those men, above all the meane subjects in his land: and so his highnes past on to *Exceter*, having given great rewards to these Maidens.

Thomas Dove and the residue of the Clothiers, against his Graces comming thither, had ordained divers sumptuous shewes; first, there was one that presented the person of *Augustus Cæsar* the Emperour, who commanded after the Romone invasion, that their citie should be called *Augustus*, after his owne name, which before time was called *Isca*, and of later yeeres, *Exeter*.

There his Majesty was royally feasted seaven daies together, at the onely cost of Clothiers, but the divers delightes and sundry pastimes which they made there before the King, and his Nobles, is too long here to be rehearsed, and therefore I will overpasse them to avoid tediousnesse.

His Grace then coasting along the country, at last came to *Gloucester*, an ancient Citie, which was builded by *Glove*, a Brittish King, who named it after his owne name, *Glocester*. Here was his Majestie entertained by *Gray* the Clothier, who profest himselfe to be of that auncient family of *Grayes*, whose first originall issued out of that auncient and Honorable Castle and Towne of *Rithin*.

Here was the King most bountifully feasted, having in his company his brother *Robert* (although his prisoner the same time.) And his Grace being desirous to see the Maidens card and spinne, they were of purpose set to their worke: among whom was faire *Margaret* with her white hand, whose excellent beauty having pierct the eyes of the amorous Duke, it made such an impression in his heart, that afterward he could never forget her: and so vehemently was his affection kindled that he could take no rest, till by writing he had bewrayed his minde: but of this we will speake more in another place: and the King at his departure said, that to gratifie them, hee would make his sonne *Robert* their Earle, who was the first Earle that ever was in *Glocester*.

Now when his Grace was come from thence, hee went to *Worcester*, where *William Fitz-allen* made preparation in all honourable sort to receive him, which man being borne of great parentage, was not to learne how to entertaine his Majestie, being descended of that famous family, whose patrimonie lay about the Towne of *Oswestrie*, which Town his predecessors had inclosed with stately walls of stone.

Although adverse fortune had so grievously frowned on some of them, that their children were faine to become tradesmen, whose handes were to them insteed of landes, notwithstanding God raised againe the fame of this man, both by his great wealth, and also in his posteritie, whose eldest son *Henry*, the Kings god-son, became afterward the Maior of *London*, who was the first Maior that ever was in that Cittie, who governed the same 23 yeares: and then his sonne *Roger Fitz-allen* was the second Maior.

The princely pleasures that in *Worcester* were shown the King, were many and marvelous, and in no place had his Majesty received more delight then here: for the which at his departure he did shew himselfe very thankfull. Now when his Grace had thus taken view of all his good townes Westward and in that progresse had visited these Clothiers, he returned to *London*, with great joy of his Commons.

CHAPTER VIII

How *Hodgekins* of *Hallifax* came to the Court, and complained to the King, that his priviledge was nothing worth, because when they found any offender, they could not get a hangman to execute him: and how by a Frier a gin was devised to chop off mens heads of it selfe

AFTER that *Hodgkins* had got the priviledge for the towne of *Halifax*, to hang up such theeves as stole their cloath in the night, presently without any further judgement, all the Clothiers of the towne were exceeding glad, and perswaded themselves, that now their goods would be safe all night, without watching them at al, so that whereas before, the town maintained certaine watchmen to keepe their cloath by night, they were hereupon dismissed as a thing needlesse to be done, supposing with themselves, that seeing they should be straight hanged that were found faultie in this point, that no man would bee so desperate to enterprise any such act. And indeed the matter being noysed through the whole countrey, that they were straight to be hanged that use such theevery, it made many lewd livers to restraine such theevery.

Nevertheles, there was at that same time living, a notable Theefe named *Wallis*, whom in the north they called *Mighty Wallis*, in regard of his valour and manhood: This man being most subtile in such kind of knaverie, having heard of this late priviledge, and therewithall of the Townes securitie, said that once he would venture his necke for a packe of Northerne cloth: and therefore comming to one or two of his companions, he asked if they would be partners in his adventure, and if (quoth he) you will herein hazard your bodies, you shall be sharers in all our booties.

At length by many perswasions the men consented: whereupon late in the night, they got them all into a Farriours shop, and called up the folkes of the house.

What the foule ill wald you have (quoth they) at this time of the night?

Wallis answered, saying good fellowes, we would have you to remove the shooes of our horses feete, and set them on againe, and for your paines you shall be well pleased.

The Smith at length was perswaded, and when he had pluckt off al the shooes from their horses feete, they would needes have

120

them all set on againe, quite contrary with the cakins forward, that should stand backward.

How? fay, fay man (quoth the Smith) are ye sicke fules? what the deele do you meane to breake your crags? gud faith I tro the men be wood.

Not so Smith (qd. they) do thou as we bid thee, and thou shalt have thy mony: for it is an old proverbe,

> Be it better, or be it worse.
> Please you the man that beares the purse.

Gud faith and see I sall (qd. the Smith) and so did as hee was willed. When *Wallis* had thus caused their Horses to be shod, to *Hallifax* they went, where they without any let laded their Horses with cloth, and so departed contrary way.

In the morning, so soone as the Clothiers came to the field, they found that they were robd, whereupon one ranne to another to tell these things. Now when *Hodgkings* heard thereof, rising up in hast, he wild his neighbors to mark and to see, if they could not descry either the footesteppes of men or Horses. Which being done, they perceived that horses had been there, and seeking to pursue them by their footesteppes, they went a cleane contrary way, by reason that the horses were shodde backward: and when in vaine they had long pursude them, they returned, being never the neere.

Now *Wallis* used his feate so long, that at length he was taken, and two more with him: whereupon according to the privilege of the Towne, they put Halters about the theeves neckes presently to hang them up.

When they were come to the place appointed, *Wallis* and the rest being out of hope to escape death, prepared themselves patiently to suffer the rigor of the law. And therewith the rest laying open the lewdnesse of his life, grievously lamenting for his sinnes, at length commending their soules to God, they yeelded their bodies to the grave, with which sight the people were greatly mooved with pity, because they had never seene men come to hanging before: but when they shold have beene tyed up, *Hodgekins* willed one of his neighbors to play the Hangmans part, who would not by any meanes doe it, although he was a very poore man, who for his paines should have beene possest of all their apparell. When he would not yeeld to the office, one of those which had his cloth stolen, was commanded to doe the deed; but he in like manner would not, saying: When I have the skill to make a man, I will hang a man, if it chance my workmanship do not like me.

And thus from one to another, the office of the hangman was posted off. At last a Rogue came by, whom they would have compelled to have done that deed.

Nay, my masters (qd. he) not so: but as you have got a priviledge for the Towne, so you were best to procure a Commission to make a hangman, or else you are like to be without for me.

Neighbor *Hodgkins* (quoth one) I pray you do this office your selfe, you have had most losse, and therefore you should be the most readie to hang them your selfe.

No, not I (quoth *Hodgkings*) though my losse were ten times greater then it is, notwithstanding look which of these theeves will take upon him to hang the other, shall have his life saved, otherwise they shall all to prison till I can provide a hangman.

When *Wallis* saw the matter brought to this passe, he began stoutly to reply, saying, My masters of the Town of *Halifax*, though your priviledge stretch to hang men up presently that are found stealing of your goods, yet it gives you no warrant to imprison them till you provide them a hangman, my selfe, with these my fellowes, have here yeelded our selves to satisfie the Law, and if it be not performed, the fault is yours, and not ours, and therefore we humbly take our leave: from the gallowes the xviii of August. And with that he leapt from the ladder, and hirld the halter at *Hodgkings* face.

When the Clothiers saw this, they knew not what to say, but taking them by the sleeves, entreated to have their owne againe.

No so (qd. *Wallis*) you get not the value of a packe or a bawby: we have stolen your cloth, then why doe you not hang us? here we have made our selves ready, and if you wil not hang us, chuse. A plague upon you (quoth he) you have hindred me God knowes what, I made account to dine this day in heaven, and you keepe me here on earth where there is not a quarter of that good cheare. The foule evill take you all, I was fully provided to give the gallowes a boxe on the eare, and now God knowes when I shall be in so good a minde againe: and so he with the rest of his companions departed.

When *Hodgekings* saw, that notwithstanding their theevery, how they flowted at their lenitie, he was much mooved in minde; and as he stood in his dumps chewing his cud, making his dinner with a dish of melancholy, a gray Frier reverently saluted him in this sort: All haile, goodman *Hodgekins*, happinesse and health be ever with you, and to all suppressors of lewd livers, God send everlasting joyes.

I am sory goodman *Hodgekings*, that the great priviledge which our King gave to this towne, comes to no greater purpose; better far had it bin that it had never beene graunted, then so lightly regarded; the towne hath suffered through their owne peevishnesse, an everlasting reproch this day, onely because foolish pitty hath hindred justice.

Consider, that compassion is not to be had upon theeves and robbers; pitty onely appertaineth to the vertuous sort, who are overwhelmed with the waves of miserie and mischaunce. What great cause of boldnesse have you given to bad livers, by letting these fellowes thus to escape, and how shall you now keepe your goods in safetie, seeing you fulfill not the law which should be your defence? never thinke that theeves will make any conscience to carry away your goods, when they find them selves in no danger of death, who have more cause to praise your pitty, then commend your wisedome: wherefore in time seeke to prevent the ensuing evill.

For my owne part, I have that care of your good, that I would worke all good meanes for your benefit, and yet not so much in respect of your profit, as for the desire I have to uphold justice, and seeing I find you and the rest so womanish, that you could not find in your hearts to hang a theefe, I have devised how to make a gin, that shall cut off their heads without mans helpe, and if the King will allow thereof.

When *Hodgekins* heard this, he was somewhat comforted in mind, and said to the Frier, that if by his cunning he would performe it, he would once againe make sute to the King to have his grant for the same. The Frier willed him to have no doubt in him: and so when he had devised it, he got a Carpenter to frame it out of hand.

Hodgekins in the meane time posted it up to the Court, and told his Majestie that the priviledge of *Hallifax* was not worth a pudding.

Why so (said the King)?

Because (quoth *Hodgekins*) we can get never a hangman to trusse our theeves: but if it shall like your good Grace (quoth he) there is a feate Frier, that will make us a devise, which shall without the hand of man cut off the cragges of all such Carles, if your Majestie will please to allow thereof.

The King understanding the full effect of the matter, at length granted his petition: whereupon till this day, it is observed in *Halifax*, that such as are taken stealing of their cloth, have their heads chopt off with the same gin.

CHAPTER IX

How the Bailiffes of *London* could get no man to bee a Catch-pole, and how certaine Flemings tooke that office upon them, whereof many of them were fleede into this Realme, by reason of certaine waters that had drowned a great part of their Countrey

THE Citty of *London* being at that time governed by Bailiffes, it came to passe, that in a certaine fray two of their Catch-poles were killed, for at that time they had not the name of Sergeants: and you shall understand, that their office was then so much hated and detested of Englishmen, that none of them would take it upon him: so that the Bailiffes were glad to get any man whatsoever, and to give him certain wages to performe that office.

It came to passe, as I said before, that two of their Officers [1] by arresting of a man, were at one instant slaine, by meanes whereof the Bailiffes were enforced to seeke others to put in their roomes; but by no meanes could they get any, wherefore according to their wonted manner, they made proclamation, that if there were any man that would present himselfe before them, he should not onely be settled in that office during their lives, but also should have such maintenance and allowance, as for such men was by the cittie provided: and notwithstanding that it was an Office most necessary in the Commonwealth, yet did the poorest wretch despise it, that lived in any estimation among his neighbours.

At last a couple of Flemings, which were fled into this land, by reason that their countrey was drowned with the sea, hearing the proclamation, offered themselves unto the Bayliffes, to serve in this place, who were presently received and accepted, and according to order had garments given them, which were of 2. colors, blue and red their coates, breeches and stockings, whereby they were knowne and discerned from other men.

Within halfe a yeare after, it came to passe, that *Thomas Dove* of *Exeter* came up to *London*, who having by his jollity and good fellowship, brought himselfe greatly behind hand, was in danger to divers men of the Citty, among the rest, one of his

[1] Officers 1632: Offices 1623.

Creditors feed an Officer to arrest him. The Dutch-man that had not bin long experienced in such matters, and hearing how many of his fellowes had bin killed for attempting to arrest men, stood quivering and quaking in a corner of the street to watch for *Thomas Dove*, and having long waited, at length he spied him: whereupon he prepared his mace ready, and with a pale countenance proceeded to his office; at what time comming behind the man, suddenly with his mace he knockt him on the pate, saying, I arrest you, giving him such a blow, that he fell him to the ground.

The Catchpole thinking he had killed the man, he left his Mace behind him and ranne away: the creditor he ranne after him, calling and crying that he should turne againe: But the Fleming would not by any meanes turne backe, but got him quite out of the Citty, and tooke Sanctuary at *Westminster*.

Dove being come to himselfe, arose and went to his Inne, no man hindring his passage, being not a little glad he so escaped the danger. Yet neverthelesse, at his next comming to *London*, another Catchpole met with him, and arrested him in the Kings name.

Dove being dismaied at this mischievous mischance, knew not what to doe: at last he requested the Catchpole that hee would not violently cast him in prison, but stay till such time as he could send for a friend to be his surety; and although kindnesse in a Catchpole be rare, yet was he won with faire words to doe him this favour: whereupon *Dove* desired one to goe to his Host *Jarrat*, who immediately came unto him, and offered himselfe to be *Doves* surety.

The Officer, who never saw this man before, was much mazed at his sight: for *Jarrat* was a great and mighty man of body, of countenance grim, and exceeding high of stature, so that the Catchpole was wonderfully afraid, asking if he could find never a surety but the devell, most fearefully intreating him to conjure him away, and he would doe *Dove* any favour.

What, will you not take my word (qd. *Jarrat*)?

Sir (qd. the Catchpole) if it were for any matter in hell, I would take your word as soone as any divels in that place, but seeing it is for a matter on earth, I would gladly have a surety.

Why thou whorson cricket (quoth *Jarret*) thou maggat-a-pie, thou spinner, thou paultry spider, dost thou take me for a Divell? Sirra, take my word, I charge thee for this man, or else goodman butterflie, ile make thee repent it.

The officer, while he was in the house, said, he was content, but as soone as he came into the street, he cried, saying: Helpe, helpe, good neighbors, or else the Divill will carry away my prisoner: notwithstanding, there was not one man would stirre to be the Catchpoles aide.   Which when he saw, he tooke fast hold on *Thomas Dove*, and would not by any meanes let him goe.

Jarret seeing this, made no more to doe, but comming to the Officer, gave him such a fillop on the forehead with his finger, that he fell the poore Fleming to the ground: and while he lay in the streete stretching his heeles, *Jarrat* tooke *Dove* under his arme and carried him home, where he thought himselfe as safe, as King *Charlemaine* in mount Albon.

The next morning *Jarret* conveyed *Dove* out of Towne, who afterward kept him in the countrey, and came no more in the Catchpoles clawes.

CHAPTER **X**

How Duke *Robert* came a wooing to *Margaret* with the white hand, and how he appointed to come and steale her away from her Masters

THE beautifull *Margaret*, who had now dwelt with her Dame the space of foure yeares, was highly regarded and secretly beloved of many gallant and worthy Gentlemen of the countrey, but of two most especially, Duke *Robert*, and Sir *William Ferris*.

It chanced on a time, that faire *Margaret* with many others of her Masters folkes, went a hay-making attired in a red stammell peticoate, and a broad strawne hatte upon her head, she had also a hay-forke, and in her lappe shee did carry her breake-fast. As she went along, Duke *Robert*, with one or two of his Keepers, met with her, whose amiable sight did now anew re-inkindle the secret fire of love, which long lay smothering in his heart. Wherefore meeting her so happily, he saluted her thus friendly.

Faire maid, good morrow, are you walking so diligently to your labour? Needes must the weather be faire, when the Sun shines so cleare, and the hay holesome that is dried with such splendant rayes.

Renowned and most notable Duke (qd. she) poore harvest folkes pray for faire weather, and it is the laborers comfort to see his worke prosper, and the more happy may we count the day, that is blessed with your princely presence.

But more happy (said the Duke) are they which are conversant in thy company. But let me intreat thee to turne backe to thy Masters with me, and commit thy forke to some that are fitter for such toyle: trust me, methinkes thy dame is too much ill advised, in setting thee to such homely busines. I muse thou canst indure this vile beseeming servitude, whose delicate lims were never framed to prove such painfull experiments.

Albeit (quoth she) it becommeth not me to controule your judiciall thoughts, yet were you not the Duke, I would say, your opinion deceived you: though your faire eyes seem cleare, yet I deemed them unperfect, if they cast before your mind any shadow or sparke of beauty in me: But I rather thinke, because it hath beene an old saying, that women are proude to heare themselves praised, that you either speake this, to drive away the time, or to wring me from my too apparant imperfections.

But I humbly intreate pardon, too longe have I fore-slowed my businesse, and shewen myselfe over bold in your presence; and therewith, with a courtly grace, bending her knees to the courteous Duke, shee went forward to the field, and the Duke to the Towne of *Glocester*.

When he came thither, he made his Keepers great cheare, intreating them they would give him respite to be awhile with old *Gray*; for we twaine must have a game or two (quoth he): and for my safe returne, I gage to you my princely word, that as I am a true Knight and a Gentleman, I will returne safe to your charge againe.

The Keepers [1] being content, the Duke departed, and with old *Gray* goes to the field, to peruse the Workefolkes, where while *Gray* found himselfe busie in many matters, he took opportunity to talke with *Margaret*; she who by his letters before was privie to his purpose, guest before hand the cause of his comming: to whom he spake to this effect:

Faire Maide, I did long since manifest my love to thee by my letter; tell me therefore, were it not better to be a Dutches then drudge? a Lady of high reputation, then a servant of simple degree? with me thou mightest live in pleasure, where here thou drawest thy daies forth in paine; by my love thou shouldst be made a Lady of great treasures: where now thou art poore and beggarly: all manner of delights should then attend on thee, and whatsoever thy heart desireth, thou shouldst have: wherefore seeing it lies in thy owne choice, make thy selfe happy, by consenting to my suite.

Sir (quoth she) I confesse your love deserves a Ladies favour, your affection a faithfull friend, such a one as could make but one heart and minde of two hearts and bodies; but farre unfit it is that the Turtle should match with the Eagle, though her love be never so pure, her wings are unfit to mount so high. While *Thales* gazed on the starres, he stumbled in a pit. And they that clime unadvisedly, catch a fall suddenly: what availeth high dignitie in time of adversity? it neither helpeth the sorrow of the heart, nor removes the bodies miserie: as for wealth and treasure, what are they, but fortunes baits to bring men in danger? good for nothing but to make people forget themselves: and whereas you alleadge poverty to be a hinderer of the hearts comfort, I find it my selfe contrary, knowing more surety to rest under a simple habite, then a royall robe: and verily there is none in the world poore, but they that think themselves poore:

[1] Keepers, brothers 1632, 1623.

for such as are indued with content, are rich, having nothing els, but he that is possessed with riches, without content, is most wretched and miserable. Wherefore most Noble Duke, albeit I account my life unworthy of your least favour, yet I would desire you to match your love to your like, and let me rest to my rake, and use my forke for my living.

Consider, faire *Margaret* (quoth he) that it lies not in mans power to place his love where he list, being the worke of an high deity. A bird was never seen in *Pontus,* nor true love in a fleeting mind: never shall I remove the affection of my heart which in nature resembleth the stone Abiston, whose fire can never be cooled: wherefore sweet Maiden give not obstinate deniall, where gentle acceptance ought to be received.

Faire sir (quoth she) consider what high displeasure may rise by a rash match, what danger a Kings frownes may breed, my worthlesse matching with your Roialty, may perhaps regaine your libertie, and hazard my life; then call to mind how little you should enjoy your love, or I my wedded Lord.

The Duke at these words made this reply, that if she consented, she should not dread any danger. The thunder (quoth he) is driven away by ringing of belles, the Lions wrath qualified by a yeelding body: how much more a Brothers anger with a Brothers intreaty? By me he hath received many favors, and never yet did he requite any one of them: and who is ignorant that the Princely Crown which adorneth his head, is my right? all which I am content he shall still enjoy, so he requite my kindnesse. But if he should not, then would I be like those men (that eating of the tree Lutes) forget the country where they were borne, and never more should this clime cover my head, but with thee would I live in a strange land, being better content with an egge in thy company, then with all the delicates in England.

The Maiden hearing this, who with many other wordes was long wooed, at last consented; where yeelding to him her heart with her hand, he departed, appointing to certifie her from *Cardiffe* Castle, what determination he would follow: so taking his leave of *Gray* he went to his keepers, and with them posted to *Cardiffe.*

Now it is to be remembred, that sir *William Ferrers* within a day or two after came unto *Grayes* house, as it was his ordinary custome, but not so much ywis for *Grayes* company, as for the minde he had to *Margaret* his Maide, who although he were a married man, and had a faire Lady to his wife, yet he laid hard siege to the fort of this Maidens chastity, having with many faire words sought to allure her, and by the offer of sundry rich gifts to tempt her. But when she saw, that by a hundred denials she could not be rid of him, she now chanced on a sudden to give him such an answere, as drove him from a deceit into such a conceit, as never after that time he troubled her.

Sir *William Ferrers* being very importunate to have her grant his desire, and when after sundry assaults she gave him still the repulse, he would needes know the reason why she would not love him (quoth he) if thou didst but consider who he is that seeketh thy favour, what pleasure he may doe thee by his purse, and what credit by his countenance, thou wouldst never stand on such nice points. If I be thy friend, who dareth be thy foe? and what is he that will once call thy name in question for any thing? therefore sweet girle, be better advised, and refuse not my offer being so large.

Truly sir *William* (quoth she) though there be many reasons to make me deny your suite, yet is there one above the rest that causes me I cannot love you.

Now I pray thee, my wench let me know that (quoth he) and I will amend it whatsoever it be.

Pardon me sir (said *Margaret*) if I should speake my mind, it would possibly offend you, and do me no pleasure because it is a defect in nature, which no phisicke can cure.

Sir *William* hearing on her so, being abashed at her speech, said, Faire *Margaret*, let me (if I may obtaine no more at thy hands) yet intreat thee to know what this defect should be, I am not wry-neckt, crook-legd, stub-footed, lame-handed, nor bleare-eyed: what can make this dislike? I never knew any body that tooke exceptions at my person before.

And the more sorry am I (quoth she) that I was so malapert to speake it, but pardon my presumption, good sir *William*, I would I had beene like the storke tonguelesse, then should I never have caused your disquiet.

Nay sweet *Margaret* (quoth he) tell me deare love, I commend thy singlenesse of heart, good *Margaret* speake.

Good sir *William* let it rest (quoth she) I know you will not beleeve it when I have revealed it, neither is it a thing that you can helpe: and yet such is my foolishnesse, had it not beene for that, I thinke verily I had granted your suite ere now. But seeing you urge me so much to know what it is, I will tell you: it is sir, your ill-favoured great nose, that hangs sagging so lothsomely to your lips, that I cannot find in my heart so much as to kisse you.

What, my nose (quoth he)? is my nose so great and I never knew it? certainly I thought my nose to be as comely as any mans: but this it is we are all apt to think well of our selves, and a great deale better then we ought: but let me see? my nose! by the masse tis true, I do now feele it my selfe: Good Lord, how was I blinded before?

Hereupon it is certaine, that the Knight was driven into such a conceit, as none could perswade him but his nose was so great indeed; his Lady, or any other that spake to the contrarie, he would say they were flatterers, and that they lied, insomuch that he would be ready to strike some of them that commended and spake well of his nose. If they were men of worship, or any other that contraried him in his opinion, he would sweare they flowted him, and be ready to challenge them the field. He became so ashamed of himselfe, that after that day he would never goe abroad, whereby *Margaret* was well rid of his company.

On a time, a wise and grave gentleman seeing him grounded in his conceit so strongly, gave his Lady counsell, not to contrary him therein, but rather say that she would seeke out some cunning Phisitian to cure him: for (said he) as sir *William* hath taken this conceit of himselfe, so is he like never to heare other opinion, till his owne conceit doth remove it, the which must be wisely wrought to bring it to passe.

Whereupon the Lady having conferred with a Phisitian that beare a great name in the countrey, hee undertooke to remove this fond conceit by his skill. The day being appointed when the Phisitian should come, and the Knight beeing told thereof, for very joy he would goe forth to meete him, when a woman of the Towne saw the Knight, having heard what rumor went because of his nose, shee looked very stedfastly upon him: the Knight casting his eye upon her, seeing her to gaze so wistly in his face, with an angry countenance, said thus to her, Why how now good huswife, cannot you get you about your busines?

The woman being a shrewish queane, answered him cuttedly, No mary can I not (qd. she).

No, you drab! What is the cause (said the Knight)?

Because (quoth she) your nose stands in my way: wherewith the Knight being very angry, and abashed, went backe againe to his house.

The Phisitian being come, hee had filled a certaine bladder with sheepes blood, and conveyed it into his sleeve, where at the issue of the bladder he had put in a piece of swanes quil, through the which the bloud should runne out of the bladder so close by his hand, that he holding the Knight by the nose, it might not be perceived, but that it issued thence. All things being prepared, he told the knight, that by a foule corrupt blood wherewith the veines of his nose were overcharged, his impediment did grow, therefore (quoth he) to have redresse for this disease, you must have a veine opened in your nose, whence this foule corruption must be taken: whereupon it will follow, that your nose will fall againe to his naturall proportion, and never shall you be troubled with this griefe any more, and thereupon will I gage my life.

I pray you Master Doctor (said the Knight) is my nose so big as you make it?

With reverence I may speake it (said the Physitian) to tell the truth, and avoid flattery, I never saw a more misshapen nose so foule to sight.

Loe you now Madam (quoth the Knight) this is you that said my nose was as well, as hansome, and as comely a nose as any mans.

Alas sir (qd. she) I spake it (God wot) because you should not grieve at it, nor take my words in ill part, neither did it indeed become me to mislike of your nose.

All this we will quickly remedy, said the Phisitian, have no doubt: and with that, he very orderly prickt him in the nose, but not in any veine whereby he might bleed: and presently having a tricke finely to unstop the quill, the blood ranne into a bason in great abundance: and when the bladder was empty, and the bason almost full, the Phisitian seemed to close the veine, and asked him how he felt his nose, shewing the great quantite of filthy blood which from thence he had taken.

The Knight beholding it with great wonder, said, he thought that no man in the world had bin troubled with such abundance of corrupt bloud in his whole bodie, as lay in his mis-shapen nose, and therewithall he began to touch and handle his nose, saying that he felt it mightily asswaged. Immediately a glasse was brought wherein he might behold himselfe.

Yea mary (qd. he) now I praise God, I see my nose is come into some reasonable proportion, and I feele my selfe very well eased of the burthen thereof; but if it continue thus, thats all.

I will warrant your worship (said the Phisitian) for ever being troubled with the like againe.

Whereupon the Knight received great joy, and the Doctor a high reward.

CHAPTER XI

How *Thomas* of *Reading* was murdered at his Hosts house of *Colebrooke*, who also had murdred many before him, and how their wickednesse was at length revealed

THOMAS OF *Reading* having many occasions to come to London, aswell about his own affairs, as also the Kings businesse, being in a great office under his Majestie, it chanced on a time, that his Host and Hostesse of *Colebrooke*, who through covetousnes had murdered many of the guests, and having every time he came thither great store of his mony to lay up, appointed him to be the next fat pig that should be killed: For it is to be understood, that when they plotted the murder of any man, this was alwaies their terme, the man to his wife, and the woman to her husband: wife, there is now a fat pig to be had, if you want one. Whereupon she would answer thus, I pray you put him in the hogstie till to-morrow.

This was, when any man came thither alone without others in his company, and they saw he had great store of money.

This man should be then laid in the chamber right over the kitchin, which was a faire chamber, and better set out then any other in the house: the best bedstead therein, though it were little and low, yet was it most cunningly carved, and faire, to the eye, the feet whereof were fast naild to the chamber floore, in such sort, that it could not in any wise fall, the bed that lay therein was fast sowed to the sides of the bedstead: Moreover, that part of the chamber whereupon this bed and bedsteed stood, was made in such sort, that by the pulling out of two yron pinnes below in the kitchin, it was to be let downe and taken up by a draw bridge, or in manner of a trap doore: moreover in the kitchin, directly under the place where this should fall, was a mighty great caldron, wherein they used to seethe their liquor when they went to brewing. Now, the men appointed for the slaughter, were laid into this bed, and in the dead time of the night, when they were sound a sleepe, by plucking out the foresaid yron pinnes, downe would the man fall out of his bed into the boyling caldron, and all the cloaths that were upon him: where being suddenly scalded and drowned, he was never able to cry or speake one word.

Then had they a little ladder ever standing ready in the kitchin, by the which they presently mounted into the said chamber, and there closely take away the mans apparell, as also his money, in his male or capcase: and then lifting up the said falling floore which hung by hinges, they made it fast as before.

The dead body would they take presently out of the caldron and throw it downe the river, which ran neere unto their house, whereby they escaped all danger.

Now if in the morning any of the rest of the guests that had talkt with the murdered man ore eve, chanst to aske for him, as having occasion to ride the same way that he should have done, the goodman would answere, that he tooke horse a good while before day, and that he himselfe did set him forward: the horse the goodman would also take out of the stable, and convay him by a hay-barne of his, that stood from his house a mile or two, whereof himselfe did alwaies keepe the keies full charily, and when any hay was to be brought from thence, with his owne hands he would deliver it; then before the horse should goe from thence, he would dismarke him: as if he ware a long taile, he would make him curtall; or else crop his eares, or cut his mane, or put out one of his eies; and by this meanes he kept himselfe unknowne.

Now *Thomas* of *Reading*, as I said before, being markt, and kept for a fat pig, he was laid in the same chamber of death, but by reason *Gray* of *Gloucester* chanced also to come that night, he escaped scalding.

The next time he came, he was laid there againe, but before he fell aslepe, or was warme in his bed, one came riding thorow the towne and cried piteously, that *London* was all on a fire, and that it had burned downe *Thomas Beckets* house in *West cheape*, and a great number more in the same street, and yet (quoth he) the fire is not quencht.

Which tidings when *Thomas* of *Reading* heard, he was very sorrowfull, for of the same *Becket* that day he had received a great peece of money, and had left in his house many of his writings, and some that appertained to the King also: therfore there was no nay but he would ride backe againe to *London* presently, to see how the matter stood; thereupon making himselfe ready, departed. This crosse fortune caused his hoast to frowne, nevertheless the next time (qd. he) will pay for all.

Notwithstanding God so wrought, that they were prevented

the likewise, by reason of a great fray that hapned in the house
betwixt a couple that fell out at dice, insomuch as the murderers
themselves were inforced to cal him up, being a man in great
authority, that he might set the house in quietnes, out of the
which by meanes of this quarrell, they doubted to lose many
things.

Another time when he should have beene laid in the same
place he fell so sicke, that he requested to have some body to
watch with him, whereby also they could not bring their vile
purpose to passe. But hard it is to escape the ill fortunes wher-
unto a man is allotted: for albeit that the next time that he came
to *London*, his horse stumbled and broke one of his legges as he
should ride homeward, yet hired he another to hasten his owne
death; for there is no remedy but he should goe to *Colbrooke*
that night: but by the way he was heavy asleepe, that he could
scant keepe himselfe, in the saddle; and when he came neere
unto the Towne, his nose burst out suddenly a bleeding.

Well, to his Inne he came, and so heavy was his heart that he
could eate no meat: his host and hostesse hearing he was so
melancholy, came up to cheare him, saying, Jesus Master *Cole*,
what ayles you to night? never did we see you thus sad before:
will it please you to have a quart of burnt sacke?

With a good will (quoth he) and would to God *Tom Dove* were
here, hee would surely make me merry, and we should lacke no
musicke: but I am sorry for the man with all my heart, that he is
come so farre behind hand: but alasse, so much can every man
say, but what good doth it him? No no, it is not words can
helpe a man in this case, the man had need of other reliefe then
so. Let me see: I have but one child in the world and that is
my daughter, and halfe that I have is hers, the other halfe my
wifes. What then? shall I be good to no body but them? In
conscience, my wealth is too much for a cupple to possesse, and
what is our Religion without charity? And to whom is charity
more to be shewen, then to decayed housholders?

Good my hoast lend me a pen and inke, and some paper, for
I will write a letter unto the poore man straight: and something
I will give him: That almes which a man bestowes with his
owne hands, he shal be sure to have delivered, and God knowes
how long I shall live.

With that, his hostesse dissemblingly answered, saying:
Doubt not, Master *Cole*, you are like enough by the course of
nature to live many yeares.

God knowes (quoth he) I never found my heart so heavy before.

By this time pen, inke, and paper was brought, setting himselfe in writing as followeth.

In the name of God, Amen, I bequeath my soule to God, and my body to the ground, my goods equally betweene my wife Elenor, *and* Isabel, *my daughter. Item I give to* Thomas Dove *of* Exeter *one hundred pounds, nay that is too little, I give to* Thomas Dove *two hundred pounds in money, to be paid unto him presently upon his demand thereof by my said wife and daughter.*

Ha, how say you hoast (qd. he) is not this well? I pray you reade it.

His hoast looking thereon, said, why Master *Cole*, what have you written here? you said you would write a letter, but me thinks you have made a Will, what neede have you to doe thus? thanks be to God, you may live many faire yeares.

Tis true (quoth *Cole*) if it please God, and I trust this writing cannot shorten my daies, but let me see, have I made a Will? Now, I promise you, I did verily purpose to write a letter: notwithstanding, I have written that that God put into my mind: but looke once againe my host, is it not written there, that *Dove* shall have two hundred pounds, to be paid when he comes to demand it?

Yes indeed (said his hoste).

Well then, all is well (said *Cole*) and it shall go as it is for me. I will not bestow the new writing thereof any more.

Then folding it up, he sealed it, desiring that his host would send it to *Exeter*: he promised that he would, notwithstanding *Cole* was not satisfied: but after some pause, he would needs hire one to carry it. And so sitting downe sadly in his chaire againe, upon a sudden he burst forth a weeping; they demanding the cause thereof, he spake as followeth:

No cause of these feares I know: but it comes now into my minde (said *Cole*) when I set toward this my last journey to *London*, how my daughter tooke on, what a coyle she kept to have me stay: and I could not be rid of the little baggage a long time, she did so hang about me, when her mother by violence tooke her away, she cryed out most mainly, O my father, my father, I shall never see him againe.

Alas, pretty soule (said his hoastesse) this was but meer kindnesse in the girle, and it seemeth she is very fond of you. But alasse, why should you grieve at this? you must consider that it was but childishnes.

I, it is indeed (said *Cole*) and with that he began to nod.

Then they asked him if he would go to bed.

No (said he) although I am heavy, I have no mind to go to bed at all.

With that certaine musitians of the towne came to the chamber, and knowing Master *Cole* was there, drue out their instruments, and very solemnly began to play.

This musicke comes very well (said *Cole*) and when he had listned a while thereunto, he said, Methinks these instruments sound like the ring of *S. Mary Overies* belles, but the base drownes all the rest: and in my eare it goes like a bell that rings a forenoones knell, for Gods sake let them leave off, and beare them this simple reward.

The musitians being gone, his hoste asked if now it would please him to go to bed; for (quoth he) it is welneare eleven of the clocke.

With that *Cole* beholding his host and hostesse earnestly, began to start backe, saying, what aile you to looke so like pale death? good Lord, what have you done, that your hands are thus bloudy?

What my hands (said his host)? Why, you may see they are neither bloudy nor foule: either your eies doe greatly dazell, or else fancies of a troubled minde do delude you.

Alas my hoste, you may see (said he) how weake my wits are, I never had my head so idle before. Come, let me drinke once more, and then I will to bed, and trouble you no longer.

With that he made himselfe unready, and his hostesse was very diligent to warme a kerchiffe, and put it about his head.

Good Lord (said he) I am not sicke, I praise God, but such an alteration I find in my selfe as I never did before.

With that the scritch owle cried piteously, and anone after the night raven sate croking hard by his window.

Jesu have mercy upon me (quoth hee) what an ill favoured cry doe yonder carrion birds make, and therewithall he laid him downe in his bed, from whence he never rose againe.

His host and hostesse, that all this while noted his troubled mind, began to commune betwixt themselves thereof. And the man said, he knew not what were best to be done. By my consent (quoth he) the matter should passe, for I thinke it is not best to meddle on him.

What man (quoth she) faint you now? have you done so many and doe you shrinke at this? Then shewing him a great deale of gold which *Cole* had left with her, she said, Would it not grieve a bodies heart to lose this? hang the old churle, what should he doe living any longer? he hath too much, and we have too little: tut husband, let the thing be done, and then this is our owne.

Her wicked counsell was followed, and when they had listned at his chamber doore, they heard the man sound asleepe: All is safe (quoth they) and downe into the kitchin they goe, their servants being all in bedde, and pulling out the yron pins, downe fell the bed, and the man dropt out into the boyling caldron. He being dead, they betwixt them cast his body into the river, his clothes they made away, and made all things as it should be: but when he came to the stable to convey thence *Coles* horse, the stable doore being open, the horse had got loose, and with a part of the halter about his necke, and straw trusted under his belly, as the ostlers had dressed him ore eve, he was gone out at the backe side, which led into a great field adjoyning to the house, and so leaping divers hedges, being a lustie stout horse, had got into a ground where a mare was grasing, with whom he kept such a coile, that they got into the high way, where one of the Towne meeting them, knew the mare, and brought her and the horse to the man that owd her.

In the meane space, the Musicians had beene at the Inne, and in requitall of their evenings gift, they intended to give *Cole* some musicke in the morning. The goodman told them he tooke horse before day: likewise there was a guest in the house that would have bore him company to *Reading*, unto whom the hoste also answered, that he himselfe set him upon horsebacke, and that he went long agoe. Anone came the man that owed the mare, inquiring up and downe, to know and if none of them missed a horse, who said no. At the last hee came to the signe of the Crane where *Cole* lay: and calling the hostlers he demanded of them if they lackt none, they said no:

Why then (said the man) I perceive my mare is good for something, for if I send her to field single, she will come home double: thus it passed on all that day and the night following.

But the next day after, *Coles* wife musing that her husband came not home, sent one of her men on horse-backe, to see if he could meete him: and if (quoth she) you meet him not betwixt this and *Colebrooke*, aske for him at the Crane, but if you find him not there, then ride to *London*; for I doubt he is either sicke, or else some mischance hath fallen unto him.

The fellow did so, and asking for him at *Colebrooke*, they answered, he went homeward from thence such a day. The servant musing what should be become of his Master, and making much inquiry in the Towne for him: at length one told him of a horse that was found on the high way, and no man knew whence he came. He going to see the horse, knew him presently, and to the Crane he goes with him. The hoast of the house perceiving this, was blancke, and that night fled secretly away. The fellow going unto the Justice desired his helpe: presently after word was brought that *Jarman* of the Crane was gone, then all the men said, he had sure made *Cole* away: and the musitians told what *Jarman* said to them, when they would have given *Cole* musicke. Then the woman being apprehended and examined, confessed the truth. *Jarman* soone after was taken in *Windsor Forest*. He and his wife were both hangd, after they had laid open al these things before expressed. Also he confessed that, he being a Carpenter made that false falling floore, and how his wife devised it. And how they had murdered by that means lx. persons. And yet notwithstanding all the money which they had gotten thereby, they prospered not, but at their death were found in debt.

When the King heard of this murder, he was for the space of vii daies so sorrowfull and heavie, as he would not heare any sute, giving also commandement, that the house should quite be consumed with fire, wherein *Cole* was murdred, and that no man should ever build upon that cursed ground.

Coles substance at his death was exceeding great, hee had daily in his house an hundred men servants and xl. Maids; he maintained beside above two or three hundred people, spinners and carders, and a great many other housholders. His wife after never married, and at her death shee bestowed a mightie summe of money toward the maintaining of the new builded monastery. Her daughter was most richly married to a Gentleman of great worship, by whom she had many Children. And some say, that the river whereinto *Cole* was cast, did ever since carry the name of *Cole*, being called The river of *Cole*, and the Towne of *Colebrooke*.

CHAPTER XII

SUTTONS wife of *Salisbury* which had lately bin delivered of a sonne, against her going to Church, prepared great cheare: at what time *Simons* wife of *South-hampton* came thither, and so did divers others of the Clothiers wives, onely to make merry at this Churching feast: and whilest these Dames sat at the Table, *Crab, Weasell,* and *Wren,* waited on the boord, and as the old Proverbe speaketh, Many women many words, so fell it out at that time: for there was such pratling that it passed: some talkt of their husbands frowardnes, some shewed their Maids sluttishnes, othersome deciphered the costlines of their garments, some told many tales of their neighbors: and to be briefe, there was none of them but would have talke for a whole day.

But when *Crab, Weasell,* and *Wren* saw this, they concluded betwixt themselves, that as oft as any of the women had a good bit of meate on their trenchers, they offering a cleane one, should catch that commodity, and so they did: but the women being busie in talke, marked it not, till at the last one found leisure to misse her meat: whereupon she said, that their boldnes exceeded their diligence.

Not so, forsooth (said *Weasell*) there is an hundred bolder than wee.

Name me one (said the woman) if you can.

A flea is bolder (quoth *Crabbe*).

How will you prove that (said the woman)?

Because (quoth he) they creepe under your coates, where we dare not come, and now and then bite you by the buttocks as if they were brawne.

But what becomes of them (qd. the woman)? their sweet meat hath sowre sauce, and their lustines doth often cost them their lives, therefore take heed.

A good warning of a faire woman (said *Wren*) but I had not thought so fine a wit in a fat belly.

The women seeing their men so merry, said it was a signe there was good ale in the house.

Thats as fit for a Churching (quoth *Weasell*) as a cudgell for a curst queane.

Thus with pleasant communication and merry quips they drove out the time, till the fruit and spice cakes were set on the boord: At what time one of them began to aske the other, if they heard not of the cruell murder of *Thomas* of *Reading*?

What (said the rest) is old *Cole* murdered? when, I pray you was the deede done?

The other answered, on Friday last.

O good Lord (said the women) how was it done, can you tell? As report goes (said the other) he was rosted alive.

O pitifull! was he roasted? Indeed I heard one say, a man was murdred at *London*, and that he was sodden at an In-holders house, and served it to the guests in stead of porke.

No neighbor, it was not at *London* (said another); I heare say twas comming from *London*, at a place called *Colebrooke*, and it is reported for truth, that the Inholder made pies of him, and penny pasties, yea, and made his owne servant eate a peece of him. But I pray you good neighbour, can you tell how it was knowne: some say, that a horse revealed it.

Now by the masse (quoth *Grayes* wife) it was told one of my neighbours, that a certaine horse did speake, and told great things.

That sounds like a lie (said one of them).

Why (said another) may not a horse speake, as well as *Balaams* asse?

It may be, but it is unlikely (said the third). But where was the horse when he spake?

As some say (qd. she) he was in the field, and had broke out of the stable, where he stood fast locked in mighty strong iron fetters, which he burst in peeces, as they had beene strawes, and broke downe the stable doore, and so got away.

The good man comming in at these speeches, asked what that was they talkt of.

Marry (said his wife) wee heare that *Cole* of *Reading* is mur-dred: I pray you is it true?

I (said *Sutton*) it is true, that vile villaine his hoast murdered him, in whose house the man had spent many a pound.

But did they make pies of him (said his wife);

No, no (quoth her husband): he was scalded to death in a

boyling caldron, and afterward throwne into a running river that is hard by.

But good husband, how was it knowne?

By his horse (quoth hee).

What, did he tell his Master was murthered? could the horse speake English?

Jesus what a foolish woman are you (quoth he) to aske such a question? But to end this, you are all heartily welcome, good neighbors, and I am sorry you had no better cheere.

So with thanks the women departed.

Thus have ye heard the divers tales that will be spred abroad of an evil deed.

CHAPTER XIII

How Duke *Robert* deceived his keepers, and got from them: how he met faire *Margaret*, and in carrying her away was taken, for the which he had his eies put out

DUKE *Robert*, having, as you heard, obtained the love of faire *Margaret*, did now cast in his minde, how hee might delude his Keepers, and carry her quite away. In the end he being absolutely resolved what to doe, sent this letter unto her, wherein he requested, that she would be ready to meet him in the forrest, betwixt *Cardiffe* and *Gloucester*.

The young Lady having secretly received his message, un-known to her Master or dame, in a morning betime made her ready and got forth, walking to the appointed place, where her Love should meete her.

During her aboade there, and thinking long ere her love came, she entred into divers passions, which indeed presayged some disaster fortune to follow.

O my deare love, said shee, how slacke art thou in performing thy promise! why doe not thy deedes agree with thy inditing? see these are thy wordes, Come, my deare *Margaret*, and with *Cupids* swift wings flie to thy friend, be now as nimble in thy footing, as the Camels of Bactria, that runne an hundred miles a day, I will waite and stay for thee, so I stay not too long. There is no Country like Austria for ambling horses, and to carry thee I have got one.

O my Love (quoth she) here am I, but where art thou? O why doest thou play the trewant with time, who like the wind slides away unseene? An ambling gennet of Spaine is too slow to serve our turnes. A flying horse, for flying Lovers were most meete. And thus casting many lookes through the Silvane shades, up and downe to espie him, she thought every minute an houre, till she might see him, sometimes she would wish her selfe a bird, that she might flie through the ayre to meet him, or a pretty squirill to clime the highest tree to descry his comming: but finding her wishes vaine, she began thus to excuse him and perswaded herselfe, saying,

How much too blame am I, to finde fault with my friend? Alasse, men that lacke their liberty, must come when they can,

143

not when they would, poore prisoners cannot doe what they desire, and then why should I be so hastie? Therefore if safely I may lay me down I will beguile unquiet thoughts with quiet sleepe: it is said that *Galino* breeds no Serpents, nor doth *Englands* forrests nourish Beares or Lyons, therefore without hurt I hope I may rest awile. Thus leaving faire *Margaret* in a sweet slumber, we will returne to Duke *Robert*, who had thus plotted his escape from his keepers.

Having liberty of the King to hawke and hunt, hee determined on a day, as he should follow the chase, to leave the hounds to the Hart, and the hunters to their hornes, and being busie in their sport, himselfe would flie, which he performed at that time when he appointed *Margaret* to meete him, and so comming to the place, his horse all on a water, and himself in a sweat, finding his love asleepe, he awaked her with a kisse, saying, Arise faire *Margaret*, now comes the time wherein thou shalt be made a Queene: and presently setting her on horse-backe he posted away.

Now when the keepers saw they had lost his company, and that at the killing of the game, he was not present, they were among themselves in such a mutinie, that they were ready one to stabbe another.

It was thy fault (said one) that he thus escapt from us, that hadst more mind of thy pleasure, then of thy prisoner, and by this meanes we are all undone.

The other said as much to him, that he had thought he had followed him in the chase: but leaving at last this contention, the one posted up to the King, while the others coasted up and downe the country to search for the Duke, who having kild his horse in travelling, was most unhappily meete on foot with faire *Margaret*, ere he could come to any towne, where he might for money have another. But when he spied his Keepers come to take him, he desired *Margaret* to make shift for herselfe, and to seeke to escape them. But she being of a contrary mind, said, she would live and die with him.

The Duke seeing himselfe ready to be surprised, drew out his sword, and said, he would buy his liberty with his life, before he would yeeld to be any more a prisoner; and thereupon began a great fight betwixt them, insomuch that the duke had killed two of them: but himselfe being sore wounded, and faint with overmuch bleeding, at length fell downe, being not able any longer to stand: and by this means the good Duke was taken with his faire love, and both of them committed to prison.

But in the meane space, when *Grayes* wife had missed her Maide, and saw she was quite gone, she made great lamentation for her among her neighbors, for she loved her as dearly as any child that ever she bore of her owne body. O *Margaret* (quoth she) what cause hadst thou thus to leave me? if thou didst mislike of any thing, why didst thou not tell me? If thy wages were too little, I would have mended it: If thy apparell had beene too simple, thou shouldst have had better: If thy worke had bin too great, I would have had helpe for thee.

Farewell my sweet *Meg*, the best servant that ever came in any mans house, many may I have of thy name, but never any of thy nature, thy diligence is much, in thy hands I laid the whole government of my house, and thereby eased my selfe of that care, which now will cumber me.

Heere she hath left me my keyes unto my chests, but my comfort is gone with her presence, every gentle word that she was wont to speake, comes now into my mind, her courteous behaviour shall I never forget: with how sweet and modest a countenance would she qualifie my over-hastie nature? It repents my heart that ever I spoke foule word unto her. O *Meg*, wert thou here againe, I would never chide thee more: but I was an unworthy Dame for such a servant: what will become of me now, if I should chance to be sicke, seeing shee is gone, that was wont to be both my Apoticary and Phisitian?

Well (quoth her neighbors) there is no remedy now, but to rest content, you shall one day heare of her doubt you not, and thinke this, that she was not so good, but you may get another as good, and therefore do not take it so heavily.

O neighbour, blame me not to grieve, seeing I have lost so great a jewell, and sure I am perswaded, that scant in a bodies life time, they shall meete with the like. I protest, I would circuit *England* round about on my bare feete to meete with her againe. O, my *Meg* was surely stole away from me, else would she not have gone in such sort.

Her husband on the other side grieved as much, and rested not night nor day riding up and downe to seeke her; but she, poore soule, is fast lockt up in prison, and therefore cannot be met withall.

But when the King understood of his brothers escape, hee was marvelous wroth, giving great charge and commandement when he was taken, that both his eies should be put out and be kept in prison till his dying day; appointing also that the Maid should lose her life for presumption of loving him.

This matter being rumored over all *England*, it came to the eares of *Gray* and his wife, who hearing that *Margaret* also was there in prison appointed to die, the good aged woman never rested till she came to the Court, where kneeling before the King with many teares she besought his Majestie to spare the Maidens life, saying, Most royall King consider, I humbly beseech you, that the Duke your brother was able to intice any woman to his love: much more a silly Maiden, especially promising her marriage, to make her a Lady, a Dutchesse, or a Queene, who would refuse such an offer, when at the instant they might get both a Princely husband and a high dignity? if death be a Lovers guerdon, then what is due to hatred? I am in my heart perswaded, that had my poore *Margaret* thought it would have bred your Highnes displeasure, she would never have bought his love so dear. Had your Grace made it knowen to your Commons, that it was unlawfull for any to marry the Duke your brother, who would have attempted such an action? if she had wilfully disobeyed your Graces commandement, she might have bin thought worthy of death; but seeing ignorantly she offended, I beseech your Grace to recall the sentence, and let me still enjoy my servant, for never will I rise, till your Majestie have granted my petition.

His Highnes, who was of nature mercifull, beholding the womans abundant teares, tooke pitie on her, and granted her suite: which being obtained, shee went home in all haste possible. And from thence, she with her husband taking their journy to *Cardiffe* castle, they came at that very instant when the Maiden was led toward her death, who went in most joyfull sort to the same, saying, that they were not worthie to be accounted true lovers, that were not willing to die for love: and so with a smiling countenance she passed on, as if she had eaten *Apium Risus*, which causeth a man to die laughing: but her dame *Gray* seeing her, fell about her necke, and with many kisses imbraced her, saying, Thou shalt not die my wench, but goe home with me; and for thy delivery, behold here the Kings letters; and with that she delivered them up to the governour of the Castle: who reading them found these words written: Wee pardon the maids life, and grant her libertie, but let her not passe, till she see her lovers eies put out, which we wil have you do in such sort, that not onely the sight may perish, but the eie continue faire, for which cause I have sent downe Doctor *Piero*, that he may execute the same.

The governour of the Castle having read the Kings letter, said thus to the Maiden: The Kings Majesty hath pardoned thy life, and allowed thy libertie: but you must not passe before you see your lovers eies put out.

O sir (said the Maiden) mistake not your selfe, they are my eies that must be put out, and not the Dukes: as his offence grew by my meanes, so I being guiltie, ought to receive the punishment.

The Kings commandement must be fulfilled, said the governour: and therewithall D. *Robert* was brought forth, who hearing that he must lose his eies, said thus: the Noble mind is never conquered by griefe, nor overcome by mischance: but as the Hart reneweth his age by eating the serpent, so doth a man lengthen his life with devouring sorrow: my eies have offended the King, and they must be punished, my heart is in as great fault, why is not that killed?

The Kings Majesty (said the Governour) spares your life of mere love, and onely is content to satisfie the Law with the losse of your eies, wherefore take in good part this punishment, and thinke you have deserved greater then is granted.

With this *Margaret* cryed out, saying, O my deare love, most gentle Prince, well may you wish that I had never bin borne, who by seeing of me must lose your sight; but happie should I count my selfe, if it so please the King, that I might redeeme thy eies with my life: or else, that being an equall offender, I might receive equall punishment: hadst thou sustained this smart for some queene or princesse of high blood, it might with the more ease be borne, but to indure it for such a one as I, it must needs cause a treble griefe to be increased.

Content thee faire *Margaret* (said the Duke): for honor ought to be given to vertue, and not riches: for glory, honor, nobility, and riches without vertue, are but clokes of maliciousnes. And now let me take my leave of thy beauty, for never must I behold thy face: notwithstanding I account my eies well lost, in that, I do forgoe them for so peerelesse a paragon. Now faire heavens farewell, the Sunne, Moone, and Starres shall I in this world never behold againe; and farewell also the fruitfull earth; well may I feele thee, but those poore windowes of my body are now denied to view thee any more: and though the world hath ever bin my foe, yet will I bid it farewell too, and farewell all my friends, whiles I live heare in this world, I must suppose to sleepe, and wake when I come in heaven, where I hope to see you all againe. Yet had it pleased the King, I had rather have lost my life then my eies. Life, why, what is it but a floure, a bubble in the water, a spanne long, and full of miserie: of such small account is life, that every Souldier will sell it for sixe pence. And trust me I doe now detest life, worse then a goat doth hate Basill.

With that the Doctor prepared his instrument, and being ready to set to the Dukes eies, he said, O stay, Master Doctor, till I have conveyed my Loves countenance downe into my heart: Come hither my sweet, and let me give thee my last kisse, while mine eies may direct me to thy cherry lips. Then imbracing her in his armes, he said, O that I might give thee a kisse of xx yeares long, and to satisfie my greedie eies with thy faire sight: yet it doth somewhat content me, because thou art present at my punishment, that I may hold thee by the hand, to comfort my heart, at the sudden pricke of my eie.

This being said, the Doctor performed his duty, and so put out the christall sight: at what time D. *Robert* started up and with a most manly courage said, I must thanke his Majestie, that though hee depriveth me of my sight, yet he leaveth me eies to weepe for my sinnes.

But so soone as *Margaret* beheld the deed, she fell downe in a swoune, and much adoe her dame had to recover her life: which when the Duke understood, hee was wondrous woe, groaping for her with his bleeding eies, saying O where is my Love? for Gods sake have regard to her. And I pray you most heartily, good goodwife *Gray*, let her have this favour for my sake, that she may be used kindly. And with that the Keepers led him into the Castle, and *Margaret* was carried away wondrous sicke and ill: but her dame was most tender over her; and would suffer her to lacke nothing. When she was somewhat well recovered, her Dame *Gray* set her on horsebacke: and at her comming to *Gloucester*, there was no small joy.

CHAPTER XIV

How *Thomas Dove* being fallen to decay, was forsaken of his friends, and despised of his servants: and how in the end he was raised againe through the liberality of the Clothiers

Such as seeke the pleasure of the world, follow a shadow wherein is no substance: and as the adder *Aspis* tickleth a man to death, so doth vaine pleasure flatter us, till it makes us forget God, and consume our substance, as by *Tom Dove* it is apparant, who had through a free heart, and a liberall minde wasted his wealth; and looke how his goods consumed, so his friends fled from him: And albeit he had beene of great ability, and thereby done good unto many, yet no man regarded him in his poverty, but casting a scornefull countenance upon him, they passed by him with slender salutation: neither wold any of his former acquaintance do him good, or pleasure him the value of a farthing; his former friendship done to them was quite forgot, and he made of as much account, as *Job* when he sate on the dunghill.

Now, when his wicked servants saw him in this disgrace with the world, they on the other side began to disdaine him. Notwithstanding that hee (to his great cost) had long time brought them up, yet did they nothing regard it, but behind his backe in most scornefull sort derided him, and both in their words and actions greatly abuse him, reverence they would do none unto him, but when they spake, it was in such malapert sort, as would grieve an honest mind to heare it.

At last it came to passe, that breaking out into meere contempt, they said they would stay no longer with him, and that it was a great discredit for them, to serve a person so beggarly: whereupon they thought it convenient to seeke for their benefits elsewhere. When the distressed man found the matter so plaine being in great griefe, he spake thus unto them:

Now do I find, to my sorrow, the smal trust that is in this false world. Why, my Masters (quoth he) have you so much forgotten my former prosperity, that you nothing regard my present necessity? in your wants I forsooke you not, in your sicknesse I left you not, nor despised you in your great poverty: it is not unknowne, though you doe not consider it, that I tooke

149

some of you up in the high way, othersom from your needy parents, and brought the rest from meere beggery to a house of bounty: where from paltrie boies, I brought you up to mans state, and have, to my great cost, taught you a trade, whereby you may live like men. And in requitall of all my courtesie, cost and good will, will you now on a sudden forsake me? Is this the best recompence that you can find your hearts to yeeld me?

This is far from the minds of honest servants. The fierce Lion is kind to those that doe him good: plucke but one thorne out of his foote, and for the same he will shew manifold favors. The wilde Bull will not overthrow his Dam: and the very Dragons are dutefull to their nourishers. Bee better advised and call to mind, I beseech you, that I have not pluckt a thorn out of your feete, but drawne your whole bodies out of perils, and when you had no meanes to helpe your selves, I only was your support, and he, that when all other forsooke you, did comfort you in all your extremities.

And what of all this (quoth one of them)? because you tooke us up poore, doth it therefore follow, that we must be your slaves? We are young men, and for our part, we are no further to regard your profit, then it may stand with our preferment: Why should we lose our benefit to pleasure you? if you taught us our trade, and brought us up from boies to men, you had our service for it, whereby you made no small benefit, if you had as well used it, as we got it. But if you be poore, you may thanke your selfe, being a just scourge for your prodigalitie, and is my opinion plaine, that to stay with you, is the next way to make us like you, neither able to helpe our selves, nor our friends: therfore in briefe; come pay me my wages, for I will not stay, let the rest doe as they will, for I am resolved.

Wel (said his Master) if needs thou wilt be gone, here is part of thy wages in hand, and the rest as soone as God sends it, thou shalt have it: and with that, turning to the rest, he said, Let me yet intreat you to stay, and leave me not altogether destitute of helpe: by your labours must I live, and without you I know not what to doe. Consider therefore my need, and regard my great charge. And if for my sake you will do nothing, take compassion on my poore Children; stay my sliding foote, and let me not utterly fall, through your flying from me.

Tush (quoth they) what do you talke to us? we can have better wages, and serve a man of credit, where our fare shal be far better, and our gaines greater: therfore the world might count us right coxcomes, if we should forsake our profit, to pleasure you: therefore adieu, God send you more mony, for you are like to have no more men: and thus they departed.

When they were gone, within a while after they met one with another, saying, What cheare? are you all come away?

In faith I, what should we doe else (quoth they)? but hear'st thou sirra, hast thou got thy wages?

Not yet (saith the other) but I shall have it, and that is as good, tis but x shillings.

Saist thou so (said he) now I see thou art one of God Almighties ideots:

Why so (said the other)?

Because (quoth he) thou wilt be fed with shales: but ile tell thee one thing, twere better for thee quickly to arrest him, lest some other doing it before, and there be nothing left to pay thy debt: hold thy peace, faire words make fooles faine, and it is an old saying, One bird in hand is worth two in bush: if thou dost not arrest him presently, I will not give thee two pence for thy x. shillings.

How shall I come by him, quoth the other?

Give me but two pots of ale, and ile betray him (said he).

So they being agreed, this smooth-fac'd *Judas* comes to his late Master, and told him that a friend of his at the doore would speake with him. The unmistrusting man thinking no evill, went to the doore where presently an Officer arrested him at his mans suite.

The poore man seeing this, being strucken into a sudden sorrow, in the griefe of his heart spake to this effect: Ah thou lewd fellow, art thou the first man that seekes to augment my miserie? Have I thus long given thee bread, to breed my overthrow? and nourisht thee in thy need, to worke my destruction? Full little did I thinke, when thou so often diddest dip thy false fingers in my dish, that I gave food to my chiefest foe: but what booteth complaints in these extreames? go wife (quoth he) unto my neighbours, and see if thou canst get any of them to be my baile.

But in vaine was her paines spent. Then he sent to his kinsfolkes, and they denied him: to his brother, and he would not come at him, so that there was no shift, but to prison he must: but as he was going, a messenger met him with a letter from Master *Cole*, wherein as you heard, he had promised him two hundred pounds: which when the poore man read, he greatly rejoyced, and shewing the same to the officer, he was content to take his owne worde. Whereupon *Tom Dove* went presently to *Reading*, where at his comming, he found all the rest of the Clothiers, lamenting *Coles* untimely death; where the wofull widdow paid him the money, by which deed all the rest of the Clothiers were induced to doe something for *Dove*. And thereupon one gave him ten pounds, another twenty, another thirty pounds, to begin the world anew: and by this meanes (together with the blessing of God) he grew into greater credit then ever he was before. And riches being thus come upon him, his former friendes came fawning unto him and when he had no neede of them, then every one was ready to proffer him kindnesse. His wicked servants also that disdained him in his distresse, were after glad to come creeping unto him, intreating with cappe and knee for his favour and friendship. And albeit he seemed to forgive their trespasses done against him, yet he would often say, he would never trust them for a straw.

And thus he ever after lived in great wealth and prosperitie, doing much good to the poore, and at his death, left to his children great lands.

CHAPTER XV

How faire *Margaret* made her estate and high birth knowne to her Master
and Dame: and for the intire love she bore to Duke *Robert*, made a
vowe never to marry, but became a Nun in the Abbey at *Glocester*

AFTER faire *Margaret* was come againe to Glocester never did
she behold the cleare day, but with a weeping eie: and so great
was the sorrow which she conceived, for the losse of Duke
Robert her faithfull Lover, that she utterly despised all the
pleasures of this life, and at last bewrayed her selfe in this sort
unto her Dame:

O my good Master and Dame, too long have I dissembled my
parentage from you, whom the froward destinies do pursue to
deserved punishment. The wofull daughter am I of the unhappy Earle of *Shrewsbury,* who ever since his banishment,
have done nothing but drawne mischaunce after mee: wherefore let me intreat you (deare Master and Dame) to have your
good wils, to spend the remnant of my life in some blessed
Monasterie.

When *Gray* and his wife heard this, they wondred greatly, as
well at her birth, as at her strange demaund. Whereupon her
Dame knew not how to call her, whether Maiden or Madam, but
said, O good Lord, are you a Lady, and I know it not? I am
sory that I knew it not before.

But when the folkes of the house heard that *Margaret* was
a Lady, there was no small alteration: and moreover her Dame
said, that she had thought to have had a match between her and
her son: and by many perswasions did seeke to withdraw her
from being a Nun, saying in this manner: What *Margaret*, thou
art young and faire, the world (no doubt) hath better fortune
for thee, whereby thou maist leave an honourable issue behind
thee, in whom thou maist live after death.

These and many other reasons did they alleadge unto her, but
all in vaine: she making this reply, Who knowes not that this
world giveth the pleasure of an houre, but the sorrow of many
daies? for it paieth ever that which it promiseth, which is
nothing els but continuall trouble and vexation of the minde.
Do you think, if I had the offer and choice of the mightiest

princes of Christendom, that I could match my selfe better then to my Lord Jesus? No, no, he is my husband, to whom I yeeld my selfe both body and soule, giving to him my heart, my love and my most firme affection: I have overlong loved this vile world: therefore I beseech you farther disswade me not.

When her friendes by no meanes could alter her opinion, the matter was made knowne to his Majestie, who against the time that she should be received into the Monasterie, came to *Gloucester* with most part of his Nobilitie, to honour her action with his princely presence.

All things being therefore prepared, the young Lady was in most princely wise attired in a gowne of pure white sattin, her kirtle of the same, embrodered with gold about the skirts, in most curious sort, her head was garnished with gold, pearles, and precious stones, having her hair like thrids of burnisht gold, hanging downe behind in manner of a princely bride: about her yvory necke jewels of inestimable price were hung, and her handwreasts were compassed about with bracelets of bright-shining Diamonds.

The streets thorow the which she should passe, were pleasantly deckt with greene oaken boughs. Then came the yong Lady most like an heavenly Angell out of her Masters house, at what time all the bels in *Gloucester* were solemnly rung: she being led betwixt the Kings Majestie, having on his royall robes, and imperiall crown, and the chiefe Bishop wearing his Miter, in a Cope of cloth of gold, over her head a Canopy of white silke, fringed about in princely manner: before her went an hundred Priests singing, and after her all the chiefe Ladies of the Land: then all the wives and Maidens of *Gloucester* followed, with an innumerable sort of people on every side standing to behold her. In this sort she passed on to the Cathedrall Church, where she was brought to the Nunry gate.

The Lady Abbesse received her: where the beautiful Maiden kneeling downe, made her prayer in sight of all the people: then with her owne hands she undid her virgins faire gowne, and tooke it off, and gave it away to the poore: after that, her kirtle, then her jewels, bracelets and rings, saying, Farewell the pride and vanity of this world. The ornaments of her head were the next she gave away: and then was she ledde on one side, where she was stripped, and in stead of her smocke of soft silke, had a smocke of rough haire put upon her.

Then came one with a paire of sheares, and cut off her golden-coloured lockes, and with dust and ashes all bestrewed her head and face. Which being done, she was brought againe into the peoples sight barefoot and bareleg'd, to whom she said: Now farewell the world, farewell the pleasures of this life, farewell my Lord the King, and to the Dukes sweet love farewell, now shall my eies weepe for my former transgressions, and no more shall my tongue talke of vanity; farewell my good Master and Dame, and farewell all good people.

With which words she was taken away, and never after seene abroad. When Duke *Robert* heard thereof, he desired that at his death, his body might be buried in *Glocester*: in that Towne (quoth he) where first my cleare eies beheld the heavenly beauty of my love, and where for my sake shee forsooke the world: which was performed accordingly.

The King also at his death requested to be buried at *Reading*, for the great love he bare to that place, among those Clothiers, who living were his hearts comfort. *Gray* dying wondrous wealthy, gave land to the Monasterie whereinto *Margaret* was taken. *William Fitzallen* also dyed a most rich man, having builded many houses for the poore, whose sonne *Henry* after was the first Maior that was ever in *London*.

Sutton of *Salisbury* did also at his death much good, and gave an hundred li. to be yeerely lent to poore weavers of the Towne, to the worlds end. *Simon* of *South-hampton* gave a most bounteous gift towards the building of a Monastery at *Winchester*. *Hodgkins* of *Hallifax* did also great good, and so did *Cutbert* of *Kendall*, who had married xxiii. couples out of his owne house, giving each of them x. li. to beginne the world withall. *Martin Briam* of *Manchester* gave toward the building of a free-schoole in *Manchester*, a great masse of money.

And thus (gentle Reader) have I finished my storie of these worthy men, desiring thee to take my paines in good part, which will incourage me to greater matters, perceiving this curteously accepted.

GREENES

CARDE OF

FANCIE.

Wherein the Folly of thofe carpet Knights is deciphered, which guiding their courfe by the compafe of Cupid, *either dafh their fhip againft moft*
dangerous Rocks, or elfe attaine
the haven with pain & peril.

Wherein alfo is defcribed in the perfon
of *Gwydemus* a cruell Combate be-
tween Nature and Neceffitie.

By ROBERT GREEN Mafter of
Art, in *Cambridge.*

Aᴛ LONDON,
Printed for *William Ponfonby,*
1 5 8 7.

SOME man, that to contention is inclin'de
With anything he sees, a fault wil finde,
As, that is not so good, the same's amisse,
I have no great affection unto this;
Now I protest, I doe not like the same,
This must be mended, that deserveth blame,
It were farre better such a thing were out,
This is obscure, and that's as full of doubt.
And much adoe, and many words are spent
In finding out the path that Humours went,
And for direction to that idle way,
Onely a busie tongue bears all the sway.
The dish that *Æsope* did commend for best,
Is now a daies in wonderful request;
But if you finde fault on a certaine ground,
Weele fall to mending when the fault is found.

SAMUEL ROWLANDS, *Humors Looking Glasse*,
1608 (J. P. Collier).

NOTE[1] [TO THE EDITION OF 1587]

There is no entry of the "Carde of Fancie" in the *Stationers' Register* (Arber); but our text is from an exemplar of the earliest known edition of 1587, from Henry Pyne, Esq., Uckfield. He has written the following note on the fly-leaf:

"'Unique, but wants title page and a leaf of dedication, and two other leaves f. 2 and f. 3.' The above note in the Bibliotheca Heberiana, Part IV, No. 796, goes far to prove two facts: 1st, that the present was the Heber copy, the four leaves referred to having been supplied in facsimile; and 2nd, that the present copy is *not* unique [i.e. the leaves in facsimile must have been derived from another exemplar].—HENRY PYNE."

See Life in Vol. I for the bibliography of "Carde of Fancie." It is somewhat odd that the name "Gwydonius" should have been misprinted "Gwydemus" in the title-page of 1587. Collation— "Carde of Fancie" 71 leaves (A to s). "Debate" 10 leaves, continuous press marks (T to x ii).—G.

[1] There is some mistake here. The Dictionary of National Biography says: "Gwydonius, the Carde of Fancie" . . . entered in the *Stationers' Register*, 11 April, 1584, and published in same year (Sir F. Freeling's Sale Catalogue); reprinted, under title of "Greene's Carde of Fancie," 1587. "Life of Greene," vol. I, repeats this (Huth Library).—[ED.]

To The Right Honorable, *Edward de Vere* Earle of *Oxen-ford*, *Viscount Bulbeck*, *Lord of Escales* and Badlesmire, and Lord Great Chamber*lain of England :* Robert Greene *wi*sheth long life with increase *of honour.*

THE poet *Castilian Frontino* (Right Honourable) being a very unskilful Painter, presented *Alphonsus*, the Prince of *Aragon*, with a most imperfect Picture, which the King thankfully accepted, not that hee liked the work, but that hee lov'd the art. The paltering Poet *Cherillus*, dedicated his duncing *Poems* to that mightie Monarch *Alexander*, saying that he knew assuredly if *Alexander* would not accept them, in [that] they were not pithie, yet he would not utterly reject them, in that they had a shew of Poetry. *Cæsar* oft times praised the Souldiers for their wit, altho' they wanted skil: and *Cicero* as well commended stammering *Lentulus* for his paynfull industrie, as learned *Lælius* for his passing eloquence, which considered (although wisdom did me not wil to strain/further than my sleeve would stretch) I thought good to present this imperfect Pamphlet to your Honours Protection; hoping your Lordship will deign to accept the matter in that it seemeth to be prose, tho' something unsavourie for want of skill, and take my wel meaning for an excuse of my boldnesse, in that my poor will is not on the wane, whatsoever this imperfect work do want. The Emperour *Trajan*, was never without suters, because courteously he would heare every complaint. The *Lapidarie* continually frequented the Court of *Adrobrandinus*, because it was his chief study to search out the nature of Stones; All that courted *Atlanta* were hunters, and none sued to *Sapho* but Poets; Whosoever *Mecænas* lodgeth, thither no doubt will Schollers flock. And your Honour being a worthy favorer and fartherer of Learning, hath forced many, thro' your exquisite virtue to offer the fruits of their studie at the shrine of your

Lordships curtesie. But though they have waded farre and found mires, and I gadded abroad to get nothing but mites, yet this I assure myself, they never presented unto your Honour their treasure with a more willing minde, then I do this simple Truth; which I hope your Lordship will so accept. Resting therefore upon your Honours wonted Clemencie, I commit your *Lordship* to the Almighty.

Your Lordship's most dutifully to command

ROBERT GREENE.

TO THE GENTLEMEN READERS, HEALTH

PAN blowing upon an Oten pipe a little homelie Musick, and hearing no man dispraised his small cunning, began both to plaie so loude, and so long, that they were more wearie in hearing his musick, than he in shewing his skill, till at last to claw him and excuse themselves, they said his pipe was out of tune: So Gentlemen, because I have before time rashlie retcht above my pitch, and yet your curtesie such as no man have accused me, I have once again adventured upon your patience (but I doubt so far) as to be rid of my follie, you will at the least saie, as *Augustus* said to the Grecian, that gave him oft times many rude verses: Thou hadst need (quoth he) reward me wel, for I take more paines to reade thy workes, than thou to write them. But yet willing to abide this quip, because I may countervaile it with your former curtesie, I put my selfe to your patience, and commit you to the Almightie. Farewell.

Robert Greene.

AD LECTOREM IN LAUDEM AUTHORIS

W

Pullulat en stirpi similis speciosa propago
Aureolusq; novo revirescit ramus amoris
Vere: (tuo verè iam VERE dicandus honori:)
Ista salus Juveni, Comiti sit gloria nosse
Accepisse decus: Comites ubi passibus æquis
Ales amor virtusq; sagax decurrere nôrunt.
Ventilat iste faces, restinguit at illa furentes
Tædas.   Nec tædet Pueri sic tædia cæci
Fallere, qui, cæcis convoluit viscera flammis.
Ergo refer grates qui devitare cupi'sti
Spumosos Veneris fluctus, scopulosq; minaces
Qui fragilem tumidis cymbam mersisse procellis

W   Possent.   Hac iter est, hac dirige, tutior ibis.

Richardus Portingtonus.

THE CARDE OF FANCIE

THERE dwelled in the Citie of *Metelyne*, a certain Duke called *Clerophontes*, who through his prowesse in all martiall exploites waxed so proude and tyrannous, using such mercilesse crueltie to his forraine enimies, and such modelesse rigour to his native citizens, that it was doubtfull whether he was more feared of his foes for his crueltie, or hated of his friends for his tyrannie: yet as the worst weede springeth up more bravely then the wholsomest herbe, and as the crookedst tree is commonly laden with most fruit, so this rigorous Duke was so favoured and fostered up by fortune, his estate being so established with honour, and so beautified with wealth, so deckt with the Diadem of dignitie, and endued with fortunate prosperitie, having in warres such happie successe against his foes, and in peace such dutifull reverence of his friends (although more for feare then favor) as he seemed to want nothing that eyther fortune or the fates could alow him, if one onely sore which bred his sorrow could have beene salved. But this griefe so galled his conscience, and this cursed care so combred his minde, that his happinesse was greatly surcharged with heavinesse, to see the cause of his care could by no meanes be cured. For this *Clerophontes*, was indued with two children, the one a Daughter named *Lewsippa*, and the other a sonne called *Gwydonius*: / this *Lewcippa*, was so perfect in the complection of her bodie, and so pure in the constitution of her minde, so adorned with outward beautie, and endued with inward bountie, so pollished with rare vertues and exquisite qualities, as she seemed a seemely *Venus*, for her beutie, and a second *Vesta*, for her virginitie: yea, Nature and the Gods hadde so bountifully bestowed their giftes upon her, as Fame her selfe was doubtfull whether shee should make greater report of her excellent vertue, or exquisite beautie. But his sonne *Gwydonius*, was so contrarie to his sister *Lewsippa*, (though not in the state of his body, yet in the stay of his minde) as it made all men mervaile how two such contrarie stems could spring out of the selfe same stocke: His personage in deede was so comely, his feature so well framed, each lim so perfectlie couched, his face so faire, and his countenance so amiable, as he seemed a heavenly creature in a mortall carcasse.

But his minde was so blemished with detestable qualities, and so spotted with the staine of voluptuousnesse, that he was not so much to be commended for the proportion of his bodie, as to be condempned for the imperfection of his minde. He was so endued with vanitie, and so imbrued with vice, so nursed up in wantonnesse, and so nusled up in wilfulnesse, so carelesse to observe his Fathers commaund, and so retchlesse to regard his counsell, that neither the dread of Gods wrath, nor the feare of his fathers displeasure, could drive him to desist from his detestable kinde of living. Nay, there was no fact so filthie, which he would not commit, no mischiefe so monstrous, which he would not enterprise: no daunger so desperate, which he would not adventure: no perill so fearefull, which he would not performe: nor no action so divelish, which he would not execute. So immodest in his manners, so rude in his jestures, yea, and so prodigall in his expences, as mines of golde were not able to maintaine such / witlesse prodigalitie. This loath-some lyfe of *Gwydonius*, was such a cutting corasive to his Fathers carefull conscience, and such a haplesse clogge to his heavie heart, that no joye could make him injoye any joye, no mirth could make him merrie, no prosperitie could make him pleasant, but abandoning all delight, and avoyding all companie, he spent his dolefull dayes in dumpes and dolors, which he uttered in these words.

Now (quoth he) I prove by experience, the saying of *Sophocles* to be true, that the man which hath many children shall never live without some mirth, nor die without some sorrow: for if they be vertuous, he shall have cause whereof to rejoyce, if vicious, wherefore to be sad, which saying I trye performed in my selfe, for as I have one childe which delights mee with her vertue, so I have another that despights mee with his vanitie, as the one by dutie brings me joye, so the other by disobedience breeds my anoy: yea, as the one is a comfort to my mynde, so the other is a fretting corasive to my heart: for what griefe is there more griping, what paine more pinching, what crosse more combersome, what plague more pernitious, yea, what trouble can torment mee worse, then to see my sonne, mine heire, the inheritour of my Dukedom, which should be the piller of my parentage, to consume his time in roysting and ryot, in spending

and spoiling, in swearing and swashing, and in following wil-
fullye the furie of his owne frantike fancie. Alasse, most
miserable and lamentable case, would to God the destinies had
decreed his death in the swadling clouts, or that the fates had
prescribed his end in his infancy. Oh that the date of his birth
had bene the day of his buriall, or that by some sinister storme of
fortune he had bene stifled on his mothers knees, so that his untimely death might have prevented my ensuing sorrowes, and
his future calamities: for I see that the young frie will alwaies
prove old frogs, that the crooked twig will / prove a crabbed
tree, that the sower bud will never be sweete blossome, how
that which is bredde by the bone will not easily out of the
flesh, that he which is carelesse in youth, will be lesse carefull
in age, that where in prime of yeeres vice raigneth, there in ripe
age vanitie remaineth. Why *Clerophontes*, if thou seest the
sore, why doest thou not apply the salve, and if thou dost
perceive the mischiefe, why doest not [thou] prevent it with
medicine: take away the cause and the effect faileth: if *Gwydonius* be the cause of thy ruth, cut him off betimes, least he
bring thee to ruine: better hadst thou want a sonne then never
want sorow. Perhaps thou wilt suffer him so long till he fall
sicke of the Father, and then he will not onely seeke thy lands
and living, but life and all, if thou prevent not his purpose:
yea, and after thy death he will be through his lascivious lyfe
the overthrow of thy house, the consumer of thy Dukedome, the
wrack of thy common weale, and the verie man that shall bring
the state of *Metelyne*, to mischiefe and miserie. Sith then thy
sonne is such a sinke of sorrowes, in whose life lies hid a loathsome masse of wretched mishaps, cut him of as a gracelesse
graft, unworthie to grow out of such a stocke. Alasse *Clerophontes*, shalt thou be so unnatural as to seeke the spoile of
thine owne childe, wilt thou be more savage then the brute
beastes in committing such crueltie: no, alasse, the least misfortune of our children doth so move us, that as the Spider
feeleth if her web be prickt, so if they be toucht but with the
point of a pinne, so if they be toucht but with the least trouble,
wee feele the paines thereof with prickinge griefe to pinch us.
Why, hath not nature then caused love to ascend as wel as to
descend, and placed as dutiful obedience in the childe as loving
affection in the father: and with that he fetcht such a deepe
sighe, that it was a signe of the extreame sorrow he conceived
for his sonnes witlesse folly. But as he was readie againe to
enter into his dole /ful discourse, to aggravate his griefe the

more, and increase his care, certaine complaints were brought
him by sundrie Citizens, of the outragious behaviour of his son
Gwydonius, which being attentively heard he in great cholar
called for his sonne, against whome he thundered out such
threatning reproches, laying before his face the miserie that
would insue of such recklesse mischiefes, and promising that
if he directed not his course by a new compasse, and levelled
his life by a new line, he would not onely repay his folly with
the penaltie of the lawe, but also by consent of his Commons
disinherite him of his Dukedome: that *Gwydonius*, greatly
incensed with the severe censure of his Father, broyling with
furious rage, sturdely burst forth into these stubborne tearmes.

Sir (quoth he) if *Terence* his *Menedemus* were alive, and
heard these your fond and fantasticall reasons, he would as
readely condemne you of crabbednesse, as he accused *Chremes*
of currishnesse: for as he by too much austeritie procured his
sonnes mishappe, so you by to much severitie seeke to breede
my misfortune. You old men most injustly, or rather injuriously measure our staylesse moode by your stayed mindes,
our young yeeres by your hoarie haires, our flourishing youth
by your withered age, thinking to directe our doings by your
doatings, our wills by your wits, our youthfull fancies by your
aged affections, and to quench our fierie flames by your dead
coales and cinders: yea, supposing that the Leveret should be
as skilfull in making of a head, as the olde Hare, that the young
Cubs should as soone tapish, as the old Fox, that the young Frie
should as well avoid the net as the olde Fish, and that the
young wantons should be as warie as the old wysards. But
this sir, is to make fire frost, to change heate to colde, mirth
to mourning, singing to sadnesse, pleasure to paine, and to tye
the Ape and / the Beare in one tedder: sith then young stemmes
will not be set on a withered stocke, that the young twig liketh
not under the olde tree, that the toyish conceites of youth are
unfit for the testie cogitations of age: I meane for your satisfaction and my solace, to depart from the Court, and to spend
my dayes in travell.

Clerophontes no sooner heard this determination of his sonne
Gwydonius, but his sorrow was halfe salved, and his care almost
cured, thinking that by travell hee should either ende his life,
or amend his lewdnesse, and therefore both hearted and hastened
his sonne in this his newe course, least delay might breede
daunger, or time by some toye cause him tourne his tippet,
furnishing and finishing all thinges necessarie for his sonnes

journie, who readie to goe (more willing to travell, than his
father to intreate him) had this friendly farewell given him
by *Clerophontes*.

Sonne (quoth he) there is no greater doubt which dooth more
deepely distresse the minde of a younge man, then to deter-
mine with himselfe what course of life is best to take, for there
is such a confused *Chaos* of contrarie conceites in young wits,
that whiles they looke for that they cannot like, they are lost
in such an endlesse laberinth, as neither choice nor chance can
draw them out to their wished desires, for so many vaines so
many vanities: if vertue draweth one way, vice driveth another
way: as profit perswades them, so pleasures provokes them: as
wit weigheth, will wresteth: if friends counsel them to take this,
fancie forceth them to choose that: so that desire so long hangs
in doubt, as either they choose none, or else chaunce on the
worst. But in my opinion, the fittest kinde of life for a young
gentleman to take (who as yet hath not subdued the youthfull
conceites of fancie, nor made a conquest of his will by witte)
is to spende his time / in travell, wherein he shall finde both
pleasure and profit: yea, and buye that by experience, which
otherwise with all the treasure in the world hee cannot purchase. For what chaungeth vanitie to vertue, staylesse wit to
stayed wisedome, fonde fantasies to firme affections, but travell:
what represseth the rage of youth, and redresseth the witlesse
furie of wanton yeeres, but travell: what tourneth a secure
lyfe to a carefull living, what maketh the foolish wise, yea,
what increaseth witte and augmenteth skill, but travell: in so
much that the fame *Ulisses* wonne, was not by the tenne yeeres
hee lay at *Troy*, but by the time he spent in travell. But there
is nothing *Gwydonius*, so precious, which in some respect is
not perillous, nor nothing so pleasant which may not be painefull: the finest Gold hath his drosse, the purest Wine has his
lees, the bravest Rose his prickles, eache sweete hath his sower,
eache joye his annoye, eache weale his woe, and everie delight
his daunger.

So travaile *Gwydonius*, is a course of lyfe very pleasant, and
yet verie perillous, wherein thou maist practise vertue if thou
take heede, or purchase discredit if thou beest carelesse: where
thou maist reape renowne if thou beest vertuous, and gaine
reproche if thou be vicious: whereout doe springe wisedome and
follie, freedome and bondage, treasure and trash, fame and
discredit, honour and shame, according to the disposition of
him which either useth it to his profit, or abuseth it to his

discommoditie. Sith then thou shalt beare saile in such perillous Straightes, take heede least thou dashe thy Shippe against most daungerous Rockes. It is a saying *Gwydonius*, not so common as true, that he which will heare the *Syrens* sing, must with *Ulisses*, tye himselfe to the mast of a ship, least happely he be drowned. Who so meanes to be a sutor to *Circes*, must take a Preservative, unlesse he will be inchaunted. He / that will fish for the *Torpedo*, must anoint his hand with the oyle of *Nemiphar*, least he be charmed, and who so meaneth to enter combat with vanitie, must first surely defence himselfe with the target of vertue, unlesse he meane to be a captive to care, or calamitie. I speake this *Gwydonius* by experience, which afterwarde thou shalt know by proofe, for to travell thou shalt finde such subtill *Syrens*, as will indaunger thee, such sorcering *Circes*, as will inchaunt thee, such poysoned *Torpedos*, as will not onely charme thy hand, but thy heart, if by my experience and other mens perills thou learne not to beware. First *Gwydonius*, be not to sumptuous, least thou seeme prodigall, nor too covetous, least they compt thee a niggard: for by spending in excesse, thou shalt be thought a vaine glorious foole, and by to much sparing, a covetous pesant. Be not wilfull in thy doings, that they count thee not witlesse, nor to rash, that they think thee not devoyde of reason: be not to merrie, that they count thee not immodest, nor to sober, least they call thee sullen, but shew thy selfe to be an olde man for thy gravitie, and a young youth for thy activitie: so shall all men have cause to prayse thee for thy manners, and commend thee for thy modestie. Be not to curious *Gwydonius*, that they deeme thee not proud, nor to curteous, least they call thee counterfaite. Be a friend to all, and a foe to none, and yet trust not without triall, nor commit any secret to a friendlye stranger, least in to much trust lye treason, and thou be forced by repentaunce to crye *Peccavi*. The sweetest Muske is sower to be tasted, the finest Pils most bitter to be chewed, and the flattering friend most tickle being tried: then beware least faire words make fooles faine, and glozing speeches cause had I wist to come to late. Lend not *Gwydonius*, a listning eare to the alarums of Love, nor yeeld not thy freedome to the assault of lust, be not dazeled with the beames of fading beautie, nor daunted with / the desire of everie delicate damsell, for in time such blisse will prove but bane, and such delightfull joy, but despitefull anoie. Lust *Gwydonius* will prove an enimie to thy purse, and a foe to thy person, a canker to thy minde, and a corasive to thy conscience, a weakener of thy wit, a molester of thy minde, a besotter of thy senses, and finallie, a mortall bane to all thy bodie, so that thou shalt finde pleasure the pathwaie to perdition, and lusting Love the load-stone to ruth and ruine. Seeke not then *Gwydonius*, greedelie to devour that bait, where-under thou knowest a hurtfull hooke to bee hidden: frequent not that pleasure which will turne to thy poison, nor covet not that companie which will convert to thy confusion, least through such follie thou have cause in time to be sad, and I to be sorrowfull. Now *Gwydonius* that thou hast heard the advertisement of a loving father, followe my advice as a dutifull child, and the more to binde thee to performe my former precepts, that this my counsaile bee not drowned in oblivion, I give thee this Ring of golde, wherin is written this sentence, *Præmonitus, Premunitus*. A posie pretie for the wordes, and pithie for the matter, short to bee rehearsed, and long to bee related, inferring this sense, that hee which is forewarned by friendlie counsaile of imminent daungers, is fore-armed against all future mishappe and calamitie, so that hee may by fore-warning prevent perilles if it be possible, or if by sinister fortune hee cannot eschue them, yet hee may beare the crosse with more patience and lesse griefe. Keepe this Ring *Gwydonius* carefullie, that thou maist shew thy selfe to respect thy owne case, and regarde my counsaile: and in so doing thou shalt please mee, and pleasure thy selfe.

Clerophontes having thus ended his discourse, embracing his sonne with fatherlie affection, and giving / him his blessing, went secretlie into his Chamber, the more to cover his griefe, which he conceived for his sonnes departure: unwilling his sonne should perceive by his sorrow how unfainedlie hee both liked and loved him.

Well, *Gwydonius* having taken his leave of his Father, furnished both with counsaile and coine, with advice of wisedome and aide of wealth, passed on his journey verie solemmlie, untill hee was past the bounds of his Fathers Dukedome, and then as merrie as might bee, he travailed by the space of seaven weekes without anie residence, untill hee came to a Citie called *Barutta*, where (whether he were delighted with the scituation of the place, or deluded with the perswasion of some Parasiticall persons) hee securelie setteled himselfe by the space of a whole yeere: in which time he so careleslie floated in the seas of voluptuousnesse, and so reckleslie raunged in licentious and lawlesse libertie, thinking himselfe a peasant if he were not

G 824

prodigall, counting nothing comelie, if not costlie, nothing
seemelie if not sumptuous, using such monstrous excesse in all
his actions, that the Citizens of *Barutta* noted him for a myrrour
of immoderate lyfe, and a verie patterne of witlesse prodigalitie:
yea, his excessive expences daylie so increased, that Mines of
golde had not beene sufficient to maintaine his pompeous magnificence, insomuch, that the Magistrates of *Barutta*, not onelie
mervailed where hee had coine to countervaile his expences,
but also beganne to suspect him eyther for some skilfull
Alcumist, or that hee hadde some large commission to take
up those purses that fell into lapse, for want of sufficient
defence: whereupon beeing called before the Magistrates and
strictlie examined what trade he used, why hee stayed / so
long in the Citie, and how hee was able to maintaine so princelie
a porte as he carried: *Gwydonius* unwilling to have them privie
to his parentage, began to coyne a scuse, yet not so cunninglie
but hee was trapt in his owne talke, and so cast in prison, where
he laie clogged with care and devoide of comfort, having not
so much as one trustie friend, amongst all those trothlesse
flatterers which in prosperitie had so frequented his companie:
the ingratitude of whom so perplexed his molested minde, as
surcharged with sorow, hee burst forth into these tearmes.

Alasse (quoth hee) now have I bought that by haplesse
experience, which if I had beene wise, I might have got by
happie counsaile: Nowe am I taught that with paine and perill,
which if selfe-love had not besotted my senses, I might have
learned with profite and pleasure, that in the fayrest Sandes is
most ficklenesse, out of the bravest Blossome moste commonlie
springeth the worste Fruite, that the finest flower seldome hath
the best smell, that the moste glistering Stone hath often-times
the least vertue, and that in the greatest shewe of good will,
lyes ofte times the smallest effect of friendshippe, in most
flatterie, least fayth, in the fayrest face, the falsest heart, in
the smoothest Tale the smallest Truth, and in the sweetest
gloses most sower ingratitude: Yea, I see nowe (quoth hee)
that in truth lies treason, that faire wordes make fooles faine,
and that the state of these fained friendes are lyke to the Marie-
golde, which as long as the Sunne shineth openeth her leaves,
but with the least Clowde, beginneth to close, lyke the Violettes
in *America*, which in Summer yeelde an odoriferous smell, and
/ in Winter a most pestilent savour: so these Parasites in prosperitie professe most, but in adversitie performe least: when
Fortune favoureth, they laughe, when shee frowneth they

lowre: at everie full Sea, they flourish, but at every dead Neape, they fade: Like to the fish *Palerna,* which being perfectlie white in the Calme, yet turneth passing blacke at everie storme: to the trees in the desarts of *Affrica,* that flourish but while the South winde bloweth, or to the *Celedonie* stone, which retaineth his vertue no longer than it is rubbed with golde.

Sith then *Gwydonius* (quoth hee) thou findes such falshoode in friendshippe, and such faithlesse deeds in such painted speeches, shake off these fawning curres with the flag of defiance, and from hence forth trie ere thou trust. I, but (quoth hee) it is too late to applie the salve when the sore is incurable, to crie alarum when the Citie is overrunne, to seeke for covert when the storme is past, and to take heede of such flattering mates, when alreadie thou art deceived by such fawning merchants: now thou wilt crie *Cave* when thy coine is consumed, and beware when thy wealth is wracked: when thou hast nothing whereof to take charge, thou wilt bee charie, and when follie hath alreadie given thee a mate, thou wilt by wisedome seeke to avoide the checke, but nowe thou triest it true that thy Father foretolde thee, that so long thou wouldest be carelesse, as at last Repentaunce woulde pull thee by the sleeve, and then had I wist woulde come too late.

Wel *Gwydonius,* sith that which is once past can never bee recald againe, if thou hast by follie made a fault, seeke by wisedome to make amends, and heape not care upon care, nor adde not griefe to sorrow, by these pittifull complaintes, but cheere up thy selfe and take heart at grasse, for the ende of woe is the beginning of weale, and / after miserie alwaies insueth most happie felicitie.

Gwydonius having thus dolorouslie discoursed with himselfe, remained not above tenne daies in prison, but that the Senate taking pittie of his case, and seeing no accusations were inferred against him, set him free from his Purgatorie, and gave him good counsaile that heereafter hee shoulde beware by such witlesse prodigalitie to incurre such suspition. *Theseus* never triumphed more after hee had escaped the danger of the perillous laborinth, than poore *Gwydonius* did when he was set free from this pernitious Limbo: now the bitternesse of bondage made his freedome seeme farre more sweete, and his danger so happelie escaped, caused his deliverie seeme far more delightfull. Yet hee conceived such discurtesie against the Citizens, for repaying his liberall good will with such loathsome ingratitude, that the next morning he departed from *Barutta,* not stored with too much monie for molesting his minde, nor overcharged with coine for combering his conscience with too much care, but having remaining of all his treasure onelie that ring which his Father gave him, travailing verie solemmlie toward *Alexandria*.

Where at that time there raigned a certaine Duke named *Orlanio*, who was so famous and fortunate, for the peaceable government of his Dukedome, administering justice with such sinceritie, and yet tempering the extremitie of the law with such lenitie, as he both gained the good will of strangers on hearing his vertue, and won the heartes of his subjects in feeling his bountie, counting him unworthie to beare the name of a Soveraigne, which knew not according to desert, both to cherish and chastise his subjects.

Fortune and the fates willing to place him in the pal/lace of earthlie prosperitie, endowed him with two children, the one a sonne named *Thersandro*, and the other a daughter called *Castania*, either of them so adorned with the giftes of Nature and beautified with good nurture, as it was hard to know whether beautie or vertue held the supremacie. But least by this happie estate *Orlanio* should bee too much puffed up with prosperitie, Fortune sparing him the mate, yet gave him a slender checke, to warne him from securitie, for before his daughter came to the age of fourteene yeeres, his wife died, leaving him not more sorrowfull for the losse of her whom he most entirelie loved, than carefull for the well bringing up of her whome he so deerelie liked. Knowing that as his Court was a schoole of vertue to such as brideled their mindes with discreation, so it was a nurse of vice to those tender yeeres that measured their willes with witlesse affection, esteeming libertie as perillous to the staie of youth, as precious to the state of age, and that nothing so soone allureth the minde of a young maide to vanitie, as to passe her youth without feare in securitie. Feared with the consideration of these premises, to avoide the inconveniences that might happen by suffering *Castania* to leade her lyfe in lawlesse libertie, hee thought it best to choose out some vertuous Ladie to keepe her companie, who might direct her course by so true a compasse, and levell her lyfe by so right a line, that although her young yeeres were verie apt to bee intangled in the snares of vanitie, yet by her counsaile and companie, shee might steddilie tread her steppes in the trace of vertue: and none hee could finde more fit for the purpose, than a certaine old Widdowe, called Madame *Melytta*, honoured for her vertuous lyfe throughout all *Alexan-*

dria, who beeing sent for to the Court, hee saluted on this manner.

Madame / *Melytta,* (quoth hee) the reporte of thy honest conditions, and the renowme of thy vertuous qualities are such, as thereby thou hast not onelie purchased great praise, but wonne great credit throughout all the Countrie. Insomuch that I incensed by this thy singular commendation, I have selected thee as the onelie woman to whome I meane to commit my chiefest treasure, I meane *Melytta,* my Daughter *Castania,* to whome I will have thee be both a companion and a counsailour, hoping thou wilt take such care to traine her up in vertue, and trace her quite from vice, to winne her minde to honestie, and weane her quite from vanitie, that she in her ripe yeares shall have cause to thanke thee for thy paines, and I occasion to regard thee as a friend, and reward thee for thy diligence.

First *Melytta,* see that shee leade her lyfe both charilie and chastlie. Let her not have her owne will, least shee prove too wilfull: or too much libertie, least she become too light. The Palme tree pressed downe, groweth notwithstanding but too fast. The hearbe *Spatania,* though troden on, groweth verie tall, and youth although strictlie restrained will prove but too stubburne.

The vessell favoureth alwaies of that licour wherewith it was first seasoned, and the minde retaineth those qualities in age wherein it was trained up in youth. The tender twigge is sooner broken than the stronge branch, the young stem more brittle than the olde stocke, the weake bramble shaken with everie winde, and the wavering will of youth tossed with everie puffe of vanitie, readie to bee wracked in the waves of wantonnesse, unlesse it bee cunninglie guided by some wise and warie Pilot.

Then / *Melytta,* youth is so easilie entrapped with the alluring traine of foolish delightes, and so soone entangled with the trash of pernitious pleasures, suffer not my Daughter to passe her time in idlenesse, least happilie being taken at discovert, shee become a carelesse captive to securitie, for when the minde once floateth in the surging seas of idle conceites, then the puffes of voluptuous pleasures, and the stiffeling stormes of unbrideled fancie, the raging blastes of alluring beautie, and the sturdie gale of glozing vanitie, so shake the shippe of recklesse youth, that it is dailie in doubt to suffer most daungerous shipwracke. But let her spend her time in reading such auncient authors as may sharpen her wit by their pithie sayings, and learne her wisedome by their perfect sentences. For where nature is vicious, by learning it is amended, and where it is vertuous, by skill it is augmented. The stone of secret vertue is of greater price if it bee bravelie polished, the Golde though never so pure of it selfe, hath the better coulour if it bee burnished, and the minde though never so vertuous, is more noble if it bee enriched with the giftes of learning. And *Melytta,* for recreation sake, let her use such honest sportes as may drive awaie dumpes, least shee bee too pensive, and free her minde from foolish conceites, that shee bee not too wanton.

Thus (Madame) as you have hearde my fatherlie advise, so I praie you give my Daughter the lyke friendlie advertisement, that heereafter shee maye have both cause to reverence mee, and to rewarde thee.

Melytta having hearde with attentive heede the minde of *Orlanio,* conceived such joye in this newe charge, and such delight in this happie chaunce, as with cheerefull countenaunce she repaied him this aunswere.

Sir / (quoth shee) although in the largest Seas are the sorest tempestes, in the broadest wayes most boysterous windes, in the hig[h]est hilles, most dangerous haps, and the greatest charge the greatest care, yet the duetie which I owe you as my Soveraigne, and the love I beare you as a subject, the care I have to please you as my Prince, and to pleasure you as a Potentate, the trust you repose in my truth without sufficient triall, the confidence you put in my concience without sure proofe, the curtesie your Grace doeth shew mee without anie desert, have so inflamed the forepassed fire of dutifull affection, and so incouraged mee to encounter your Graces curtesie, with willing constancie, that there is no happe so harde which I would not hazard, no daunger so desperate which I would not adventure, no burthen so heavie which I would not beare, no perill so huge which I would not passe, no charge so great, which both willinglie and warilie I would not performe. For, since it hath pleased your Grace to vouchsafe so much of my simple calling, as to assigne me for a companion for your daughter *Castania,* I will take such care in the charie performance of my charge, and indeavour with such diligence both to counsaile and comfort *Castania,* as your Grace shall perceive my dutie in pleasuring you, and my diligence in pleasuring her.

The Duke hearing the friendlie and faithfull protestation of the good Ladie *Melytta,* tolde her that although it were great trouble for one of her age to frame her selfe as a companion to such yong youth, and that some care belonged to such a charge, yet hee woulde so countervaile her painfull labour with princelie liberalitie, that both shee and all *Alexandria* should have cause to speake of his bountie.

Melytta / thanking the Duke for such undeserved curtesie, setting her householde affaires in good order, repaired to the Court as speedelie as might be. But leaving her with *Castania*, againe to *Gwydonius*. Who now being arrived in *Alexandria*, pinched with povertie, and distressed with want, having no coine lefte wherewith to countervaile his expences, thought it his best course, if it were possible, to compasse the Dukes service: repairing therefore to the Court, he had not staied there three daies before hee found fit opportunitie to offer his service to *Orlanio*, whome verie dutifullie he saluted in this manner.

The report (right worthie Prince) of your incomparable curtesie and peerelesse magnanimitie, is so blazed abroad throughout all Countries, by the golden trumpe of Fame, that your Grace is not more loved of your subjects which tast of your liberall bountie, than honoured of straungers, which onelie heare of your princelie vertue. Insomuch that it hath forced me to leave my native soile, my parents, kindred, and familiar friends, and pilgrime like to passe into a straunge Countrie, to trie that by experience heere, which I have heard by report at home. For it is not (right worthie Sir) the state of your Countrie that hath allured me (for I deeme *Bohemia*, whereof I am, no lesse pleasant than *Alexandria*), neither hath want of living or hope of gaine intised mee, for I am by birth a Gentleman, and issued of such parents as are able with sufficient patrimonie to maintaine my estate, but the desire, not onelie to see, but also to learne such rare curtesie and vertuous qualities as fame hath reported to be put in practise in your Court, is the onelie occasion of this my journey. Now if in recompence of this my travaile, it shall please your Grace, to vouchsafe of my service, I shall thinke my selfe fullie satisfied, and / my paines sufficiently requited.

Orlanio hearing this dutifull discourse of *Gwydonius*, marking his manners, and musing at his modestie, noting both his excellent curtesie and exquisite beautie, was so inflamed with friendlie affection toward this young youth, that not onelie he accepted of his service, but also preferred him as a companion to his sonne *Thersandro*, promising that since he had left his Countrie and parents for this cause, he would so countervaile his dutifull desert with favour and friendship, as he should never have cause to accuse him of ingratitude.

Gwydonius repaying heartie thankes to the Duke for his undeserved curtesie, being now brought from woe to weale, from despaire to hope, from bale to blisse, from care to securitie, from want to wealth, yea, from hellish miserie to heavenlie prosperitie, behaved himselfe so wiselie and warilie, with such curtesie in conversation, and modestie in manners, that in short time he not onelie purchased credit and countenance with *Orlanio,* but was most entirelie liked and loved of *Thersand[r]o.*

Now there remained in the Court, a young knight, called Signor *Valericus,* who by chance casting his glancing eies on the glittering beautie of *Castania,* was so fettered in the snare of fancie, and so entangled with the trap of affection, so perplexed in the Laborinth of pinching love, and so inchaunted with the charme of *Venus* Sorcerie, that as the Elephant rejoyceth greatlie at the sight of a Rose, as the Bird *Halciones* delighteth to view the feathers of the *Phœnix,* and as nothing better contenteth a Roebuck, than to gaze at a red cloth, so ther was no object that could allure the wavering eies of *Valericus,* as the surpassing beautie of *Castania,* yea, his onelie blisse, pleasure, joy, and delight, was in feeding his fancie with staring on the heavenlie face of his Goddesse. But alasse her beautie bredde his bane, her lookes, his losse, / her sight his sorrow, her exquisite perfections his extreame passions, that as the Ape by seeing the Snaile is infected, as the Leopard falleth in a trance at the sight of the Locust, as the Cockatrice dieth with beholding the Chrisolite, so poore *Valericus* was pinched to the heart with viewing her comelie countenance, was griped with galing griefe, and tortured with insupportable torments, by gazing uppon the gallant beautie of so gorgious a dame: yea, he so framed in his fancie the forme of her face, and so imprinted in his heart the perfection of her person, that the remembraunce thereof would suffer him take no rest, but he passed the daie in dolour, the night in sorrow, no minute without mo[u]rning, no houre without heavinesse, that falling into pensive passions he began thus to parle with himselfe.

Why how now *Valericus* (quoth hee) art thou haunted with some hellish hagge, or possessed with some frantike furie? art thou inchanted with some magicall charme, or charmed with some bewitching Sorcerie, that so sodainlie thy minde is perplexed with a thousand sundrie passions? alate free, and now

fettered, alate swimming in rest, and now sinking in care, ere-
while in securitie, and now in captivitie, yea, turned from mirth
to mourning, from pleasure to paine, from delight to despight,
hating thy selfe, and loving her who is the chiefe cause of this
thy calamitie. Ah *Valericus*, hast thou forgot the saying of
Propertius, that to love howsoever it bee, is to loose, and to
fancie, how charie so ever thy choice be, is to have an ill chance,
for Love though never so fickle, is but a *Chaos* of care, and
fancie, though never so fortunate, is but a masse of miserie:
for if thou injoye the beautie of *Venus*, thou shalt finde it small
vauntage, if thou get one as wife as *Minerva*, thou maiest put
thy winninges in thine eie, if as gorgeous as *Juno*, thy accountes
beeing cast, thy gaine shall be but losse: yea, bee shee vertuous,
be / she chast, be she curteous, be she constant, bee she rich,
be shee renowmed, be she honest, be she honourable, yet if thou
bee wedded to a woman, thinke thou shalt finde in her sufficient
vanitie to countervaile her vertue, that thy happinesse will bee
matcht with heavinesse, thy quiet with care, thy contentation
with vexation: that thou shalt sowe seede with sorrow, and
reape thy corne with sadnesse, that thou shalt never live without griefe, nor die without repentaunce, for in matching with
a wife there is such mischiefes, and in marriage such miseries,
that *Craterus* the Emperour wishing some sinister fortune to
happen uppon one of his foes, praied unto the Gods, that he
might be married in his youth, and die without issue in his
age, counting marriage such a cumbersome crosse, and a wife
such a pleasant plague, that hee thought his foe could have
no worse torment, than to bee troubled with such noisome
trash. Oh *Valericus*, if the consideration of these premises be
not sufficient to perswade thee: if the sentence of *Propertius*
cannot quench thy flame, nor the saying of *Craterus* coole thy
fancie, call to minde what miseries, what mischiefes, what woes,
what wailings, what mishappes, what murthers, what care,
what calamities have happened to such, as have beene besotted
with the balefull beautie of women, enjoying more care than
commoditie, more paine than profite, more cost than comfort,
more griefe than good: yea, reaping a tunne of drosse for everie
dramme of perfect golde.

What carelesse inconstancie ruled *Eriphila*? What currish
crueltie raigned in *Philomela*? How incestuous a life lead
Aeuropa? And how miserable was that man that married
Sthuolea? What gaines got *Tereus* in winning *Progne*, but a
loathsome death for a little delight. *Agamemnon* in possessing

*G 824

the beautie of *Crecida*, caused the Grecian armie most grievouslie to be plagued. *Candau/les* was slaine by his murthering wife whom so intirelie he loved. Who was thought more happie than the husband of *Helena*, and yet who in time lesse fortunate? What haplesse chances insued of the chastitie of *Penelope*? What broiles in *Rome* by the vertue of *Lucrecia*? The one caused her sutors, most horrible, to be slaine, and the other that *Tarquine* and all his posteritie were rooted out of their regall dignities. *Phaedra* in loving killed her haplesse sonne *Hippolitus*, and *Clitemnestra* in hating slewe her loving husband *Agamemnon*. Alasse *Valericus*, how daungerous is it then to deale with such dames, which if they love, they procure thy fatall care: and if they hate thee, thy finall calamitie?

But ah blasphemous beast that I am, thus reckleslie to raile and rage without reason, thus currishlie to exclaime against those, without whom our life though never so lucklie, should seeme most loathsome: thus *Tymon* like, to condemne those heavenlie creatures, whose onelie sight is a sufficient salve against all hellish sorrowes: is this right, to conclude generallie of particular premises? Is it justice to accuse all for the fault of some? Is it equitie to blame the staie of vertuous women, for the state of vicious wantons? Doest thou thinke *Valericus* to shake off the shackles of fancie with this follie? Or to eschue the baite of beautie, by breathing out suche blasphemie? No, no, assure thy selfe, that these thy raging reasons, will in time bee most rigorouslie revenged, that the Gods themselves will plague thee for braying out such injurious speeches. Alasse, Love wanting desire, maketh the minde desperate: and fired fancie bereaved of love tourneth into furie. The loiall faith I beare to *Castania*, and the loathsome feare of her ingratitude, the deepe desire which inforceth my hope, and the deadlie despaire which infringeth my happe, so tosseth / my minde with contrarie cogitations, that I neither regard what I saie to my harme, nor respect what I doe, to my owne hurt: yea, my senses are so besotted with pinching love, and my minde so fretted with frying fancie, that death were thrice more welcome, than thus to linger in despairing hope.

And with that to passe awaie those pensive passions, hee floung out of his Chamber with his Hauke on his fist, thinking by such sport to drive awaie this melancholie humour, which so molested his minde.

But as hee was passing through the Court, hee was luckelie encountered by *Melytta* and *Castania*, who minding to have some sporte with *Valericus* before hee did passe: had the onset thus pleasantlie given him by *Castania*.

It is hard Signor *Valericus* (quoth she) to take you either without your Hauke on your fist, or your heart on your halfepenie, for if for recreation you bee not retriving the Partridge with dogs, you are in solempne meditation driving awaie the time with dumpes, neither caring for companie to solace your sadnesse, nor pleasantlie discoursing of some amorous *Parle*: which makes the Gentlewomen of this Court thinke, that you are either an Apostata to Love, as was *Narcissus*, or have displayed the flagge of defiance against Fancie, as dyd *Tyanæus*. If these their surmised conjectures bee true, *Valericus*, I warne thee as a friend to beware by other mens harmes, least if thou imitate their actions, thou bee mangled with the like miserie, or maimed with the lyke misfortune.

Valericus hearing his Saint pronouncing this sugered harmonie, feeling himselfe somewhat toucht with this quipping talke, was so rapte in admiration of her / eloquence, and so ravisht in the contemplation of her beautie, that hee stoode in a mase, not able to utter one word, untill at last gathering his wits together, he burst forth in these speeches.

Madame (quoth he) what it pleaseth the Gentlewomen of this Court to surmise of my solitarinesse, I know not, but if they attribute it to curiousnesse, or coinesse, to strangenesse or statelinesse, either that I am an enimie to love, or a foe to fancie, that I detest their bountie with *Narcissus*, or contempne their beautie with *Tianeus*, they offer me great injurie so rashlie to conjecture of my disease, before rightlie they have cast my water. But to put your Ladiship out of doubt what is the cause of my dumpes, so it is that of late raunging the fieldes, my heart (my Hauke I should saie Madame), hovered at such a princelie praie, and yet mist of her flight, that since she hath neither prunde her selfe, nor I taken anie pleasure. Marie, if the fates should so favour mee, or fortune so shrowde mee up in prosperitie, that my desire might obtaine her wish, I would not onelie chaunge my mourning to mirth, my dolour to delight, and my care to securitie, but I would thinke to have gotten as rich a praie as ever *Cæsar* gained by conquest.

Surelie Signor *Valericus* (quoth *Melytta*) no doubt the praie is passing princelie, since the value thereof is rated at so precious a price, and therefore we have neither cause to condemp[n]e your Hauke of haggardnesse, for want of pruning, nor you of foolishnesse for want of pleasure. And if your heart (your

Hauke I should saie, Signor *Valericus*) hath reacht farther with her eie, than she is able to mount with her wing, although I am no skilfull Fawlkener, yet I thinke you had better keepe her on the fist still, and so feede her with hope, than let her misse / againe of her flight, and so she turne taile and be foiled.

In deede Madame (quoth *Valericus*) your counsayle is verie good, for as there is no better confect to a crazed minde, than hope, so there is no greater corasive to a carefull man, than dispaire, and the Fawlkeners also jumpe with you in the same verdite, that the Hauke, which misseth her praie, is doubtfull to soare aloofe and prove haggard. Yet if shee were so tickle, as she wold take no stand, so ramage as she would be reclaimed with no lure, I had rather happelie hazard her for the gaining of so peerelesse a praie, though I both lost her, and wanted of my wish, than by keeping her still in the Bines, to prove her a kite, or me a coward.

In deede Sir (quoth *Castania*) Fortune ever favoureth them that are valiant, and things the more hard, the more haughtie, high and heavenlie: neither is anie thing harde to bee accomplished, by him that hardelie enterpriseth it. But yet take heede that you fishe not so faire, that at lengthe you catch a Frogge, and then repentaunce make you mumble up a masse with *Miserere*.

No Madame (quoth hee) it is never seene that he which is contented with his chance, should ever have cause to repent him of his choice.

And yet (quoth shee) hee that buies a thing too deere, may be content with his chaffer, and yet wish he had ben more charie.

Truth Madame (quoth *Valericus*) but then it is trash and no treasure, for that which is precious is never over-prised, and a bad thing though never so cheape is thought too chargeable.

Oh Sir (quoth *Melytta*) and is it not an olde saying, that a man maye buy golde too deare, and that Jewelles though never so precious, may bee set at too high / a price. I see if you had no better skill in manning of a Hauke, than in making of a bargaine, you woulde prove but an ill Fawlkener. But since we have so long troubled you with our talke, we will now leave you to your sport, and so bid you farewell.

Valericus with a courteous *Conge*, repaying their curtesie, and with a glauncing eie giving his Goddesse the dolefull *A dio*, went solitarilie into the secret woods, where laying him downe in the shade, he fell into these musing meditations.

What greater prosperitie (quoth hee) can happen unto anie

earthlie wight, than if hee bee crossed with care, to finde a confect to cure his calamitie: then if hee bee pinched with paines,
to get a plaister for his passions: if hee bee drenched in distresse,
to finde a meanes to mittigate his miserie, which I see by proofe
performed in my seelie selfe: for the sight of my Goddesse hath
so salved my fore-passed sorrowes, her sweete wordes hath so
healed my heavie woundes, that where before I was plunged in
perplexitie, I am nowe placed in felicitie: where before I was
oppressed with care, I am now refreshed with comfort. O
friendlie Fortune, if from hence forth thou furiouslie frowne
uppon mee, if thou daunt mee with disaster mishappe, or crosse
mee with perpetuall care, yet this thy friendlie courtesie shall
bee sufficient to countervaile all future enormities.

But alasse, I see everie prosperous puffe hath his boisterous
blaste, everie sweete hath his sower, everie weale his woe, everie
gale of good lucke, his storme of sinister fortune: yea, everie
commoditie his discommoditie annexed: the bloud of the Viper is
most healthfull for the sight, and most hurtfull for the stomacke,
the / stone *Celonites* is verie precious for the backe, and verie
perillous to the braine: the flower of *India* pleasant to be seene,
but who so smelleth to it, feeleth present smart: so as the joye
of her presence procureth my delight, the annoie of her absence
breedeth my despight: yea, the feare that she will not repaie
my loue with liking, and my fancie with affection, that she
will not consent to my request, but rather meanes to stiffle
me with the raging stormes of repulse, and daunt me with the
doome of deadlie denialls, so fretteth my haplesse minde with
hellish furie, that no plague, no paine, no torment, no torture
can worse molest mee, than to be distressed with this dreadfull
despaire.

Alasse, her calling is too highe for me to climbe unto, her
roiall state is farre above my reach, her haughtie minde is too
loftie for mee to aspire: no doubt if I offer my sute unto her,
shee will prove lyke the Stone of *Silicia*, which the more it is
beaten, the harder it is: or like the spices of *Ionia*, which the
more they are pounded the lesse savour they yeeld: lyke to the
Isiphilon, which yeeldeth forth no juyce though never so well
brused: so, though I should with never so great devotion offer
up at her Shrine, prayers, promises, sighes, sobbes, teares, troth,
faith, freedome, yea, and my heart itselfe, as a pledge to pleade
for pittie, yet shee would make so small account of these my
cares, and as lyttle regarde my ruth and ruine, as *Eriphila*
did her faithfull friend *Infortunio*.

But oh vilde wretch that I am, why doe I thus without cause condemne *Castania*? Why doe I accuse her of crueltie, in whom raigneth nothing but curtesie? Why doe I appeach her of coinesse, in whome bountie sheweth small curiousnesse? How / friendlie, how familiarlie, yea, how faithfullie did she talke with me, what a cheerfull countenance did shee carrie towards mee, what sodaine glaunces, what lovelie lookes, which no doubt are signes, that though shee repulse mee at the first, she will not refuse mee at the last: though she be straight in words, she will not be straunge in minde: though she give mee some bitter pilles of deniall, it shall bee but for the better triall. And shall I then beeing fedde with this hope prove such a mecocke, or a milkesoppe, as to bee feared with the tempestuous Seas of adversitie, when as at length I shall arrive at the haven of happie estate: shall I dread to have my ship shaken with some angrie blasts, hoping to be safelie landed on the shore, and so have my share of that, which the showers of shrewd Fortune for a time hath denied mee. No, no, *Dulcia non meruit, qui non gustavit amara.* Hee is not worthie to sucke the sweete, which hath not first favoured the sowre: he is not worthie to eate the kernell which hath not crackt the shell, hee deserveth not to have the crowne of victorie, which hath not abidde the brunt of the battaile: hee meriteth not to possesse the praie, which will not willinglie take some parte of the paine: Neyther is hee worthie of so heavenlie a Dame as *Castania*, that woulde not spend the most precious bloud in his bodie, in the pursuite of so peerelesse a peece.

Valericus thus mittigating his paine with the milde medicine of hope, and rooting out the dead flesh of despaire with the plaister of trust, determined to strike on the Stith while the yron was hot, and to pursue his purpose while his Mistresse was in her good moode. And therefore leaving his sport for this time, highed him to / the Court in hast; where insinuating himselfe into the societie of the Ladies and Gentlewomen, hee shewed himselfe in sport so pleasant, in talke so wittie, in manners so modest, in conceites so cunning, in *parle* so pithie, and in all his conversation so comelie, that whereas before hee was speciallie loved of none, now hee was generallie liked of all: insomuch that for a time there was no talke in the Court but of the Metamorphosis of *Valericus* minde. Who oftentimes determining in plaine tearmes to present his sute to *Castania*, when he came to the point, feare of offence, and dreade of deniall, disappointed his purpose, that hee remained mute in the matter: but at last perceiving delaie bredde daunger, seeing his mistresse sit alone in his presence, hovering betweene feare and hope, hee began the assault with this march.

Madame (quoth he) for that I see you sitting thus solitarie in dumps, I am the bolder to prease in place, although the most unworthie man to supplie it. Hoping you will pardon my rudenesse for troubling thus rashlie your musing meditations, and count my companie the lesse offensive in that I see you busied with no such serious matters whereunto my presence may bee greatlie prejudiciall. *Cyneas* the Philosopher, Madame, was of this minde, that when the Gods made beautie, they skipt beyond their skill, in that they framed it of greater force than they themselves were able to resist: if then there is none so wise or worthie whome beautie cannot wracke, nor none issued of such princelie birth whome beautie cannot bend, though I have beene intangled with the snare of fancie, and have listned to the lure of beautie, I am the more to be borne with, and the lesse to be blamed. For I must of force confesse Madame, that the giftes of nature so abundantlie bestowed uppon you, your / excelent / beautie and exquisite vertue, have so scaled the wals of my fancie, and sacked the fort of my freedome, that for my last refuge I am forced to appeale unto your curtesie, as the onelie medicine which may cure my intollerable disease. Naie incurable I may wel call it, for (I speak with teares outwardlie, and droppes of bloud inwardlie) unlesse the misling showers of your mercie mittigate the force of my fancie, the droppes of your princelie favour quench the flame of my affection, and the guerdon of your good will give a soveraigne plaister for my secret sore, I am like to passe my life in more miserie, than if I had taken the infernall torments. But I hope it is not possible, that out of a sugered Fount should distill a bitter streame, out of a fragrant flower a filthie sappe, and from such divine beautie should proceed hate and hellish crueltie.

It is Madame, your beautie which hath wrought my wo, and it is your bountie which must worke my weale. It is your heavenlie face which hath deprived mee of libertie, and your curteous consent must be the meanes to redeeme mee from captivitie: for as he that eateth of the Briane leafe, and is infected, can by no meanes bee cured, unlesse hee taste of the same roote: As hee which is wounded of the Porcuntine, can never be healed unlesse his woundes be washt with the bloud of the same beast: as there is nothing better against the stinging of a Snake, than to be rubbed with an Adders slough, and as he which is hurt of the Scorpion [must] seeke a salve from whom he received the sore, so Love onelie is remedied by Love, and fancie by mutuall affection: You Madame, must minister the medicine, which procured the maladie, and it onelie lies in your power to applie the plaister which inferred the paine.

Therefore I appeale to your good grace and favour, and at the barre of your beautie, I humblie holde up my handes,/ resting to abide your sentence, either of consent unto life, or of deniall unto death.

Castania hearing this solempne discourse of *Valericus*, was driven into a maze with this unlookt for motion, musing that hee woulde so farre overshoote himselfe, as to attempt so un-likelie a match, and therefore with disdainefull countenance shee gave him this daunt.

As your present arivall Signor *Valericus*, dooth not greatlie prejudice my muses, so I thinke it will as little profit your motion: as your companie pleaseth me regarding the person, so it much misliketh me, respecting the *parle*: that your countes beeing once cast, you shall finde your absence might have more pleasured you, and better contented mee. For it is unpossible *Valericus*, to call the Fawlkon to that Lure wherein the pens of a Camelion are pricked, because she doth deadlie detest them, it is hard to traine the Lyon to that trappe which savoureth of Diagredium, because he loatheth it. And it is as impossible to persuade mee to enter league with fancie, which am a mortall foe to affection, and to vow my service to *Venus*, which am alreadie addicted to *Diana*. No, no sir, I meane not to love least I live by the losse, nor to choose, least my skill being small, I repent my chance. She that is free and willinglie runneth into fetters is a foole, and who so becommeth captive without constraint, may be thought either wilfull or witlesse. It is good by other mens harmes to learne to beware, and to looke before a man doth leap, least in skipping beyond his skill, he light in the mire. Who so considereth the ficklenesse of mens affections, and the fleeting fondnesse of their fading fancie, who carefullie looketh at the lightnesse of their love, and marketh the inconstancie of their wavering / minde, who readeth the records which make mention of their deepe dissemb-lings, faithlesse protestations, false vowes, perjured promises, fained love, and forged flatterie: how poore *Ariadne* was abused, how *Medea* was mocked, how *Dido* was deceived, how *Oenone* was rejected, and how *Phillis* was forsaken, and yet would be allured to the traine with such filthie scraps, I woulde count

her chaunce too good, were her choice never so bad. But
leaving these necessarie doubtes, *Valericus*, I tell you for troth,
if I meant to love, it is not you I meane to like, if affection
forced me, it is not your person I meane to fancie: your patrimonie is not sufficient to countervaile my parentage, nor your
bringing up my birth, and therefore I would wish you to sow
the seede of your sute in a more fertile soile, for in me you shall
finde no grafts of grant to grow, nor no consent to bee cropped,
for I neither like of your unlikelie love, nor meane not to be
framed to your fancie.

Valericus being pricked with this pike, thought it a signe of
small courage to yeeld at the first soine, and therefore looking
more narrowlie to his ward, and gathering himselfe within his
weapon, he stood to his tackling with this replie.

Madame (quoth hee) if you condemne mee of follie for
climbing a staffe too high, or accuse me of fondnesse for laying
my love on a person of such princelie parentage, if I seeme to
make an ill market in cheaping such precious chaffer, as the
price thereof is far above my reach, yet my offence is to small
to beare anie waightie penance, sith where the fault proceedeth
of love, ther the pardon insueth of course, but your beautie
shall beare all the blame, as the onelie spurre of this my rash
enterprise. For as it is impossible for the yron to resist the
operation of the Adamant, or the silie strawe the vertue of
the sucking / Jeat, so as impossible it is for a lover to with-
stande the brunt of beautie, to freeze if he stand by the flame,
or to pervert the lawes of Nature. So that madame, if you
knew what a breach your beautie hath made into my breast,
and how deepely I have shrined the Idoll of your person in
my happelesse heart, I assure my selfe though my person and
parentage, my birth and bringing up be farre unfit for such a
mate, yet you would deeme my love and loyaltie to deserve no
lesse. Loyaltie I call it madame, for as all things are not made
of one mould, so all men are not of one minde, as the Serpentine
pouder is quickly kindled, and quickly out, so the Salamander
stone once set on fire can never be quenched, as the soft Waxe
is apt to receive everie impression, so the hard mettall never
chaungeth forme without melting. *Jason* was never so trouth-
lesse as *Troylus* was trustie: *Paris* was never more fickle then
Pyramus was faithfull: *Aeneas* was never so light as *Leander*
was faithfull: And sure madame, I call the Gods to witnesse,
I speake without faining, that sith your beautie and vertue
eyther by fate or fortune is so deepely shrined in my heart, if

it please you to accept mee for your slave or servaunt, and admitte mee so farre into your favour, as that I may freely enjoy the sight of your sweete face, and feede my fancie in the contemplation of your beautie: in liewe thereof, I will repaie such dutifull service, as the betrothed faith of *Erasta* to his *Persida*, shal not compare with the love of *Valericus* and *Castania*.

Castania hearing these perplexed passions, proceede from wofull *Valericus*, pricked forwarde to take some remorse of his tormentes, felte within her minde a carefull conflict betweene fancie and the fates, love and the destinies: fancie perswaded her to take pitie of his paines, the fates forced her to give him the repulse: love wisht / her to retourne his good will with gaine, the destinies drave her to denie his request: tossed thus with contrarie cogitations, at last she burst forth into these doubtfull speeches.

Valericus, as I am not altogether to rewarde thy good wil with hate, so I cannot repaie it with love, because fancie denies me to like: to mary I meane not, to retaine servants I may not. Marie, to let thee either to love or looke, take this for an aunswere, I neither can nor will.

And with that she went her waye, leaving *Valericus* greatlie daunted with this doubtfull aunswere, with feare and hope so fiercely assailed, that being left alone, he beganne thus to consider of his amorous conceits.

If ever wofull creature had cause to complaine his wofull case, then undoubtedly may I preace for the formost place, for there is no sorrow more sower, no torment more terrible, no griefe more grievous, no heavinesse more hurtfull, then to have desire requited with despight, and good will with hate, then to like upon hope of courtesie, and to finde nothing but hate and hellish crueltie.

Alasse poore *Valericus*, is thy true love thus triflingly accounted of? is this the guerdon for thy good will? Doeth thy deepe desire merite no better desert? then hast thou no choice, but either to dye desperatelie, or else to live loathsomelie? Why fonde foole, doest thou count her cruell, that at the first gives not a free consent? Doest thou thinke her coye that commeth not at the first call? wouldest thou have the match made at the first motion? Shee that is wonne with a word, will be lost with a winde, the Hauke that bates at everie cast of the / Lure will never be stedfast on the stonde, the woman that frame[th] her will to everie wish will prove but a blinde wanton. No, no *Valericus*, let not her denials daunt thee, let not the sower taste of her talke quat thy queasy stomacke, conster all things at the best: tho' her censure was very severe, yet shee knit up her talke with a courteous close. The hound which at the first defaulte giveth over the Chace, is called but a curre. The Knight that finding the first encounter cumbersom giveth over the quest, is counted but a coward, and the lover that at the first deniall is daunted with despayre is neyther worthie to obtaine his desire, nor to enjoye his desert. And with that he flung out of his chamber both to avoid the melancholy which tormented his mind and see if he could have a sight of his goddesse.

But *Castania* altogether unwilling to *parle* with her new patient, kept herself out of his sight: which *Valericus* espying was no whit amazed, but like a valiant souldier gave the fort a fresh assault, with a new kinde of batterie, seeking to obtaine that with writing which he could not gaine with words, and therefore speedilye framed a letter to this effect.

Signor Valericus, to the Ladye Castania, health.

There is no Creature (Madame *Castania*) so bereaved of reason, or deprived of sense, which being oppressed with direfull calamities, findeth not by mere instinct of nature, a present remedy for his malady, man only excepted, who by reason of this want, may justly accuse the injurious gods of justice with injustice. The Tigre, though never so deadlye wounded taketh the roote of the Tamariske, and is presently cured: The Deere beeing stroken, though never / so deep, feedeth on the herb *Dictaninum*, and forth with is healed: The Lyon salveth his sicknesse by eating the Sea Woolfe, and the Unicorne recovereth his health, by swallowing up the buds of a Date-tree. But man being crossed with care, or oppressed with griefe, pinched with fancie, or perplexed with love, findeth no herbe so wholesome, nor medicine so milde, no plaister so perfect nor no salve so soveraigne, which by their secrete virtues can appease his passions: the which *Madame*, I knowe by proofe and now speake by experience: for your divine beautie and secrete vertue, the perfection of your bodie and the beautie of your mind, hath kindled such a flaming fire in my hoplesse heart that by no meanes it may be quenched, but will turne my bodie into

drie earth and cinder, unlesse by the droppes of your pittie it
be speedily redressed. Then *Madame* sith your beauty is my
bale, let it be my blisse: since it hath wrought my woe, let it
work my weale, and let not my faithfull service and loyal love
be recompenced with such rigorous refusals. Strive not for
my life, since you have my liberty, seeke not my death, since
you are the Saint to whom I offer up my devotion. But good
Madame, let the sweete balme of thy benevolence salve the sore
that so painfully afflicteth my carefull conscience. And with
the deawe of your grace redeame him from most hellish tormentes, whose life and death standeth in your aunswere, which
I hope shall be such as belongeth to the desert of my love, and
the shewe of your beautie.

Yours, if he may be,
Don Valericus.

Valericus / having thus finished his Letter, sent it, with as
much speed as might be by his Page, to *Castania*, who finding
her at convenient leisure, with most reverent dutie delivered
it. *Castania*, at the firste sight, conjecturing the contents,
with scornfull looks, and disdainfull countenance, unripped the
seales, where seeing and reading his deep devotion, she perceived that his affection was no lesse indeede than he professed
in word; She notwithstanding would take no remorse at his
torment, but to drive him more into dolefull dumps shee returned
him this damp.

Castania to Seignor Valericus

As it is impossible (*Seignor Valericus*) to straine moist liquor
out of the dry flint, and procure flaming heate in that which is
already nipped with the chilling cold, to force the sturdy
streames to run against their common course, so as hard is it
to win unwilling love, either with tears or truth. For if thy
birth or patrimony could countervaile my Parentage, if my
Father were content to knit the knot, yet neither his command
nor thy entreatye, should make me to choose without my owne
love and liking. Sith then thou art the man whome I rather
loathe then like, cease from thy sute, make a vertue of necessitie,
and assuage the flame thy selfe which no other will quench.
By importunate persisting in thy purpose, where no hope is,
thou provest thy selfe rather a desperate sot, then a discrete
souldier. To hop against the hill, is extreme fondnesse; to

strive against the streame, mere folly: then *Valericus*, avoid the one, and eschewe the other, for if thou wilt seeke to gain my good-will, thou shalt turne the endlesse stone with *Sisiphus*, and therefore take my nay for aunswer. For / if I would I cannot, and if I could I will not, and so farewell.

No way yours
Castania.

Valericus having received this rigorous Letter from ruthlesse *Castania*, seeing with what great disdain she rejected his dutifull devotion, and how with coy countenance she rewarded his loyall love, he began with reason somewhat to vent his rage, and with wisdome to redresse his witlesse folly; for comparing her crueltie with his own curtesie, and her wilful disdaine with his willing dutie, his disordinate desire began not only to decay, but his extreame love turned to his extreame hate, insomuch, that forced to despight, he sent her (in revenge) these raging lines.

Valericus the despised, to despightfull Castania.

Diogenes being demaunded why so extreamely hee hated woman, answered, (quoth hee) because they be women. So if thou aske of me why so rudely I raile against thy recklesse folly, I aunswere, because thou art *Castania*, whose mercilesse minde is so misled with ingratitude, and whose currish nature is foyled with carelesse inconstancy, that like *Menechmus Subreptus* his wife, thou doest not begin to love, ere again thou seekest to hate. Thou plaiest like the young Eagles, which being hatched by the bird *Olyphaga*, never seek to peark on loftie mounts but to / sitte in durtie Dales, and lyke the greedie Kyte which leaveth the sweete fleshe, to pray on the stincking carrion. But why doe I so farre forget my selfe? Is she to be blamed that leaveth her choyce to have a better chaunce, or is the Faulchon to be accused of bastardie, that leaveth the Starling to praye on the Larke? No: and no doubt such is thy case, for if it bee true that all speaketh, or at the least suspecteth, thou art lyke by thy lovers Parentage to become a great Potentate: for if armes bee the bewrayer of auncient discentes, no doubt hee is come of an olde house. Yea, thy Father *Orlanio* may rejoyce if he live to see the daye that his Daughter shall be so well wedded as to such a wrangling Wisard. But *Pasiphae* preferred a Bull before a King, and *Venus* a smeered Smith before *Mars* the God of battaile. Tush, *Psammeticus* was father to *Rhodopes* children, whosoever begat them,

and that cloake is of a course spinning, that cannot keepe of
the raine.   Farewell.

> *Living he hopes to revenge*
> *thy injuries.*
>
> *Wofull Valericus.*

Castania no sooner hadde read these despitefull lynes of
Valericus, but her minde fired with the flames of furie, and her
breast boyled with raging wrath, in such sorte, that she could
not be in quiet nor take any rest: she busied her selfe so carefullie in studying with what kinde of revenge she might best
wreake her wrath uppon him, and requite his spitefull speeches.
At last womanlike, she found her tongue the beast weapon,
and with that she plagued him in this sort.

Castania / to Valericus, neither health nor good hap.

The Mastiffe Dogge (*Valericus*) can never quest like a Spaniell,
but he must alwaies barke lyke a Curre: it is naturall for the
Pie to chatter, for the Jaye to jangle, and for thee to raile and
rage like a frantike foole.   Doest thou thinke (*Valericus*) by
brawling lyke a beggar to become a King, or by thy moodelesse
follie to obtaine my favour? no, as I knowe thy knaverie, so
I passe not for thy braverie: neither can those vauntes stand
for paiment, where the partie is prickt for a peevish paltering patch.   It is no mervaile if thy doggish Letters favour of
Diogenes doctrine, for in troth thou art such a Cinicall kinde
of Dunce, that thy fond felicitie is in biting bitterlie those whom
otherwise thou canst not revenge.   In deede, gentle *Balaams*
Asse, if I had beene so light as to have loved you, I might
justlie have beene accused to have beene a Curre or a Kistrell,
for in faith shee that feedes her fancie on thy face, may onelie
reape this profite, to fill her eyes full with the figure of a foole.
For my lovers armes, *Valericus*, they are imblased in such a
coate, as it is harde for thee to controule.   But I knowe thou
boastest that thou hast gotten thy antiquitie by conquest, and
keepest thy Letters pattents in the beggars boxe.   Thus adieu
Sir Dunce, the more you mislike mee, the better I love my selfe.

> *Thy detested foe,*
>
> *Castania.*

Valericus his heart was so hardned with hate, as hee was
nothing dismaied with this rigorous replie, but thought himselfe halfe satisfied, that he hadde thus kind / lie toucht her to

the quicke, praying the Gods, that sith it was not in his possibilitie to make anie sufficient revenge, they would by some
sinister meanes requite her crueltie. But leaving him to his
dumpes, at last to *Gwydonius*, who besides the beautie of his
bodie, and the bountie of his minde (whereat all *Alexandria*
wondered) had by good government and perfect practise,
obtayned such a dexteritie in all thinges, as in feates of armes
no man more forward, in exercise none more active, in plaie
none more politike, in *parle* none more pleasant, amongst his
auncients verie wise, amongst the youthfull who more merrie:
so that there was no time, person, nor place, whereto aptlie
he applied not himselfe: insomuch that hee entered into such
favour and familiaritie with *Thersandro* and *Castania,* that
hee was the onelie man whose companie they desired to injoy.
But especiallie *Castania,* who by casting a gazing glaunce sometime upon the beautie of *Gwydonius,* felte a certaine restraint
of lybertie in her affections, an alteration of minde, and as it
were a civile assault within her selfe: but having small practise
in the pangs of love, shee could not conjecture the secrete cause
of these her sodaine passions, thinking that as it was a toie
lightlie taken, so it would as lightlie be left: and upon this still
she rested, conceiving onelie an ordinarie kinde of liking towardes
Gwydonius.

Who bathing thus in the streames of blisse, and safelie harboured in the haven of happinesse, wanting nothing which
might content his minde, either for pleasure or profit, thought
it a point of meere follie either to seeke or wish for more than
inough, knowing that to strain further than the sleeve would
stretch, was but to make the arme bare, and to skippe beyond
a mans skill, was to leape, but not to know where to light: to
avoid therefore hasti/nesse in hazarding, he fell a slumbering
in the carelesse seate of securitie.

But as it is impossible for a man to sleepe by the viper and
not bee invenomed, to gaze upon the Cockatrice and not be
infected, to stare upon the Sunne and not be dazeled, to looke
upon *Medusas* head and not be transformed, to wade in the
waves and not be drenched, to handle coales and not be scorched,
so it was as impossible for yong *Gwydonius* to gaze upon the
beautie of *Castania* and not be galled, to fixe his eies upon her
feature and not be fettered, to see her vertuous qualities and
not be inveigled: for her curtesie had so encountred him, her
modestie had so amazed him, and her charie chastitie so
inchaunted him, that whereas he came to *Orlanio* his Court

free from affection, hee was now become a servile slave
to fancie, before a foe to lust, now a friend to love, yea hee
felte such an alienation of his senses, and such a straunge
Metamorphosis of his minde, as reason was tourned to rage,
mirth to mourning, joye to annoie, delight to despight, weale
to woe, blisse to bale: in fine, suche contrarie passions so perplexed the doubtfull Patient, as maugre his face, hee yeelded
the fort toe fancie, and pulde in the former flagge of defiance,
intreated for truce, and beganne to enter *parle* with *Cupide*
on this manner.

O *Gwydonius* (quoth hee) what straunge chaunce, nay, what
rare chaunge, what solempne motion, nay, what sodaine mad-
nesse, what foolish phrenzie, or rather what frantike affection
hath possessed thee? Is thy lawelesse lybertie tourned to a
slavish captivitie? Is thy freedome fettered? Are thy senses
besotted? Is thy wit inveigled? Wert thou of late a defier
of *Venus*, and art thou now a defender of vanitie? Didst thou
of / late renounce beautie as a foe, and wilt thou nowe embrace
her as a friend? Is this the carefull keeping of thy Fathers
commandement? Or is this the dilygent dutie in observing
the counsayle of thy olde Sire *Clerophontes*? Hast thou so
soone forgot his fatherlie preceptes, or committed to oblivion
his friendlie advertisement? Did hee carefullie warne thee to
beware of love, and wilt thou careleslie wed thy selfe to
lust? Did hee shew thee what poisoned bane is hidden under
the painted baites of beautie, and wilt thou bee haled to the
hooke?

O haplesse case: nay rather, if the charie charge thy Father
gave thee will bee no constraint, if his counsayle will not commaund thee, if his warning will not make thee warie, nor his
advice bee thy advertisement: yet let imminent perilles, and
insuing daungers bee a precious preservative against future
calamities. Consider with thy selfe *Gwydonius*, what difference
is betweene freedome and bondage, betweene libertie and captivitie, mirth and mourning, pleasure and paine, rest and care,
happinesse and heavinesse: and so farre doth hee which is free
from affection, differ from him which is fettered in fancie.

Why but *Gwydonius*, why doest thou thus reckleslie rage
against reason? Why doest thou thus fondlie exclaime against
thine owne welfare? Why doest thou condemne thy selfe of
that crime whereof thou art not guiltie?

Thy Father warned thee to beware of fickle fancie, but this

thy lyking is firme affection. His counsayle was to perswade
thee from lewde lust, but not from lawfull love, from vanitie,
not from vertue: yea, his will was to wish thee from liking such
a lewde minion, who had neither birth, wealth, nor vertue,
but / a little fading beautie to be either her credite or thy
countenance, not to warne thee from loving such a chast maiden,
nay, a peereles Princesse, whose birth may countenance thy
calling, whose power maye promote thee, whose livings may
inrich thee, whose vertue may advance thee: yea, in obtaining
whome, thou shalt gaine both honour, and perhappes the
inheritaunce of a Dukedome.

Doest thou thinke then *Gwydonius*, in winning so worthie a
peece, to purchase thy Fathers displeasure, nay assure thy selfe
he will not onelie be content with thy chaunce, but he will
thinke thou hast runne a happier race, than *Hyppomanes* did in
winning *Atlante*. Content with thy chance. Why *Gwydonius*,
art thou so fond a foole, as to count the Castle conquered,
that as yet thou hast not compassed: to suppose the Citie
sacked, which thou hast not besieged: to thinke the Bulwarke
beaten, which as yet thou hast not battered: or to count
the Ladie wonne, whome as yet thou hast not wooed? Naie
Gwydonius, if thou weigh thy case in the equal ballance, thou
hast more cause of feare than of hope, of doubt than of assurance,
of missing thy pretence, than of obtaining thy purpose.

The Faulkon (*Gwydonius*) seldome pearketh with the Merline,
the Lion seldome lodgeth with the Mouse, the Hart seldome
feedeth with the Pricket, *Aquila non capit Muscas*, and a Dame
indued with Nobilitie vouchsafeth not to match with a man of
meane Gentilitie. Of meane Gentilitie *Gwydonius*? Yea trulie,
for *Castania* rather thinketh thee sprong of some poore peasant,
than of anie princelie personage.

Besides, alasse, Fortune her selfe denieth mee anie such
favour: my good will as yet hath deserved no such guerdon,
my desire is farre above my deserts, my ambition / above my
condition, and the poore staie of wandering *Gwydonius*, farre
unfit for the princelie state of worthie *Castania*. But put case
shee did will as I did, with that shee were pricked in the same
veine, caught in the same snare, trapped with the like traine,
and fired with the like fancie, yet the Duke her Father wil
neither condescend to her minde, nor consent to my motion,
neither thinke well of her liking nor of my love, nay if he should
but once heare of such recklesse follie, as he hath wrought my
promotion, soe he would worke my confusion, as hee hath

beene my friend, so he would be my foe, and in troth *Gwydonius*, not without cause, for art thou so voide of vertue, or vowed to vice, so nursed up in vanitie, and nusled up in villanie, as to requite his liberalitie with such disloialtie, to returne the trust which he reposeth in thee, with such treason? Tush, Love is above Lord or Lawe, friend or faith. Where Love leadeth, no maister is made account off: no king cared for, no friend forced off, no dutie respected, but all things done according to the qualitie that is predominant. Why *Gwydonius*, what doubts are these that thou thus dreamest on? Why dost thou cast beyond the Moone, and feare before thou art in daunger to fall: knowing that Love and fortune desireth not them that are dastards, nor careth not for them that are cowards? The Captaine that retyreth from the walles before he hath the repulse, shall never returne a conquerour, the souldiour that fainteth before the battaile bee fought, shall never vaunt him-selfe of victorie. Hee that feareth everie tempest is not fit to bee a travailer. Hee that doubteth everie wave shall never prove a perfect Pilot, and he that in love dreadeth everie chip of mischance, may well encounter, but never obtaine the con-quest. Sith then *Gwydonius*, harde venturing is a signe of happie victorie, sound out the march with the trumpet of trust, begin the assault, give the onset. Laie the battering / peeces of love, against the bulwarke of beautie, and no doubt thy successe shall be such as thou shalt triumph with *Cæsar*, and saie, *Veni, Vidi, Vici*. And art thou so presumptuous fond foole, as to promise thy selfe the conquest? knowest thou not that the path of love is perillous? And with that he fell into such melancholike passions, such contrarie cogitations, such doubtfull thoughts, such fearefull supposes, that as hee which eateth of the Goorde roote looseth his memorie, and as the Elephant when hee eateth of the Heliotropian leafe, is then verie sleepie, so *Gwydonius* was so perplexed with these un-acquainted passions, that contrarie to his custome he had driven mirth into mourning, pleasant conceites into painfull cares, laughing into lowring, singing into sorrowe, as beeing thus besotted: to solace himselfe, he went into a Parke adjoyning to the Dukes Pallace, where sitting under the shade of a Beech tree, leaning his head on his hand, he laie as one in a slumber. But fortune willing somwhat to favour this young novice, brought it so to passe, that *Thersandro, Valericus, Castania*, and *Melytta*, with diverse other Gentlemen, were for recreation sake ranging in the same Parke, who espying ghostly *Gwydonius* sitting as one in a trance, *Castania* passing before the rest, pulling him by the sleeve, drave him thus out of his dumpe.

Why how now *Gwydonius* (quoth she) are you dreaming or doubting, or is your minde musing upon some metaphysicall motions, that you sit thus as a man halfe mortified? your solemne jesture makes me remember the picture of *Pigmalion*, which once I sawe portraied out by a skilfull painter, who leaning his head on his Marble mistres (that so unfainedlie he loved) sate with his eyes as one in a slumber, having his face notwithstanding so bedewed with brinish teares, as his outward plaintes / did sufficientlie bewraie his inward passions. In truth *Gwydonius*, I had taken thee for *Pigmalion*, if thou haddest had teares as thou wert in a trance, for thou doest not greatlie differ from him neither in countenance nor colour: well, if it were but a dreame *Gwydonius*, that thus cumbered thy conscience, or a doubt that made thee thus dumpish, I will devine the one if it be not too darke, or decide the other if it bee not too secret: marie, if the case be cumbersome, I leave it to the judgement of these Gentlemen.

Gwydonius wakened out of his musing slumber with this sugered harmonie, seeing before his eies his gorjeous Goddesse, the verie Saint, at whose shrine he was offering up scalding sighs, farre fetcht sobs, plaints, praiers, and protestations, was so apalde with her presence, that as the Basiliske looseth his senses, with the sight of a naked man, as the Torteise seeing the North starre is benummed, as the Hermeline looking on the stone Echites, is greatly amazed, so *Gwydonius* seeing the incomperable beautie of his best beloved *Castania*, was so astonished, yea, so inchanted with the rare perfection of this heavenlie *Pallas*, that as one besotted he sate senselesse, not beeing able to utter one word, untill at length revived with the view of her cheerefull countenance, hee repaide her with this pleasant answere.

Madame (quoth he) whereas jestinglie you saie, that at the first sight you had taken mee for perplexed *Pigmalion* by my pittifull plaintes and carefull countenance, but that I wanted trickeling teares to decypher my sorrowe, I aunswere, that woe maye verie well bee without watrie wailinges, for when the Stone *Garatides* frieth without, it freezeth within, the Germaunder leafe, when it is most full of moisture, looketh then / most drie, where the streame is most deepe, there it is most still, and where is the smallest shew of teares, there is the greatest signe of sorrow. And also I call the heavens to witnesse, that when you wakened mee out of my dreame by your divine eloquence, I tooke you either for beautie to bee *Venus*, for comelinesse to bee *Pallas*, or for porte and honour to bee *Juno*, so that both your presence and curtesie daunted my minde: your presence in dazeling my eyes so sodainlie with so solempne a sight, your curtesie, in that your Ladyship without curiositie would vouchsafe to talke with so meane a Gentleman. But Madame, sith that I perceive your skill in navigation to be greate, in that you made so cunning a conjecture, and without anie great aiming, so rightlie hit the marke, to put you out of doubt, I confesse I was both in a dreame and a doubt, wherein sith it pleaseth your honour to take so much paine, I will crave your aide to devine the one, and decide the other.

The Dreame

I was walking (Madame *Castania*) in my dreame (as I supposed) solitarilie by the sea side, whereas I tooke delight to see the Dolphins leape, (which as the Mariners saie, is a signe of imminent tempest) I forthwith espied a rocke in the Sea, whereupon stood a Ladie araied with roabes of burnisht golde, so formed and framed, so adorned and decked with the giftes of Nature, as at the first I tooke her to be *Thetis*, that had so gorjeouslie clad her selfe, to welcome home her lover and Lord *Neptunus*. But viewing her countenance more narrowlie, I perceived her to be a mortall creature (though unworthie such divine beautie shoulde be shrouded in the substance of an earthlie carcasse) which so inflamed my affection, so fired my fancie, and so kindled my desire, that the torments / of *Tantalus*, the torture of *Ixion*, the sorrow of *Sisiphus*, were not halfe comparable to the perplexed passions that pinched my haplesse heart, when I saw all hope cut awaye from injoying this earthly Goddesse: the sea which compassed the rocke was so deepe and daungerous, the cliffes so steep-downe and feareful, as to descend was no lesse daunger then death it selfe: thus as I surged in griefe, and wandered up and downe in woe, I spied a bridge a farre off, whereby was a passage to the rocke, which sight so salved my forepassed sorrow, and so revived my daunted minde, as I was driven into an extasie for joy, to see so good meanes to injoy my wished desire. Comming to the bridge, I found it built of glasse so cunningly and so curiously, as if Nature her selfe hadde sought to purchase credit by framing so curious a peece of workmanship. But yet so slenderly, as the least waight was able to pash it into innumerable peeces, and underneath the bridge did run so terrible a sea, such bouncing billowes, such tumbling waves, such fearefull surges, such roaring streames, such hideous goulfs, as it made the passage seeme a thousand times more perillous. This terrible sight was such a cooling Card to my former conceits, as hope was turned to feare, blisse to bale, and supposed happinesse to assured heavinesse. And yet my fancie was not quenched, but rather far the more inflamed, my desire was not diminished, but augmented, and my liking no lesse, but rather inlarged, so that to live in love without hope was loathsome, to seeke redresse was losse of life, to want my wish, was horror: to injoy my will, was hel: to live in care without comfort, was calamitie: to seeke for cure, was more then miserie: not to possesse the pray, was hellish daunger: to venture for the prise was haplesse death. Thus crossed with cares, and daunted with such divers doubts, desperate hope so repulsed direfull feare, that incouraged by ventrous desire, I had either obtained my / wish, or wanted of my will, if your Ladiship hadde not so sodainly wakened mee out of my slumber. Thus madame *Castania*, you have heard my dreame: now the doubt is, whether it had beene better to have ventured upon the brickle bridge, and so either desperately to have ended cares with death, or else valiantly to have injoyed desire with renowne, or still like a fearefull dastard to have ended my dayes in lingering love with miserie?

Castania hearing the surmised dreame of *Gwydonius*, both smelled the fetch, and smiled at the follie of this young youth, knowing that these fantasticall visions and pre-supposed passions, would in time (if he tooke not heede) prove but too true: to prevent therefore such imminent perills, she nipt her young novice on the pate with this *parle*.

Gwydonius (quoth shee) I have listened to thy drousie dreame, with deepe devotion, by so much the more desirous attentively to heare it, by how much the more I finde it strange and wonderfull: yea, so straunge, as if I my selfe had not wakened thee out of thy slumber, I would either have thought it a fained vision, or a fantasticall invention, but sith these Gentlemen heere present, and mine owne Eyes, are witnesses, and thine owne tongue a testimonie of thy talke, suffice I beleeve it, though I cannot divine it: to give a verdit where the evidence is not understoode, is vanitie: to yeelde a reason of an unknowen case, is meere follie: and to interpret so straunge a dreame without great practise, is but to skip beyond my skill, and to lye fast in the mire.

Yet least I might seeme to promise much and performe nothing, I will decide your doubt, if you please to take my doome for a censure.

It is a saying *Gwydonius*, not so common as true, that the hastie manne never wants woe, and that hee which / is rash without reason, seldome or never sleepeth without repentaunce. To venture amiddest the Pikes when perills cannot bee eschewed, is not fortitude but folly, to hazarde in daungers, when death ensueth, is not to live worthely minded, but wilfully mooved. Vertue alwayes consisteth between extremities, that as too much fearefulnesse is the signe of a quaking coward, so too much rashnesse betokeneth a desperate Ruffian. Manhoode *Gwydonius* consisteth in measure and worthinesse, in fearing to hazard without hope. But to give a verdite by thine owne voyce, I perceive thou art guiltie of the same crime, for when the bricklenesse of the Bridge portendeth, and the surging Seas inferred losse of lyfe, yet desire drave thee to adventure so desperate a daunger.

Better it is *Gwydonius*, to live in griefe, then to die desperately without grace: better to choose a lingering life in miserie, then a speedie death without mercie, better to be tormented with haplesse fancie, then with hellish fiends, for in life it is possible to represse calamitie, but after death never to redresse miserie. *Tully*, *Gwydonius*, in his *Tusculans* questions, discoursing of the happinesse of life and heavinesse of death, saith, that to live we obtaine it of the loving Gods, but to dye, of the un- luckie destinies: meaning heereby, that life though never so loathsome, is better then death, though never so welcome: whereby I conclude *Gwydonius*, that to live carefully, is better then to die desperately.

Gwydonius perceiving that *Castanias parle* was nothing to the purpose, and that she toucht not that point whereof hee desired moste to bee absolved, but meant to shake him off with a sleevelesse aunswere, beganne to drawe her to the Trappe with this traine.

Madame *Castania* (quoth he) I confesse that rashnesse never raigneth without repentance, nor hastie hazarding without hap- lesse harmes, that he which adventureth desperate dangers is a foole, and he that passeth inevitable perills is worse than an asse: yet from these so generall rules, Madame, I exempt these particular exceptions, namelie Love and Necessitie, which two

are tied within no bonds, nor limitted within no lawe, for whom
the divell drives he must needs runne, be the passage never so
perilous: and whom Love or Necessitie forceth he must v[e]n-
ture, be the danger never so desperate: for as there is no enterprise so easie, which to an unwilling man seemeth not verie
hard to be atchieved, so there is no encounter so cumbersome
where will wisheth, that seemeth not passing easie to be performed: now this will is with nothing sooner pricked forward,
than either with the force of Love, or sting of Necessitie. So
that whosoever adventureth in a danger, though never so
desperate, is not to be blamed, if inforced by fancie, or incouraged by affection, and especiallie where the perill is in
possibilitie to bee passed without death, and in the performance
thereof, the possession of such a prise, as the passionate person
more esteemeth than landes, lims, or life it selfe, bee it never
so sweete.   In which case (Madame) my cause consisteth. For
the Ladie who was an heavenlie object to my glazing eies, was
so beautified with the gifts of nature, and so perfectlie pollished
with more than naturall perfection, that with the onelie view
of such divine beautie, my senses were so besotted, my wit and
wil so inveigled, my affection so inflamed, and my freedome so
fettered, yea, love alreadie hath made so great a breach into
the bulwarke of my breast, that to obtaine so gorjeous a Goddesse
I thought death no daunger, though never so direfull, nor losse
of life no torment, though never so terrible.

In /deed *Gwydonius* (quoth *Thersandro*) I agree with thee in
this point, that there is no carpet Knight so cowardly, that
would not passe most perillous pikes to possesse so lively a Dame
as thou dost decipher, nor no dastard so daunted with dread,
which would not greatlie indanger himselfe to injoy so lovely
a damsell, in the fruition of whome consisteth nothing but joy,
blisse, rest, contentation of minde, delight, happinesse, yea,
all earthlie felicitie.

And yet Sir (quoth *Gwydonius*) your sister *Castania*, con-
demnes mee of follie, in ventring for so precious a price, when
as hope perswaded mee, that no hazarde could be haplesse, and
assured mee that Love and Fortune favoureth them that are
bold: that the gods themselves seeing my perplexed passions,
would of pittie defend mee from those perillous daungers. For
if *Theseus* by Divine power, were ayded againste the force of
the monstrous *Minotaure*, or if *Jason*, who constrained with a
covetous desire to obtaine the golden Fleece, arriving at *Colchos*,
was preserved by the Gods, from the dint of the deadly Dragons,

no doubt *Jupiter* himselfe would either have made the staggering
bridge more strong (considering that no hope of wealth, no
desire of riches, no greedinesse of gaine, no love of lucre, but
beautie hir selfe was the victorie I meant to vaunt off,) or
else if I had sowsed in the roaring Seas, he would have provided
some happie Dolphin, that *Arion* like, I might arive at the
desired Rocke: and then my daungers should have bene tourned
into delight, my perills into pleasures, my hazarding into
happinesse: yea, I should have possessed that heavenly paragon,
and enjoyed the love of that lovelie *Venus*, whose onely sight
were a sufficient salve, against all fore-passed sorrowes.

Stay there Master *Gwydonius* (quoth the Ladie *Me/lytta*) for
I see to graunt one false proposition, is to open a doore to
innumerable absurdities, and that by suffering you to long, of
these supposed premisses, you will inferre some cavilling conclusion to your former reasons: thus I replye.   That I confesse
necessitie to have no law, but I graunt not the same of Love:
for if it be lawlesse, it is lewde: if without limits, lascivious:
if contained within no boundes, beastlie: if observed with no
order, odious: so that lawelesse Love without reason, is the
verie Load-stone to ruth and ruine.

Sith then Master *Gwydonius*, as your selfe affirme, this was
the pricke that pusht you into perill, how can the effecte be
good, when the cause was naught, or how can you clarkely
defend your desperate motion, proceeding of such a fond and
foolish occasion.   But it was the perfection of her comelie
person, her exquisite feature, and rare beautie, that so kindled
thy desire, and so bewitched thy sences: for, who is so fearefull
that beautie will not make bolde? who so doubtfull, that beautie
will not make desperate? yea, what so harde that a man will not
hazard, to obtaine so divine a thing, as beautie.

Oh *Gwydonius*, hast thou not heard that the Fish *Remora*,
lystening to the sound of a Trumpet is caught of the Fishers,
that while the *Porcupine* standeth staring at the glimmering
of the starres, he is overtaken with dogges, that the Deare
gazing at the bow is striken with the bolte, that the Leopard
looking at the Panthers painted skinne, is taken as a praie,
and that hee which taketh too much delight to gaze upon
beautie, is oftentimes galled with grief and miserie.   Yea, his
pleasure shall inferre such profite, and his good will such gaine,
as if he reapt the beautifull apples of *Tantalus*, which / are no
sooner toucht, but they tourne to ashes.

Beautie *Gwydonius*, no sooner flourisheth but it fadeth,

and it is not fullie ripe before it beginne to rot: it no sooner
blossometh, but it withereth, and scarcely beeing toucht it
staineth, like to the *Guyacum* leafe, that hath the one halfe
parched, before the other halfe be perfect: to the Birde *Acanthus*,
which hatched white, yet tourneth blacke at the first storme:
or lyke to the Stone *Astites*, that chaungeth colour with the
onelie breath of a man.

If then *Gwydonius*, Beautie be so fading, so fickle, so momentarie, so mooving, so withering, so waning, so soone passed, and
so soone parched: is this the Jewell, which you count more
deere than life? and the Jemme which you thinke worthie to
be purchased with the danger of death? No doubt *Gwydonius*,
if you wonne the victorie, you might vaunt of a great Conquest,
and if your long hope were repayed with a great happe, it
shoulde be much lyke to his, which thinking to embrace *Juno*,
caught nothing but a vanishing clowde.

You doe well Madame (quoth *Castania*) to put an If, in it,
because hee that vaunteth of victorie before hee hath wonne
the fielde, may prove himselfe a foole: hee that bragges of
gaines before the accompts be cast, may perhappes put his
winnings in his eyes: and hee that bloweth the Mort before
the fall of the Buck, may verie well misse of his fees: so hee that
counts himselfe a speeder before he be a woer, sheweth himselfe
a vaine person or a vaunting patch.

Might it not be I pray you master *Gwydonius*, that passing
the bridge, scaping the dangerous seas, and happely arriving
at the desired Rock, yet you might misse of your purpose?
Yes forsooth: for many a man bendeth his bow, that never
killeth his game, layeth the strap that never catch/eth the
foole, pitcheth the Net that never getteth the Fish, and long
time are heavie woers that never prove happie speeders.

So perhaps *Gwydonius*, you might be crossed with a chippe of
the same mischaunce, and the gorgeous Dame whome you adore
for a Goddesse, might repaie your liking with loathing, your
love with hate, your good will with despite, and your fixed fancie
with small affection, either that she liked you too little, or loved
another too much. All these doubts *Gwydonius*, are carefully
to be cast, and wisedome it is to feare the worst, and finde
the best: but you Sir, like a lustie champion, thinke a
Ladie wonne at the first looke, and the good will of women
gained at the first glaunce, thinking the Gods themselves are to
be accused of injustice, if they be not aiders to your enterprise,
insomuch that if in ventring over the perillous passage, you had

by disaster Fortune fallen into the dangerous Seas, you doubted not but that *Jupiter* would have sent a Dolphin, that *Arion* like, you might escape the fearefull surges: but *Gwydonius,* be not so ventrous, least though you harpe verie long, you get not the like hap. These premisses considered, if my censure might stande for a sentence, I deeme it better to be counted a dastardly coward, than a desperate caitife, better to forsake your Goddesse than your God, better to live pinched with a few momentarie passions, than with desperate death to destroy both soule and bodie: for there is no sore such, which in time may not be salved, no care such which cannot be cured, no fire so great which may not be quenched, no love, liking, fancie, or affection, which in time may not either be repressed, or redressed.

Valericus hearing this rough replie of *Castania,* supposed that although she levelled at *Gwydonius,* yet shee shot at him, and fearing the forte should be to much shaken / with this fierce assault, hee stiflie defended the walls with this fresh alarum.

Madame (quoth he) I see you will sit nigh the wals eare you bee thrust out for a wrangler, and that you will speake against your owne conscience, but you will have the conquest: for my owne parte Madame, howsoever I seeme to like it, I will not saie I mislike it, but I am sorrie you Madame *Melytta* shoulde so blasphemouslie imblaze the armes of beautie, and so reckleslie raile against the sacred lawes of love: take heede for crossing *Cupide* so crabbedlie, for though hee forgive and forget, *Venus* is a woman, and wil seeke revenge.

Valericus (quoth shee) take no care what daunger I incurre for speaking the truth: if I chaunce to bee harmed, it is mine owne mishappe, and for *Venus* revenge I care for it the lesse, because I feare it not: if I speake against my selfe, you may see I am the fitter to bee a Judge, because I am not partiall, nor have anie respect of persons.

These quips Madame (quoth *Gwydonius*) are nothing to the purpose, therefore in the behalfe of my selfe and beautie, thus I answere. That as there is nothing that so soone procureth a man to loath, as deformitie, so there is nothing which sooner procureth a man to love than beautie: for the most precious stone is chosen by the most glistering hiew, the purest golde by the most perfect coulour, the best fruit by the bravest blossomes, and the best conditions by the sweetest countenaunce, so that

where beautie raigneth, there vertue remaineth, and under a
faire face resteth a faithfull heart. Since then beautie and
bountie cannot bee parted, what man is hee so brutish, whome
the least of these will not make to breake or bend?

And / whereas you condemne me of vanitie in vaunting before
the victorie, I saie, that if fortune had so favoured me, that
I had gained the presence of my Goddesse, I would never have
doubted to have obtained my desire: for if shee had seene the
desperate daunger which I adventured, and the fearefull perills
which I passed for her sake, shee could not but of conscience,
repaie my love with unfained loialtie, and my good will with
treble gaine. And in troth I thinke it unpossible, that such
heavenlie beautie should bee eclipsed with crueltie, and such
perfect comelinesse bee blemisht with curious coynesse.

Why *Gwydonius* (quoth shee) doest thou call it crueltie, not
to condescend to the request of everie one that wooeth, or doest
thou tearme it coinesse, not to yeeld to the assault of everie
flattering lover? Then in my judgement, it were good for
everie woman to be both cruel and coie, that by crueltie she
might avoide the traine of trothlesse wooers, and by coinesse
eschue the troupe of faithlesse sutors.

And so Madame (quoth *Valericus*) she shoulde reape small
comfort and lesse credit.

Tush Signor *Valericus* (quoth *Gwydonius*) it pleaseth her thus
merilie to jest, whereas I know shee doth account more of a
curteous dame, than of a curious damsell, and that her Ladishippe so detesteth the name of crueltie, that shee would bee
loth to bee thought to have a minde devoide of mercie. And in
troth to leave these perticular instaunces, women in generall,
or for the most parte, are bountifull, courteous, sober, chast,
demure, not imbrued with vice, but indued with vertue: so
that by how much womens bodies are weaker than mens, by
so much their mindes are more strong and vertuous.

What *Gwydonius* (quoth she) doe you thinke to be a free /
man in *Wales*, for offering a Leeke to Saint *Davie*, or to bring
Pan into a fooles Paradise by praising his Pipe.

Not so Madame (quoth hee) but I hope in extolling a souldiers
life to have Saint *George* to my friend, and in giving verdit with
Venus, to gaine her good will, and to reape the reward that
Paris had for his censure.

Marie sir (quoth *Castania*) if you have no better gettings,
you may gaine long inough, and yet live by the losse: for in
obtaining one friend, you shall reape two foes, as *Paris* did,

who was more plagued by *Pallas* and *Juno,* than pleasured by flattering *Venus.*

And yet Madame (quoth he) his mishap shal not make me to beware: for if *Venus* woulde graunt me but one Ladie in the world, whom most entirelie I love, I wold neither respect *Pallas, Juno,* nor *Diana* her selfe, were she never so despitefull.

Yes but you would (quoth she) if she pinched you but with *Acteons* plague, to pester your head with as many hornes as a a Hart: It woulde cause you conjecture your new mistres were too much given to the game, or that you were come from *Cornetto* by descent.

Tush Madame (quoth he) doe you count *Acteons* hap such a great harme? the onelie sight in seeing *Diana* naked, was a recompence for all his insuing sorrowes, and if my selfe might injoy my wish, and obtaine the heavenlie dame that so hartilie I desire, the plague of *Acteon,* nay, the griping griefes the ghostlie spirits doe suffer, should not countervaile the joy I should conceive in injoying so peerelesse a jewell.

Trulie (quoth *Thersandro*) thou art worthie *Gwydonius* to bee a chapman, that thou bidst so well for thy chaffer, and in my mind she is not in *Alexandria,* who for her beautie is so to be loved, or at the least would deeme thee not worthie to be liked. But leaving these amorous dis/courses, let us hie us in hast to the Court, least in tarrying *Orlanio* misse us, and so we be shent. The companie obeying the minde of *Thersandro,* passed as speedilie as might be to the pallace, where being arived, they departed everie man to his owne lodging.

Castania had no sooner conveied her selfe closelie into her chamber, but her mind was moved with a thousand sundrie motions, and she felt such a cruell conflict in her haplesse heart, by the assault of diverse contrarie passions, that how stoutlie so ever she defended the wals, she found her force too weake to resist the rage of so recklesse a tyrant. Now the praiers *Valericus* poured forth came to effect, now *Venus* meant to bee revenged for the crueltie she used to her valiant Captaine, *Valericus,* who so valiantlie had fought under the flagge of affection, and yet could by no meanes prevaile. For *Castania* hearing the sugered eloquence, which so sweetlie flowed from the sappie wit of *Gwydonius,* framing in her fancie the forme of his face, and printing in her heart the perfection of his person, was so intangled in the snares of love, as shee could by no reason redresse her miserie, but will she, nill she, fell into these bitter complaints.

Alasse witlesse wretch (quoth she) that I am, what firie
flames of fancie doe frie within mee? What desire, what lust,
what hope, what trust, what care, what dispaire, what feare,
what furie? That to be pained with these perplexed passions,
to me that never felt the force of them before, is no lesse dolour
than death it selfe, be it never so direfull. O Gods, where are
now become those loftie lookes I used to *Valericus*? Where is
the disdainfull dealings, the coie countenaunces, the curious
congies, the causelesse crueltie? Yea, the hard heart, which
so rigorouslie rejected the love of him / which so entirelie liked
mee? Could I, fond foole that I am, valiantlie withstand the
assaultes of a worthie Gentleman, and shall I cowardlie yeeld
to an unknowen straunger? Did I loath him, whose parentage
was little inferiour to mine, and shall I love another of base and
vile birth? Did I disdaine to looke at the lure, and shall I
now stoope without stall, come without call, yea, and to such
an emptie fist? O lawlesse Love, O witlesse will, O fancie,
fraught full of phrensie and furie. Alasse, if I should bee so
carelesse as to consent to this frantike toie, what will they saie,
that praised me for my vertue? Will they not as fast dispraise
me for my vanitie? Will not my father fret, my kinsfolkes
crie out, my friends bee sorrie, my foes, and especiallie *Valericus*,
laugh me to scorne, and triumph of this my mishap? Yea,
will not all the world wonder to see me alate given to chastitie,
and now shake hands with virginitie, to yeeld my deerest jewell
and chiefest treasure into the hands of a stragling straunger,
who came to my fathers Court without countenance or coine,
wealth or worship, credit or calling: yea, who by his owne
report is but a person of small parentage. Seeke then *Castania*
to asswage this flame, and to quench this fire, which as it
commeth without cause, so it will consume without reason:
For the greatest flow hath the soonest ebbe, the sorest tempest
hath the most sodaine calme, the hottest love hath his coldest
end, and of the deepest desire oft times insueth the deadliest
hate: so that she which settles her affection with such speede
as shee makes her choice without discretion, may cast her corne
she knowes not where, and reapes she wots not what, and for
her hastie choosing, may perhaps get a heavie bargaine. Alasse,
I know this counsaile is good, but what then? Can I denie
that which the destinies have decreed? Is it in my power to
pervert that which the Planets have placed? Can I resist that
which is stirred up by the starres? No, what neede / I then
make this exclamation, sith I am not the first nor shall not be

the last, whom the frantike phrenzie of flickering fancie, hath with more wrong and greater vantage pittiouslie oppressed. What though *Gwydonius* be not wealthie, yet he is wise, though he be not of great parentage, yet he is of comelie personage: it is not his coine that hath conquered me, but his countenaunce, not his vading riches, but his renowned vertues, and I farre more esteeme a man than money: I, but the Duke my father is not so base minded, as to bestow me upon so meane a Gentleman, he never wil consent that poore *Gwydonius* should enjoy that which he hopeth some peerelesse Prince shall possesse. What then? Shall I prefer my Father's weale before mine owne will, his liking before mine owne love? no, no, I will choose for my selfe whatsoever my choice bee. Why, but perchance *Gwydonius* will no more esteeme thee than thou didst *Valericus*, and repaie thee with as small fancie, as thou him with affection? Tush, doubt it not *Castania*, thou art the dame which he so deciphered in his dreame, thou art that *Venus* which he saw in his vision, thou art that Goddesse, whose beautie hath so bewitched him, thou art that jewell to possesse the which there is no hap so hard which he wold not hazard, no danger so desperate which he would not adventure, no burthen so heavie which he would not beare, nor no perill so huge which he would not passe. And shall not then *Gwydonius* be my servant, sith I am his Saint, shall not I like him which loveth me, sith he is my joy, shal I not injoy him? Yes, *Gwydonius* is mine, and shalbe mine in despite of the fates and fortune.

Castania having thus pittifully poured out her plaints, would gladly have given *Gwydonius* intelligence (with modestie if she might) of her good will towards him, and God knowes how faine *Gwydonius* wold have discovered his fervent affection, if too much feare had not astonished him, / and too great bashfulnesse staied her. She therefore hovering betweene feare and hope, persevered so long in her pensive passions and carefull cogitations, that by covert concealing of her inward sorrow, the flame so furiouslie fired within her, that she was constrained to keepe her bed. Whereupon *Melytta* conjecturing the cause of her care by the coulour of her countenance, thought to sift out the occasion of her sorrow, that by this meanes she might applie a medicine to her maladie, and finding fit opportunitie, she brake with her in this wise.

Madame *Castania* (quoth she) since I have by the Duke your father ben assigned to you as a companion, I have in such loving wise both comforted and counsailed you, as I hope you have just cause to saie, that I have most carefullie tendered your estate, for perceiving how willing you were to follow my direction, I counted your wealth my weale, your pleasure my profit, your happinesse my joy, and your prosperitie my felicitie. Which friendlie care if it were not to be considered, if I should shew you what great sorrow I sustaine by your heavinesse, you would judge my wordes to proceede either of follie or flatterie, but if your sore be such as it may be salved, if your care may be cured, if your griefe may be redressed, or your maladie mitigated by my menes, command me good *Castania*, in what I may to pleasure thee, and thou shalt finde me so charilie to performe my charge, as my willing minde shall evidentlie bewraie my wel meaning. I see *Castania*, of late, such a strange Metamorphosis in thy minde, as for pleasant conceits thou doest use pensive cogitations, thy cheerefull countenance is changed into lowring lookes, thy merrie devises into mournfull dumps, and yet I cannot conjecture no cause of this sodaine alteration. If want of riches should work thy wo, why, thou swimst in wealth, if losse of friends, thou hast infinite of noble parentage, which loves thee most entirelie. If thou meanest no longer to leade / a single life, no doubt thy father will provide thee of such a princelie match, as shal content thee for his person, and countenaunce thee with his parentage. But if in all these supposes I have mist the marke, and have not toucht the case of thy calamitie, unfolde unto me *Castania*, what the paine is that thus doth pinch thee, and assure thy selfe I will be so secret in thy affaires, as ever *Lampana* was to her Ladie *Cleophila*.

Castania hearing this friendlie discourse of *Melytta*, thought for all this faire glose, the text might bee too intricate, and that these painted speeches would prove but rotten pillers: fearing therefore the fetch, and doubting the worst, if she bewraie her minde, she framed her this answere.

Madame (quoth she) the incomparable curtesie and unfained friendship which since your first comming I have found in you by experience, will neither suffer mee to suspect your Ladishippe of flatterie, nor my selfe willinglie to bee accused of ingratitude, for your diligence hath bene so great, and my deserts so small, that if I might but live to requite some part of your good will, it were the second felicitie I looke for in this life. But touching the pensive passions which thus diverslie perplexed mee, I answere, that as he which is wounded of the Bores tuske, if his sore take aire, is verie hardlie healed, as hee which is stroken

with a Scorpion, if his wound take wind can never be cured:
so Madame, many inward maladies carrie this nature, that if
they be once discovered, they are farre the more hardlie recovered, that it is better to conceale them with griefe, than
reveale them in hope of releefe.

Not so *Castania*, your principle is not true, for if your passions
proceeded of love, which of all other inward sores requireth
greatest secrecie, yet undoubtedlie the more it / is discovered,
the sooner it is cured, for as the stone of *Armenia* beeing covered
with Sand, burneth most extreamlie, and no sooner taketh aire,
but it cooleth, so the firie flames of love raked up in silence,
frie most furiouslie, but being by discourse disclosed, they soone
convert from flame to fume and smoke. Wherefore good
Castania impart unto me the matter which doth import thee
so neere, and I sweare unto thee by the sacred rites of *Cæres*,
which is so honoured in *Alexandria*, that if thou doest love where
thy friends doe not like, and thy wish be contrarie to their will,
yet I will seeke all meanes possible to redresse thy sorrow.

Alasse good Madame, rather than you should thinke mee so
incredulous or suspitious, as not to beleeve your oth, or doubt
of your secret dealing, I will without delaie make you privie
to the cause of my paine, what perill so ever I incurre by revealing it. So it is *Melytta*, that the perfection of *Gwydonius*,
his exquisite qualities, and excellent vertues, have fiercelie
assaulted the forte of my fancie, as I am perforce constrained
to resigne my libertie captive unto his curtesie, and to make
his person the prison of my heart. This lucklesse and unlikelie
love madame, is the cause of my care, and the sum of my
sorrow: this frantike affection hath driven my drooping heart
to shew forth these drousie lookes, this is it which hath made
me an enimie to my selfe, a foe to all good companie, and to
delight in nothing but sorrow and solitarinesse: yea, this is the
sore, which if in time it be not salved, will prevent by death
all other miseries.

And is this (quoth *Melytta*) the paine that so greatlie per-
plexeth you? Is this the care which so cumbers your conscience? Is this the danger which drives you into such deepe
distresse? Do you thinke so superstitiouslie of *Gwydonius*, or
so abjectlie of your selfe, that you deeme this matter impossible
to bee brought to passe? no, no, doubt not / *Castania*, I my
selfe dare absolutelie promise thee, that thy love shall sort to
such happie successe, as thou thy self doest seeke for.

And with that *Melytta* staied by a sodaine sight shee had of that Saint that *Castania* so hartely served, for *Gwydonius* was entering in at the chamber doore with a dish of delicates, which *Orlanio* hearing his Daughter was sicke, had sent her. *Melitta* seeing that Cupid began to favour the cause of his clients, in giving them such fit opportunitie to discover their cares, went her waie, leaving *Gwydonius* the first man to plaie his part in this tragicall Comedie, who seeing his goddesse thus surprised with sicknesse, was so galled with griefe, so pinched with hellish passions, and so tortured with extreame torments, that his colour began to change and he fetcht a deep sigh or two, which, *Castania* hearing, she perceived without touching his pulses, the cause of these his sodaine passions. In fine, such melancholike motions so amazed his minde, that he was almost mute in his message, yet at length incouraging himselfe, he presented it unto her in this wise.

Madame (quoth he) the Duke your Father hearing of your sodaine sickenesse, in token of his fatherlie affection, amongst all his dainties, hath sent you this dish, which hee thinkes most meete for your diet, wishing your Ladiship to let no doubtfull motions distresse your minde, nor no carefull thoughts cumber your conscience, for you shall lacke nothing if you reveale to him your want, which either your will or wish can desire. And trulie Madame, to manifest my willing duetie (if the praiers of a poore Gentleman may be heard of the heavenlie Gods) I wish that before you tast of this foode, it may turne to *Nectar,* whereby not onelie your sickenesse should bee salved, but your divine beautie and vertue according to desert, should be crowned with immortalitie.

Castania perceiving with what fervent affection *Gwydonius* / uttered these words, began to cheere up her selfe, in hope that her good will should not be repaied with ingratitude: taking therefore the present at his hands, and liking it never the worse for his sake that brought it, she returned him this replie.

Gwydonius (quoth she) as I have cause most reverentlie to accept of my fathers loving curtesie, and to repaie his naturall affection with most dutifull obedience, so I have cause to thanke thee for thy paines, and to thinke well of thee for thy wish, promising in recompence of thy good will, if in any respect I may pleasure thee, to seeke and sue to my father for preferment.

Madame, I account the performance of my message no paine, but pleasure, and I thinke my selfe as much honored by this office, and thrice more happie than if I should in *Ganimedes*

*H 824

place, present the cup to *Jupiter*. But Madame, sith that to stop the streame, is to make the floud flow more fiercelie, to represse the fire, is to make it flame more furiouslie, and to restraine the force of love, is to kindle a greater flame, least too long delaie should breede too greate daunger, and by concealing my sorrow I should make the sore incurable, I thought good eyther presently to heare the curteous sentence of my life, or the cruell doome of my death. So it is Madame, that too long gazing upon the beames of your heavenlie beautie, and too narrowlie construing over your vertuous conditions, I remaine so caught in the snare of your bountie, and so thraled in the threed of your vertue, that the staie of my life hangeth in your hands, either to drive me downe to hellish miserie, or to hoist mee up to heavenlie felicitie. For although I have not heere-tofore by dutifull service made manifest the loyaltie of my love, yet since I first framed in my fancie (as in a mirrour) the shape of your surpassing beautie, my heart hath beene crossed with such cruell Camizados for your sake, as if with the Target of / hope, I had not withstoode the furious force of such raging furies, I had by dispaire bene dashed against most dangerous rockes. Sith then Madame, the sight of your sweete face hath fast fettered my fancie in the linkes of love, as with-out your meanes I can neither be redressed nor released: I humblie desire you neither to resist the motion of my well meaning, nor to reject the devotion of my good will, but to accept your poore *Gwydonius* as a faithfull servant.

Castania hearing diligentlie the faithfull discourse of distressed *Gwydonius*, perceiving by his sighs, the pinching sorrow of his thoughts, and seeing him so fast fettered in follie, on a sodaine to give her the slip, had that she desired: and now her loving lookes was turned to lowring glances, her delightfull curtesie, to disdainfull coinesse, and she thought to repaie the sweet meate wherewith before she fed him, with most sowre sauce: not that she misliked of his love, for it was the onelie thing she desired, but to make him the more fervent in affection, uttering these or such like wordes to her selfe secretelie.

And is not (*Castania*) the victorie most accounted of, where he conquest is most doubtfull? Is not the Castle which abideth the longest batterie, thought the richest bootie? Are not those pearles which are scarcelie found and hardlie gotten, ever of greatest value? what so is gained by perill, is thought alwaies precious, hardlie come by, warilie kept. The maide that by long sute and much travel is obtained, by how much the more she was hard in the winning, by so much the more she wil be sweet in the wearing: she which in her virginitie is charie of her chastitie, in her marriage will be as warie of her honestie: therefore I will qualifie the hot love of *Gwydonius* with a colde potion: and with that she made him this waspish answere.

Why *Gwydonius*, shall the olde Proverbe be verified in thee, that the Priest forgets himselfe that ever he was a / clarke, that too much familiaritie breedes contempt. I see well if *Appelles* that cunning Painter, suffer the greasie Souter to take a view of his curious worke, hee will grow so malapert, as to meddle with his picture: if the proude Centaure *Ixion* bee bidden to the Feast of the Gods, no lesse than *Juno* her selfe will suffice him for his choice.

Set a beggar on horse backe, they saie, and hee will never alight. Extoll one of base stocke to anie degree of dignitie, and who so proud and haughtie? I speake this *Gwydonius* to thy reproofe: is thy stomacke alate waxen so queasie, that no diet will downe but my Fathers owne dish? Will no meaner mate suffice thee, unles thou match with a Prince? Is there no Ladie will like thee, but my love? Is there no courser Dame to covet, unlesse thou court unto me? Did my Father promote thee to this thou art, from the state of a begger, and wilt thou now presume to be my better? Have my lookes bene so loving, my countenance so curteous, my glaunces so full of good will, as to promise so much as thou doest presume? No: but one onelie countenance in a servile mind is too much incouragement. Doest thou thinke *Gwydonius*, that I account so meanelie of my person, as to match with a man of thy pitch? Shall I so farre cracke my credit, as to cumber my selfe with one of thy calling? Shall I so staine my state, as to stoope to thy lure? No. Where is thy coine to maintaine my countenance? Where is thy wealth to uphold my worship? Where is thy patrimonie to countervaile my personage? But put case I accepted of thy sute, doest thou thinke ever to gaine my fathers good will? Doest thou thinke it is possible to compasse his consent? Doest thou hope ever to take him in such a vaine, as he will be willing to give his verdite on thy side? No *Gwydonius*, but if he were privie to this thy presumption, hee would repaie thy follie with / too much furie, hee would unplume thee of all his feathers, that like *Æsops* Crowe thou mightest receive the reward of thy rashnesse. If therefore thou love thine owne welfare, keepe thy selfe within thy bounds, and strive not farther than thy sleeve will stretch, least in climing to high, thou catch the sorer fall.

Castania having thus sharplie shaken up my young youth *Gwydonius*, thought she had given him a sufficient cooling Card: but he no whit dismaied with this denial, like a lustie champion entered peece meale with her in this wise.

Madame (quoth he) the poore shoomaker was not blamed for viewing *Appelles* picture, but because in finding fault hee went beyond his shoe: the Centaure *Ixion* was not reproved for his familiaritie with *Juno* as he was a guest, but in that his sute tended to the sacking of her honestie: familiaritie never breeds contempt in a good minde, neither am I to be accused of that crime, for the most servile slave in *Alexandria* (I call the heavens as witnesses of my wordes) doth not with more loving duetie reverence and honour your person and parentage, than doth your poore servant *Gwydonius*. Well Madame, though my nature and nurture be such in your sight, as they bewraie my bringing up and birth to be so base, as if I meane to drawe my descent (I must as you saie) imblaze mine armes in the beggers coate: yet thus much I answere in respect of my parents, and without arrogancie, thus farre I stand on my pantuffles, that the credite I have in your fathers Court, is not coequall with the calling I have in mine owne Countrie, if I did not count it more greater credite and honour, in that I have sometime injoyed a curteous countenance of your sweete selfe since my comming. But if I were the most famous Prince in the world, I so esteeme your divine beautie and exquisite vertue, as I would thinke my selfe farre / unworthie to possesse such heavenlie perfection: which if I could obtaine, the displeasure of your Father could no whit discourage mee, his thundering threates could no whit amaze mee, no, death itselfe could never daunt my minde, were it never so despitefull. But who (saie you) can laie their love where is no desert, and where want breeds a flat deniall?

Ah *Castania*, Nature by her secret motion hath indued all creatures with some perfect qualities, to supplie that want which breedes misliking. The Moule deprived of sight hath a wonderfull hearing: the Hare beeing verie fearefull is most swift: the fish having no eares, hath most cleare eies: so though want of dignitie disgrace mee, though want of coine discountenance mee, though lacke of wealth impaires my credit, yet Nature hath given mee such a loyall and loving heart, as I hope in the perfection of that, shee hath supplied the want of all the rest: so that Madame, though I want coine, I doe not want constancie, though I have no lands, yet I lacke not loyaltie, though I want wealth, yet I want not will to end my life to doe you good, or spend my time to doe you service.

Gwydonius having thus pithelie replied, drave *Castania* into a great doubt, whether she should presentlie consent to his demand, or still drive him off with delaies, whether she should yeelde the forte at the first skirmish, or stand to the doubtfull event of battaile: at length least she should digresse from the course of womankinde, she thought best to denie that she most of all desired, and therefore then gave him this answere.

Gwydonius (quoth shee) in what state you came to my Fathers Court I knowe, what you are by descent I know not, nor I care not, and if I did, it availeth not, / but this I saie, that it is harde taking of Fowle, when the net is descried, and ill catching of fish, when the hooke is bare: impossible it is *Gwydonius*, to inferre beleefe, when no credite will bee given, and to deceive her that spieth the fetch: when the string is broken, it is harde to hit the white, and when a mans credite is called in question, perswasions can little prevaile. It is a religion amongst lovers to sweare and forsweare, to promise mountaines, and performe moulhilles, to bee ripe without and rotten within, to carrie a rustie blade in a velvet scabberde, and a silver Bell with a leaden clapper. Therefore *Gwydonius*, I had rather mistrust too soone than mislike too late, I hadde rather feare my choice than rue my chaunce, I had rather stop at the brim than at the bottome: for the Signet being set, it is too late to reclaime affection. For the love of a woman is lyke the Oyle of Flint, which being once conjeald will never bee dissolved: lyke the Diamond, which being once rubbed with the gum of a Pine tree, will never bee broken: so if I fancie anie, sith I meane not to fleete, it shall bee such a one, as I neede not repent mee.

And whereas you saie *Gwydonius*, that in despight of Fortune, Nature hath given you a loving heart, I my selfe surely did never deeme anie lesse, but thought you of the crue of those lovers that love too much, having as many Ladies as they have wits, and that is not a few: who count that everie face must have a new fancie, and if they see a thousand, they must be all viewed with a sigh, which considered *Gwydonius*, I meane not to like nor to love neither you nor anie other.

And shall then Madame (quoth hee) my merite be repaide with no meede? Shall my good wil be requited with / no gaine? shal I have in lieu of my love no liking? will you so swarve from Justice, as not to give everie one according to his desert? at the least recompence not desire with despight and heartie love, with loathing hate, for as the Poet saythe: *Quis enim succenset amanti.*

Well *Gwydonius*, as I wil not be thy privie friend, so I will not be thine open foe, and as I cannot bee so curteous as to requite thee for thy paines, so I will not be so cruell as to despight thee for thy presumption, and whereas thou cravest gaines for thy good will, I am content to remaine thy unwilling debter.

Yet Madame (quoth he) where the debte is confest, there remaineth some hope of recoverie, for though the creditor be never so unwilling to pay, the debt being due, hee shall by constraint of lawe and his owne confession (maugre his face) be forced to make restitution.

Truth *Gwydonius* (quoth she) if he commence his action in a right case, and the plea he puts in, prove not imperfect. But yet take this by the way, it is hard for that plaintiffe to recover his costes, where the defendant beeing Judge, sets downe the sentence.

Gwydonius feeling himselfe pincht to the quick with this pretie quip, made no further reply, but least his long tarying might breed suspition, wishing his mistres welfare, tooke his leave verie solemnely and sorrowfully, of *Castania*: who seeing him gone and her selfe alone, began thus to muse and meditate uppon the sharpe aunsweres she had given her best beloved *Gwydonius*.

Why *Castania*, what frantike follie hath made thee thus far to forget thy selfe? Is the bird inticed to the strappe by the shew of the nettes? is the Foxe allured to the traine by the view of the trappe? will the Mouse march under that Ensigne, where the Cat proclaimeth her / selfe Captaine? wil the sillie Dove lay her Egges in the Fawlchons neast? or is it the meanes to have him to thy frend, whome with bitter blowes thou doest rebuke? is there no other call for courtesie but crueltie? doest thou finde no fitter meanes to obtaine a reasonable request but by a rigorous repulse? or is it the nature of women to defie that outwardlie which they most desire inwardlie, to loath that in their mouth, which they love in their minde, to reject that with their hand, which they most willinglie would receive in their heart? Dost thou thinke *Castania*, to draw *Gwydonius* to thy desire, by detesting him? Doest thou thinke to allure him to thy love, by loathing him? Doest thou suppose to win him to thy will by these waspish aunsweres? No: and what, doest thou know what perill will insue of this repulse, what daunger will follow of this deniall? Is it like he will put it up patientlie? No sure, either looke to have his extreeme love tourned to extreeme hate, or that he will persist no longer in the pursute of his purpose.

Oh would to God *Gwydonius*, thou wert againe to begin thy demaund, and I to frame mine aunswere: then would I salve thy sores with sweet sirops, not with cutting corasives: then would I mittigate thy maladie with easie medicines, not with pinching plaisters: then would I comfort thee with consent, not daunt thee with denials. But alas, had I wist now comes to late, and therefore *Castania*, if thou haste made a faulte, seeke to make amends, and recompence this his injurie with most friendly courtesie.

And with that came *Melitta*, who comforting *Castania*, passed away the rest of the day in *parle*.

But *Gwydonius*, who all this while hadde a flea in his eare, was driven into a quandarie with the taunting quips of his Mistresse, fearing that although his accompts / were great, his gaines should be little, and though he made a verie long harvest, yet he should reape but a verie small croppe, thinking that under such sower speeches, a sugred minde could not be contained: yet at last entring into deeper consideration with himselfe, he fell into these tearmes.

But by the sweete (quoth hee) how should we know the sower: but by the blacke how should we know the white: he never greatlie accompteth of prosperitie which hath not bene before pinched with adversitie: which perchaunce *Castania* meanes to make me trie by experience, thinking to feede me first with bitter broaths, that hereafter daintie fare may more delight mee: to daunt mee with the raging stormes of deniall, that the calme of her consent may more content mee: to make mee tast the bitter pills of annoie, that hereafter I maie enjoie the greater joye: for the chilling colde of winter makes the sprowting spring time seeme farre more pleasant, the parching heate of Summer, makes the coole shade more delightfull, and the frowning lookes of *Castania*, will make her smiling countenaunce seeme more cheerefull. Then cease *Gwydonius*, to pursue thy sute with endlesse paine, either to enjoy her curtesie, or tast of her crueltie, to thy great happinesse or extreeme heavinesse.

Gwydonius thus like a valiant champion, never amazed with

anie chip of misfortune, never feared to give the assault for all
the first repulse, but onely sought opportunitie how he might
in close combat once againe incounter with *Castania*, vowing
either to return with some signe of victory, or else to put lim
and life in hazard. But fortune meaning pleasantlie to sport
with this young novice, wold never minister such fit occasion,
that he might have solitarie accesse to his goddes, for *Castania* of
pretended purpose / so warelie avoided his companie, and with
such disdaineful lookes so rejected his dutie as *Gwydonius* was
constrained to seeke his course by a new compasse, delyvering
unto one of her maides, a friendlie letter, to this effect.

Disdained Gwydonius to his desired Castania, health.

Who so tasteth (Madame *Castania*) of the River *Licos* in
India, feeleth such a continuall flame to frye and fret his in-
trayles, as it is more torture than to bee tormented with the
hellish furies, and this griefe can never be redressed, but with
drinking the bloud of his deerest frend. And as he that is
venomed by the *Phalanga*, feeleth such painefull passions, as
he runneth mad, and is onely cured [by] the meanes of most
harmonious Musicke: so Madame, the furious heate of fancie,
dooth so scorch and scale my haplesse heart, and doth perplexe
mee with such hellish pangues, as death it selfe were thrice
more desired, than thus to drive my dayes in dolour. And I
have so greedely swallowed up the sugred poyson of your divine
beautie, as through the extremitie of pinching griefe, which so
direfullie distresseth mee, I rest as one distracte from his senses,
not possible to obtaine a cure for this my calamitie, unlesse
with the deaw of mutuall affection you mittigate my maladie,
or with the pleasant harmonie of your Musicall consent, you
appease my miserie.

Sith then madam, my care proceedeth from your beautie,
let my sore be cured by your bountie, sith the perfection of
your person hath wrought my bane, let the effect of your
courtesie procure my blisse, and reject him not so / rigorously
which respecteth you so reverently: loath him not so hatefully,
which loveth you so heartelie: nor repaie not his dutifull amitie,
with such deadlie enmitie. The pike fatallie prosecuteth the
fish *Mugra*, as his mortall foe, and yet seeing him snared on the
fishers hooke, he speedelie shreddeth the line in sunder, to
deliver him: the Snake most deadlie detesteth the field-mouse,
and yet shee heapeth up in her hole store of provision to prevent

her enimies penurie: and shall then madame, your crueltie so farre exceede these sencelesse creatures? shall your rigour be so voide of reason, as to requite your friend with paine, when they repaie their foes with pleasure? to drive your friends into distresse, when they redeeme their foes from daunger? no, madame, I hope you will not countervaile my constancie with such discurtesie, nor so reckleslie regard your poore *Gwydonius,* whose love and loyaltie is so great, that as the stones which are founde in the river *Lyncestis,* the lower the winde bloweth, and the deeper they are drencht in the water, the more they burne and blaze: so the more you seeke to coole my fancie with disdaine, the more my affection is kindled with desire: the more you loath, the more I like: the greater dispaire you drive me into by denialls, the greater hope (incouraged by constancie) I have to obtaine my request: in which fervent affection, I meane to remaine without chaunge, craving in liewe of this my loyaltie, that you will speedelie sende the messenger of present consolation, to him which pineth awaie, and is yours onelie, and ever.

Still in hope, Gwydonius.

Castania, having received this letter from her assured friend *Gwydonius,* although she perceived by the contents / that his love was not counterfait, but constant: not light, but loiall: not floting, but faithfull: and that she should not finde him immutable in prosperitie, which was so permanent in adversitie. Yet (whether it were for coinesse in consent, or charinesse of choise I know not) she once againe thought to sound him more deeper, to keepe out still the flagge of defiaunce, and to spende one Vollee of shot in the face of her enimie, to see if a hot skirmish would make him flie the fielde. And if like a valiant souldier he did manfullie march on, and not refuse the brunt of the battaile, she would then resigne the fort of her freedome into his hands, and yeeld up the bulwarke of her breast, which so long he had battered, that triumphantlie he might sette up *Trophees* in signe of a most victorious conquest. To put therefore the matter in question, she returned him this answere.

Castania to Gwydonius, which hopeth in vaine, health.

Maister *Gwydonius,* your letter being more hastelie received then heartelie read, I perceive by the contents, that you are stil perplexed with your pen-sick passions, and that your disease is incurable, for if your paines may be appeased, or your maladie mittigated by no medicine, but by my means, you are like either to pay your due unto death, or still to linger in distresse. My cunning is to smal to enterprise the composition of anie secrete simples, and my calling to great to become a Phisition to such a paltering patient, so that I neither can nor wil cure another mans harme by mine owne mishap. To love him whome I cannot like, were but to wreast against mine owne will, to flatter him whome I meane not to fancie, is but a meere tricke of extreame follie.

What the cause is *Gwydonius*, that thy good will reaps so small gaine, and that so rigorouslie I repaie thy love with hate, I know not, unlesse the constellation of the Starres by some secrete influence have so appointed it in the calculation of our nativitie. But this I am sure, that as no Serpent can abide the smell of a harts horne, as the Panther escheweth the companie of the Ownce, as the Vulture is mortal enimie to the Eele, and as it is impossible to hatch up a Swanne in an Eagles neast, to temper Oile and Pitch together in one vessel, to mixe the bloud of a Lion and a Woolfe, in one bowle, and to procure amitie betweene the Fawlcon called *Tilo*, and the Foxe, so hard is it to procure me by ruthful request to be thy friend, which am by instinct of nature thy protested foe, and as hard to winne me to thy wife, who so little likes of thy love, that the verie remembrance of thy person makes me fal into most hatefull passions. Cease then *Gwydonius*, to condempne me of crueltie, and leave off at last to appeale to my curtesie, for thou shalt alwaies bee sure to feede the one, and never to finde the other. Yet least thou shouldest accuse me of ingratitude, though I cannot inwardlie mittigate thy miserie, yet I will outwardlie teach thee to applie such plaisters (as if the experience of them prove true) shall greatlie appease thy paine. *Plinie Gwydonius* reporteth, that he which drinketh of the River *Averna*, cooleth and mortifieth his affections, but if the water be toucht by anie meanes before it be drunk, the vertue thereof is of no value. He that weareth the feathers of the Birde *Ezalon* about him, shall ever bee fortunate in his love, but if they be not pulde when the Sunne is eclipsed, they are of no force: and to conclude, there is nothing that sooner driveth awaie amorous conceits, then to rub the temples of thy head with the sweat of an / Asse, which if you canne performe it, as no doubt you may put it in practise, I hope you shall be redressed from your intollerable griefe, and I released from such an importunate sute.

Forced by the destinies still
to denie thee, Castania.

Gwydonius having viewed and reviewed over this letter, seeing the rigorous resolution of his mistres, could by no meanes be removed, and that a most severe sentence was pronounced against him by a most injurious Judge, was driven into a doubt whether he should still with plaints sue for pittie, or else blasphemously exclaim against her brutish crueltie, whether he should bewraye his parents and parentage to the Duke and her, or still stand to the doubtfull chaunce of Fortune, to pursue his purpose still with plaints: her hellish crueltie perswaded him, to blaspheme against her: the sinceritie of his love, would not let him to bewray his birth: diverse daungers might insue: to stande to the chaunce of Fortune, was still to hazard without hope: combred thus with divers cogitations, at last he determined to breake up the batterie, and to laie too an invincible hold, but to returne with as much speede as might bee to his Father *Clerophontes* Court, there by absence to mittigate the maladie which so grievouslie molested him: yet he thought before his departure to give her a friendlie farewel, that might both confirme his constancie, and contempne her crueltie: which he framed to this effect.

Gwydonius to Castania, prosperous successe in all her affaires. /

I meane not, most mercilesse mistresse, any longer to sue for mercie, nor with pittifull plaints to trouble your patience, sith to stirre that which the Starres hath staied, is to strive against the streame, and to force that which the fates have framed, is to covet to be counted a foole, but as one whome fortune meanes to make a myrrour of miserie, and over whome *Venus* her selfe meanes to vaunt as of a most haplesse vassal, I sorrowfully send you this fainting farewell, as a faithfull token of my fervent affection: for seing neither my person can please, nor my living like you, nor my base calling content you, nor I my selfe reape anie guerdon for my good will, to avoid remembrance of these passions, which renue my pains, and to asswage the rigour of my raging love, I purpose as speedelie as winde and weather wil permit me, to abandon the place of your abode: not incensed by furie, as one in despight, but inforced by the rage of fancie to deprive my selfe of all delight, either to consume in solitarie cares without compassion, or by absence to mittigate some part of my martirdome: for to hope stil, I see is but to heap wo upon wretchednesse, and care upon calamitie.

Yet madame thus much I say, that *Dido* Queene of *Carthage* loved *Aeneas*, a banished exile, and a stragling stranger. *Euphinia* daughter to the king of *Corinth*, and heire apparent to his crowne, who for her feature was famous throughout all the East countries, vouchsafed to applie a soveraigne plaister to the furious passions of *Acharisto*, her fathers bondman. The dutchesse of *Malphey* chose for her husband her servant *Ulrico*: and *Venus*, who for her surpassing beautie, was canonized for a Goddesse, disdained not the love of limping *Vulcan*. They madame, respected the man, and not their money, their wills, and nor their wealth, their love, not their livings: their constancie, not their coine: their person, not their parentage: and the inward vertue, not the outward value. But you are so addicted to / the opinion of *Danae*, that unlesse *Jupiter* himself be shrouded in your lappe, under the shape of a shower of golde, he shall have the repulse, for all his deitie: seeing then it is not in my poore power, either to performe or practise it, I cease off to seake for impossibilities: promising in what coast or Countrie so ever I shall remaine, to have my heart whollie dedicated to your divine beautie and vertue, both by dutie and service, and so commending my health to the Gods, I bid you farewell.

> *Yours while he is Gwydonius,*
> *sans espoier.*

Castania having received this Letter from *Gwydonius*, perceiving the constant minde of the yong Gentleman, that these his protestations were not vanitie, but veritie: not trifling, but troth: no signes of fleeting fancie, but of a firme affection: standing a while in a dump, at last she fell into this discourse.

I now (quoth she) both see and trie by experience, that there is no fish so fickle, but will come to the baite: no Doe so wilde, but will stande at the gaze: no Hauke so haggard, but will stoope at the lure: no Niesse so ramage, but will be reclaimed to the Lunes: no fruit so fine, but the Caterpillar will consume it: no Adamant so hard but will yeelde to the File: no mettal so strong, but will bend to the stampe: no maide so free, but Love will bring her to bondage and thraldome. And doe I call it bondage, fond foole, to bee bound unto beautie? is it slaverie to be subject unto vertue? is it thraldome to live in league with him who will like mee in my youth, and love mee in my age, in whome I shall finde nothing but pleasure and contentation: who will be the haven of my happinesse, wherein I may rest: and the port of my prosperitie, wherein I may be safe harboured from the tempests / of froward fortune, and shroud mee from the bitter blasts of bale? Shall I repent mee sith my bargaine is good, or complaine of the losse of libertie, sith I have a change for farre more worthie chaffer? Shall I grudge when the gods are agreed, or defer it, when the destinies drive it: or froune at it, sith fortune frames it? No, *Gwydonius* is my Saint, and him will I serve, he is my joye, and him will I injoye. He hath laide the siege, and he shall sacke the citie, he hath abode the batterie, and he shall have the bulwarke of my breast: he hath fought the combat, and he shall be victor in the conquest. For I cannot be so unnaturall, to reward his love with loathing: so without reason, to defraude him of his right: so divellish for his deepe desire, to give him a dolefull dish of dispaire. No, no, I have setteled with my selfe, that if ever I marrie, *Gwydonius* shall bee the man I will match with. And therefore as I have driven him with delayes, and fed him with follie, so now I will send him a setteled aunswere of my good will and favor, as I have given him cutting corasives, so I will send him confects of comfort. As I have bene fearefull to shew my liking for the better tryall, so now I will be bolde to shew my love in token of a better trust, and with that she wrote him a Letter to this effect.

Castania to Gwydonius, wishing him such happie successe, as either fortune or the fates can allow him

Plato Gwydonius, being demanded why he wold never condescend to the requests of his most deerest friends without great entreaty and long sute, answered, that things lightly granted (though never so costly) are smally accounted off: which saying *Gwydonius,* I take as a sufficient excuse for my folly: for my straightnes in words was no strangnes in minde, / my bitter speeches were written with my hand, not wrought with my heart, my deniall was onelie for the better triall, and those rigorous repulses were either to rip up thy fained fancie, or fervent affection: for if thou hadst retired at the first foile I would have thought thy fancie but a flash, readie to bee quenched with the least misling deaw of misfortune. But since thou hast kept thy course so rightlie by thy compasse, amidst most dangerous rockes, and hast stoode to thy tackling against all the blustering blasts of fortune. Assure thy selfe in lieu of this thy love, thou hast not heeretofore found me so disdainfull, as hereafter thou shalt finde me dutifull, neither did I ever reject thee so currishlie, as I will accept thee curteouslie, being readie to restore the injurie I have offred thee, with anie curtesie that thou maist either honestlie require, or I justlie affoord. But alasse *Gwydonius*, what curtesie shall I ever be able to shew thee, that may countervaile thy kindnesse? How entirely shal I love thee to requite thy loialtie? What dutie can be a due recompence to this thy good will: yea, if by anie meanes I can quit this thy love, I never doubt to be deemed ungratefull while I live. Thy worthie constancie (*Gwydonius*) hath won the castle which many have besieged, and thou hast obtained that which diverse have sought to gain: yet it is not the shape of thy beautie, but the hope of thy loialtie, which entiseth me, not thy faire face, but thy faithfull heart: not thy comelie countenance, but thy modest curtesie, not thy wordes, but thy vertues: not thy wealth, but thy wit: for she that builds her fancie upon such fading subjects, tieth her love to the inconstant wheele of fortune. And what though the Duke my father be incensed against me, for making (in his minde) so carelesse a choice? What care I for his friendship, so I have thy favour: let him fret, let my friends frowne, let livings be lost, hap what hap will, no misling showers of mischance, no / boysterous blasts of adversitie, no terrible tempeste of disaster fortune, shall make my constant minde in any respect to move: no torments, no travaile, no care, no calamitie, no penurie, no povertie, no, onelie the losse of life, shall diminish my love: in liew whereof remaine thou but constant, and in pledge of my protested good will, have heere my heart and hande, to be thine in dust and ashes.

> *Thine, though the Gods say no:*
>
> *Castania.*

This Letter being most luckelie delivered into the hands of *Gwydonius*, I leave you to judge Gentlemen into what a quandarie this young youth was brought, to see such a sodaine chaunge, and so happie a chaunce, as to have his hellish bale requited with heavenlie blisse, his despightfull annoy, with delightfull joye: his heavinesse with happinesse, and doubtfull despaire tourned to assured hope: to see Fortune which of late defied him as a foe, now to imbrace him as a friend, and to wil that he did wish: to see his mistresse crueltie tourned to curtesie, her disdaine to desire, her bitter pilles to sugered potions, her stormie repulses to calme consent, and her contemptuous protestations, to most constant promises. For if the carefull

captive, who by the doome of the Judge expecteth eache houre
to dye, rejoyceth when he heareth his pardon pronounced, no
doubt *Gwydonius* joye could be no lesse, sith deniall was his
death, and consent the conserve to heale his woundes: the
greater care, the greater joy, the more paine, the greater
pleasure, the more hellish miserie, the more heavenlie felicitie.
Yea, *Gwydonius* was driven into such an extasie for joye, that
he was in doubt, whether this letter was preferred to him / in
deede, or presented to him in a vision, whether hee were wrapt
into a Traunce, or ravished with some drowsie slumber: but at
last perceiving it to be no fained fantasie, such a deepe desire
inforced his affection, as hee thought everie moment a month,
everie houre a yeare, everie day a thousand, untill he might
freelie injoye the presence and sight of his love and Ladie
Castania. Fortune meaning to advance him to the toppe of
her inconstant wheele, brought it so to passe, that before the
weeke was ended, he spied *Castania* walking alone in the garden:
which sodaine sight so revived his sences, that without any
dread or doubt, he manfullie marcht on towards her, and was
as hastelie and hartelie incountred by *Castania*: who embracing
Gwydonius in her armes, welcommed him with this salutation.

As the Whale (*Gwydonius*) maketh alwaies signe of great
joye at the sight of the fishe called *Talpa Marina*, as the Hinde
greatlie delighteth to see the Leopard, as the Lion fawneth at
the view of the Unicorne, and as he which drinketh of the
Fountaine *Hipenis* in *Scithia*, feeleth his mind so drowned in
delight, that no griefe though never so great, is able to assuage
it: so *Gwydonius* I conceive such surpassing pleasure in thy
presence, and such heavenlie felicitie in the sight of thy perfection, that no miserie though never so monstrous, is able to
amaze mee, no dolour though never so direfull, is able to daunt
mee, nor no mishap though never so perillous, is able to make
mee sinke in sorrow, as long as I injoy thy presence, which I
count a soveraine preservative against all carefull calamities.
That as he which tasteth of the hearbe *Hyacinthus* is never
combred with care, and as he that weareth the stone *Agathes*
about him, is surelie defenced against all insuing sorrowes, so
injoying the sight of thy seemly selfe, and feeding / mine eyes
with the forme of thy feature, I think my selfe sufficiently
shrowded against all the tempestuous showers of sinister fortune.
And to prove these my promises to be no fained vanities but
faithfull veritie, I commit my selfe, my staye, and state, into
thy hands, to dispose of mee at thy pleasure, wishing rather

to live with thee in most distressed penurie, than to linger heere in most fortunate prosperitie.

Gwydonius listening attentivelie to this sugred harmonie, was so ravished with the sight of her sweete face, and so rapt into a traunce with the contemplation of her beautie, that as the Lyon tasting of the gumme Arabicke becommeth senselesse, as the Bull by brousing on the barke of a Juniper tree falleth a sleepe, as the Camill standeth astonished at the sight of a Rat: so *Gwydonius* seeing in his armes the Saint whome in heart he did honour, and imbracing the Goddesse whome with most deepe devotion he did adore, was so amazed, that he was not able to utter one worde, as witnesse of his happinesse: untill at last gathering his wits together, he began thus to replie.

Castania (quoth hee) it is an axiome in Philosophie, that the colour joyned hard to the sighte, hindereth the sence, the flower putte into the nose-thrill, stoppeth the smelling: the Wine vessell being full, lettes passe no Wine, though never so well vented: the water-pot beeing filled to the brimme, yeelds foorth no licour, though having a thousand holes: so where the minde is surcharged with overmuch joy, or to much pleasure, ther the tongue is both tied, and the sences so restrained, that the heart is neither able to conceive the joye, nor the tongue able to expresse the pleasure. Which *Castania* I now speake / by proofe, and know by experience, for I am so drowned in delight by injoying that princely Jemme, which I esteeme the rarest and richest Jewell, not onelie in *Alexandria*, but in all the worlde, and so puffed up in pleasure by thy divine presence. Yea, thy faithfull and unfained affection, the promise of thy constancie, and the hope of thy loyaltie, the report of thy chastitie, and the renowme of thy modestie, the force of thy beautie, and the fame of thy vertue. But above all, thy prodigall bountie, in bestowing these heavenlie perfections on thy poore *Gwydonius*, being by person and parentage most unworthie to possesse them, so surchargeth my sillie heart with excessive joye, that my tongue not being able in part to expresse the extreame pleasure of my minde, I am with *Philistion* the Comicall Poet, constrained by silence to unfold that affection, which in words, the filed phrase of *Demosthenes*, were not able to decipher. But this assure thy selfe *Castania*, that if *Juno* would advance mee to bee Monarch of the world, if *Pallas* would preferre mee to exceede hautie *Hercules* in valour, if *Venus* would present mee with some princelie peece of heavenlie perfection, yet would I not so gladlie receive their proffers, as I doe gratefullie accept the promise of thy love and loyaltie. No, I accompt the treasure of *Crœsus* but trash, in respect of the guerdon of thy good will: I accompt the fortune of *Cæsar* but follie, respecting the fruites of thy favor: I esteeme the dignities of *Priamus* as dregs, in respect of thy divine perfection. Yea, *Castania*, I am so snared with thy beautie, and so intangled in the trap of thy bountie, as I shall never leave to love thee, nor ever beginne to like anie other.

It is easie *Gwydonius* (quoth *Castania*) to purchase credite, where the partie is alreadie perswaded, and to infer beleefe, wher every word is counted an Oracle: there / fore omitting these frivolous protestations, thus much I say touching the purpose. *Cecillius Metellus* was wont to say, that as it was necessar[i]e that olde men should be grave in counsaile, so it was expedient yong men should be secret in love, and therefore when the contract was made between *Fulvius* and his daughter, he sealed up their lippes with his signet, meaning that to violate the secret conference of lovers, was to commit a second sacriledge. I speake thus *Gwydonius*, as one carefull of thy staye and my state: for if *Orlanio* my father should but once heare of our love, or suspect our liking, it would breede thy mishap and my miserie: yea, no doubt hee would speedelie prevent our pretence, which would bee thy care and my calamitie. Dispose our affaires at thy pleasure, but discover not our purpose: if thou hast won the castell, vaunt not of the conquest: if thou hast made a good market, bragge not of thy gaines: least by boasting of thy bootie, thou loose thy praie, and be thought a pratler. And *Gwydonius* above all men beware of *Valericus*, least under the shape of a friend, he prove in time thy mortall foe, least his fained amitie prove faithlesse enmitie: that in trusting too much without triall, thou finde not treason: and then though thou repent, yet had I wist commeth too late, and so thou wish thou hadst never loved, and I never liked.

Tush *Castania* (quoth *Gwydonius*) he that is afraide to venter on the Bucke, because he is tapisht in the briers, shall never have hunters hap, and he that puttes his doubt in love for everie chaunce, shall never have lovers lucke. Cannot the Cat catch Mice, without she have a bell hanging at her eare? Cannot the Hobbie seaze on his praie, but he must check? Cannot the Spaniell retrive the Partridge, but he must quest? / And cannot we deale so warilie but all the world must wonder at it? Yes, it is a subtile Bird that breedes among the aerin of Hawkes, and a shifting sheepe that lambes in the Foxes den, and he shall looke narrowlie that spies mee halting. Let *Orlanio* not onelie weigh our workes, but our wordes, and let *Valericus* both deeme our deedes and devine our thoughtes, and yet I hope wee will deale so secretlie in our affaires, as neither the one shall have cause to suspect our familiaritie, nor the other to detect our affection. And therefore *Castania*, least (if wee bee spied) the time and place give occasion of mistrust, I will leave you as I found you, and so farewell.

Well, these two lovers placed thus by fortune in the pallace of earthlie prosperitie, floated so securelie in the streames of blisse, as they thought no chippes of mischance might change their present happinesse to future heavinesse, as long as their privie contract was kept so secret to themselves. But as they which cannot see fire in the strawe are stone blind: so he that cannot see the flame of fancie is a foole. It is harde to cover smoake, but more harde to conceale love, which these two lovers in tract of time tried true. Who as closelie as they kept their cloake, yet it was most easie to espie the lining: for fancie secretlie restrained, is like the sparke covered with ashes, which at length bursteth into a great flame. For there passed betweene *Gwydonius* [and *Castania*] such amorous glaunces, such loving lookes, such curteous congies, such countenances, and such friendlie familiaritie, such often meetinges, such open greetinges, such sighes, such sobbes, and such strange passions, as not onelie *Valericus*, but all the Court (though they poore soules thought to daunce in a Net and not bee seene) / perceived how entirelie they loved and liked eache other. Which as it dyd not displease many which loved *Gwydonius* as their friend, so it greatlie despighted *Valericus* which was his foe, to see one of small countenance preferred before one of his calling: that *Gwydonius* should winne the bulwarke which he so long had battered: that he pitching the field, another should obtaine the conquest: that he laying the siege, another shoulde vaunt of the victorie: that while he beate the bush, another should catch the birds: and that the meede of his merite, should be given to one of small desert. Being cumbered with these cholerike cogitations, and perplexed with these despightfull passions, inflamed with wrathfull furie, he fell into these tearmes.

O Gods (quoth hee) what curtesie is there to bee found in such Kites of *Cræsus* kinde? Or what constancie is there to be hoped for in such daintie disdaining Dames? Whose wavering willes and staylesse wits, both waxe and wane with the Moone, whose lunatike mindes chaunge with everie sodaine motion: yea, whose lightnesse and lewdnesse is such, as they delyght with the Raven to feede on the moste loathsome flesh, with the shee Wolfe to choose the foulest make, with *Æsops* Cocke to prefer the Barlie Corne before a most precious Pearle, and with *Glaucus* to make a change of his golden armour for brasen Harnesse.

Did not *Euphinia* forsake most famous Princes, and embrace a most infamous bondslave? Did not *Sirithia* the Princesse of *Denmarke* reject most princelie Potentates, and at last accepte a poore peasant? Yea, dydde not *Venus* her selfe with the Beetle disdaine / all daie to light on the most fragrant flowers, and at night vouchsafeth to lodge in a filthie cow-sheard: I meane, did not refuse the renowned Gods, and choose a most deformed Smith?

Why, but *Valericus*, is it fancie that forceth them in this follie? Doth love leade them? Do the destinies drive them? Doth beautie allure them? Is it their countenance that constraineth them? No, they are clownes: Is it their person or parentage that perswadeth them? No, they are pesants. But like craftie *Calipsos*, they thinke by these unequall matches to rule the roast after their owne diet, to be soveraigne mistres of their owne mindes, with *Venus* to let *Vulcan* possesse the tree, and *Mars* injoy the fruit, to have their husbands feede the sheepe, and some other reape the fleece: under the shadowe of his head, doe defend themselves from such heate as would otherwise greatlie scorch their credite, to make him followe the bent of their bowe, although he set the Cuckoldes end up ward. It is a simple cloake that cannot cover one from a shower of raine, and a seelie husband that is not able to father that another doth beget. But to see howe these gallant girles if they like not the partie, what shew of shamefastnesse they will make, howe they will vale their face with the visour of virginitie, how they will cloake themselves with the coulour of continencie, how charie they will be of their chastitie: whereas if they fancie, who so loose of their lippes, and free of their flesh as they? But *Valericus*, why doest thou thus reckleslie raile and rage against womankinde? It is not *Castania* that thus crosseth thee with care, but *Gwydonius* that breedeth thy griefe. It is not she that inferreth thy sore, but he that procureth thy sicknesse. She is not the meanes of thy maladie, but hee the hinderer of thy medicine. She is not the worker of thy woe, but he is the sower / of thy sorrow. And shall he be puffed up with prosperitie, and I pressed downe with miserie? Shal he swim in wealth, and I sinke in want? Shall he bath in blisse, and I waile in woe? Shall he be pampered up with pleasure, and I pinde awaie with penurie? No, I will either spoile him, or spill my selfe, in despite of the fates and fortune.

While thus *Valericus* sought opportunitie to revenge his wrath uppon guiltlesse *Gwydonius,* Fortune minding to bewraie her immutabilitie, brought it so to passe, that whereas *Orlanio* was accustomed to paie a yeerelie tribute to the Duke of *Metelyne,* which surmounted to the sum of thirtie thousand Duckets, either wilfullie or wittinglie he with-held this debt, which *Clerophontes* claimed as his due, insomuch that beeing demanded by embassage for the paiment of this tribute, hee flatlie answered, that he would not from hence forth disburse one denier, and he was sorie that in paying it heeretofore he proved himselfe such a foole. Whereupon *Clerophontes* being fraught with raging furie, was so incensed against *Orlanio,* that taking counsaile of his nobilitie, hee determined with as much speede as might bee, to wage battaile against him, and to obtaine that by constraint, which he denied him of curtesie. As thus he was musing with himselfe whom he should appoint Captaine generall of his armie, because hee meant not in proper person to abide the hazard of the battaile, the remembrance of his sonne *Gwydonius* came into his minde, which not onelie amazed him, but so molested him, as he was driven into most distressed dolour: now hee called to minde his mercilesse crueltie in correcting his faults, and his moodlesse rigour in rebuking his follie: now hee bewailed his long absence, and wished his speedie presence: yea, he was so diverslie perplexed, as he began thus dolorous / lie to discourse with himselfe.

Alasse (quoth he) now I see the saying of *Cicero* to bee true, that who so wilfullie perverteth the lawes of nature, seemeth to proclaime himselfe an enimie to the Gods, for that Nature never framed anie thing amisse: wherein I have most grievouslie offended: For in beastlie rage I have surpassed the brute beastes, and in crueltie, the senselesse creatures: I have beene more devoide of pittie than the Fowles of the aire, and more un-naturall than the Fishes of the sea. The Birde called *Apis Indica,* seeing the venimous Viper readie to devour her yong ones in the neast, presenteth her selfe to death, to preserve them from destruction. The Eagle is so carefull over her young, that if it happe by her default one of them doe perish,

shee willinglie woundeth her selfe in many places with her
owne beake. The Lion so lovinglie fostereth up her Whelpes,
that shee never tasteth of the praie untill they bee fullie satisfied.
The Foxe is so carefull over her cubbes, that shee willinglie
falleth into the Hunters handes to defend her young from
harme. But I vilde wretch (as though I had drunke of the
River *Lincestis* in *Bohemia*, which presentlie turneth whatsoever it toucheth into stones). In stead of friendlie courtesie
I have abused mine owne sonne with frowning crueltie, the
fatherlie affection I have shewed him, hath beene raging furie:
yea, my rigorous Nature, naye rather my unnaturall rage hath
beene such towardes him, as hee liveth a bannished exile in a
straunge Countrie, perhappes pinched with penurie, oppressed
with povertie, wandering in the wilde Desartes, in daunger of
devouring, in perill of spoyling, afflicted not onelie with the
maladie of the bodie, but the miserie of the minde: so that no
doubt hee wisheth that / I had never bene Father to such a
sonne, or he never sonne to such a Father.

Alasse what joy can I now injoy when I want my onelie
joye? What comfort can I have to see my childe in calamitie?
What pleasure can I take while hee toyleth in penurie, who
nowe in mine age should bee the staffe whereon to staie, that
by his valiant courage and warlike prowesse (wherewith from
his infancie hee hath beene indewed) might defend mee from
mine enimies, and revenge mee of my foes. But alasse I lament
too late, the calme commeth out of time, when the Shippe
alreadie hath suffered shipwracke, and these pittifull plaintes
little prevaile, where the Patient is alreadie pushed into perill.
No, no, my rage hath beene too greate to heare of his hastie
returne, my perverse furie hath beene such, as hee dare not
abide my presence: and surelie my sorrowe is too greate ever
to be salved.

And with that *Clerophontes* start up, minding to revenge
these his cholerike cogitations by bloudie battaile upon the
confines of *Alexandria*, and therefore in great hast mustered
all his men, made great provisions for the warre, and caused
his Navie to bee rigged, for that hee meant to conveie his armie
by sea into *Alexandria*.

While thus there was no worde through the whole Dukedome
of *Metelyne* but warre, warre and no newes but of the cruell
conflict that shoulde insue betweene the two Dukes. Certaine
Merchants of *Alexandria*, which then roade in the Haven, durst
not goe a shoare to sell their Commodities, but as fast as winde

and weather would serve them, highed them out of the harbour, and coasted speedelie into their owne Countrie: where they no sooner arived, but they made reporte thereof to *Orlanio*, who driven into a dumpe with this noisome / newes, whether he doubted of the puisant power of *Clerophontes*, who was such a worthie warriour, and in battaile so bolde, that no man durst abide him, or whether he feared his owne force was not able to resist the furie of his raging enimie. He presentlie summoned all his Lordes to a Parliament, where after some conference, it was concluded that *Thersandro* should bee sent Embassadour to *Metelyne* to *parle* of peace with *Clerophontes*: which determination was no whit deferred, but with as much speede as might be, the Barke wherein he should passe was provided, the charge of the Embassage was given him, and he accompanied with a traine of brave Gentlemen, departed.

But if this newes was dolefull to *Orlanio*, no doubt it was death it selfe to *Gwydonius*, who hearing that his Father would bend his force against the place, wherein hee was, sawe all possibilitie taken awaie from obtayning his purpose: for hee feared death if hee were knowen to *Orlanio*, and hee doubted despightfull hate at the least, if he bewraide himselfe to *Castania*. Which double dolour so distressed him, as he felt himselfe diverslie perplexed with dumpish passions: his mirth was turned to mourning, his pleasant conceites, to painfull cogitations: his wanton toies, to wailing thoughtes: now he abandoned all good companie, and delighted onelie in solytarie life, the wildsome woods were his wished walkes, and the secret shades the covert he chieflie courted. In fine, he seemed rather a *Tymon* of *Athens* than a Gentleman of *Alexandria*, so that all the Court mervailed at this so sodaine a chaunge, but especiallie *Castania*, who conjecturing his dolefull heart by his drousie lookes, was astonished at this his strange state, casting in her minde whether she had given him anie cause of this care, or whether by her occasion, he was crossed with this calamitie. But alas poore soule, howsoever she aimed she mist the marke, for / *Gwydonius* felt his disease so secret, as he knew none could but himself devine the cause of his maladie, which no doubt was such, that it would have inferred present death, if he hadde not hoped for some happie newes by *Thersandro*.

Who no sooner luckely arived at *Metelyne*, but *Clerophontes* was certified that the Dukes sonne of *Alexandria* was come to impart with his grace some waightie matters of importaunce. Now at this instant when the message was brought him, his

Daughter *Lewcippa* was by, who (as the nature of women is, desirous to see and bee seene) thought she should both heare the *parle*, and view the person of this young Embassadour, and therefore found fish on her fingers, that she might staye still in the chamber of presence: whether presently *Thersandro* was sent for: who curteously and curiously dooing his obeysance to the Duke, delivered his Embassage in this manner.

Whereas (right worthie sir) *Orlanio*, the Duke of *Alexandria*, more unwittingly then wilfullie denied certaine tribute, which hee confesseth both hee and his predecessours have paide to you and your auncestours.   Hearing that hereupon your grace meaneth rather to wage battaile, then to loose any part of your due, although he feareth not your force, as one able every way to withstand it, nor passeth of your puissaunce, as a Potentate sufficient to resist your power.   Yet, the care hee hath of his subjects safetie, and the love he hath to preserve the life of his commons, the regard he hath to paye and performe that which conscience and custome requireth: and lastly, meaning with *Tully, Iniquissimam pacem justissimo bello anteponere.* He hath sent mee both to sue for conditions of peace, and to paye the tribute, which if your grace shall refuse, of force he must put his hope / in the hazard of Fortune.

Thersandro havinge thus pithelie performed his charge, *Clerophontes* tolde him that uppon a sodaine he would not dispatch so waightie a matter: but meant first both to consult and take counsaile of his Nobles: which done, within three dayes hee shoulde have an aunswere.   In the meane time hee commaunded *Lucianus* the Steward of his house, verie courteouslie to entreate both *Thersandro* and his traine, and to feast them with such sumptuous fare, as they might have cause most highlie to extoll his magnificence.

But leaving *Clerophontes*, to consult with his learned counsailours, and *Thersandro* to accompanie with the lustie Courtiers, againe to *Lewcippa*, who while this young youth was telling of his tale, never markte the matter, but the man: nor regarded not the *parle*, but respected the person: never noted the contentes, but viewed his countenaunce: In such sort, that she was so scorched with the fire of fancie, and so scalded with the flame of affection, so bewitched with his beautie, and so inveigled with his bountie, as hee was the onely man that made her checke at the praie, bate at the Lure, and willinglie yeelde to the first assault of fancie.   And on the other side, Fortune so favoured, that *Thersandro* printing in his heart the perfection of *Lewcippas* person, felt his freedome so fettered by the view of her heavenlie face, and so snared in the beames of her amorous glaunces, that hee wisht that either this discention had never growen, or that hee hadde not beene the deliverer of the message: for hee felte his heart alreadie so overgrowen with good will, towards this young Princesse, as no salve but her selfe was able to mittigate his sorrow, no medicine but her courtesie was able to cure his / calamitie: and hee thought to preferre his sute to his professed foe, was follie: to linger still in love, was death and miserie: to seeke for helpe at her handes, neither would the present state permitte him, nor time suffer him to prosecute his purpose: daunted with these diverse doubts, to avoyde the melancholike motions that molested his minde, hee presentlie went from his lodging to the Court, that by companie he might drive away these dumpes: where hee found in the great chamber diverse Ladies and gentlewomen, passing awaye the time in pleasaunt *parle*: amongst whome was that pearelesse Paragon, princely *Lewcippa*: who (after due reverence done to the Gentle-women in generall) was singled out by *Thersandro*, and courted in this wise.

Madame (quoth hee) if any creature hath just occasion to accuse either nature or the gods of injustice, man onelie hath the greatest cause to make this complaint: for there is none either so deprived of reason, so devoide of sense, which by some naturall instinct doth not skilfully presage of perills before they come, and warily prevent ere they be past.

The Goates of *Lybia*, know certainlie when the Canicular daies beeginne, wherein commonlye they fall blinde, and therefore by eating the hearbe *Polopodium*, they providentlie prevent their disease.   When the Lion leaveth his Lawnes, and raungeth in forraine Deserts, hee alwaies foresheweth a drought.   When the Fish called *Uranascapos* sinketh downe to the bottome of the Sea, hee beewrayeth great tempestes to bee imminent.   But man is so farre from this secret foresight, that not onely he cannot devine of these ensuing daungers, but rather wilfully or willing: pusheth himselfe into most manifest perills, which Madame, I speake, as / feeling my selfe distressed with this want.   For if I had bene indued with this sacred prescience, perfectly to presage of ensuing perills, I had not bene crossed with such cares as I am like to incurre, nor hadde cause to repent this my present arivall.   But sith lacke of such skill hath

procured my losse, and that when the hurt is hadde it is too late
to take heede, though revealing of my mishappe cannot heale
my miserie, nor repeating of my paines redresse my sorrow:
yet, I meane to participate my passions to your good grace,
that though you cannot or will not mittigate my maladie, yet
you may pittie my estate, which will somewhat ease my
heavinesse.

I came to your Fathers Court, Madame, a free man of *Alexandria*, and am like to retourne a captive of *Metelyne*: I arived
devoide of care, and am like to departe, drenched with calamitie:
I landed free from affection, but feare to passe hence fraught
with fancie: my charge was onely to *parle* of peace, but my
chaunce is to discourse of passions. Yea, your beautie hath so
fettered my freedome, and so snared my heart in the linkes of
your love, that it shall never bee raced out by anie sinister
meanes of Fortune, although I see it is almost impossible to
obtaine it.

For I doubt our parents are lyke to proclaime themselves
professed foes, and the urgent necessitie of my affaires, forceth
mee to departe so speedelie, as want of time will not suffice to
make tryall of my love, whereby I might claime a sufficient
guerdon for my good wil: yet howsoever the matter shall happe,
whether my hope be voide, or my happe be vaine, I meane
madame to remaine yours for ever.

Lewsippa took such delight in hearing *Thersandro* discourse
so lovingly as she could scarcely keep her countenaunce from
bewraying the pleasure she conceived in this / *parle*, seeing that
her love was requited with liking, and her fancie incountered
with the like affection. Yet, least *Thersandro* should thinke
her to curteous if shee should come at the first call, and verie
light of love, to like at the first looke, she framed this aunswere.

Sir (quoth she) if of your sute for conditions of peace there
insue no better successe than the revealing of your passions shall
reape pittie at my hands, or if the intreatie for truce be as
lightlie respected by my Father, as either your person or petition
is regarded by mee, you are like to carrie home colde newes to
your countrie, and to vaunt that you bad faire, but bought
little: that your Harvest was long, but your corne not worth
the cropping: that your venter was much, but your gaines such,
as if your winning prove no better, you are like to live by the
losse. For sir, doe you suppose mee so sottish, as to thinke
everie one that flatters doeth fancie, or so addicted to selfe

love, as by a few filed phrases to be brought into a fooles Paradice: knowing that it is the fashion of men by their fained
subtiltie to deceive our faithfull simplicitie. No, for if you
meane to counterfaite, take this for a rule, it is ill halting
before a creple. But sir, this your sodaine liking bewraies
the lightness of your love: this your fond affection, im-
ports the ficklenesse of your fancie: for soone hot, soone colde:
easely inflamed, as quicklie quenched: like to the Apples
of *Arabia*, which begin to rot, ere they be halfe ripe. And if
I meant to love, had I none to like but my Fathers foe? should
I desire him whome my Father doth detest? And if I should
so farre forget mine owne stay or my Fathers state, as to consent, it were impossible either to appease his wrath, or to get
the graunt of his good will, so / that to desire that which I can
never injoy, were to drive my selfe whollie into dispaire, which
would smally profit you, and greatlie displeasure mee: and
therefore cease to sue for that, which may well be wisht, but
never obtained.

Thersandro although he heard *Lewcippa* decide the case
sufficientlie, yet he was so wilfull, that he would not take her
doome for a verdite, but retourned her this replie.

Madame (quoth he) where in liew of hate there insueth love,
it is alwayes the signe of the greater affection: and that it is a
thing either confirmed by the Fates, or appointed by the Gods.
Tereus the Prince of *Thrace*, being sent by his Father to defie
Pandion the king of *Athens*, was enamoured of his daughter
Progne, whereby betweene the Parents in steede of fatall enmitie,
there insued friendly amitie. When as the blouddie warres
betweene *Atis* the king of *Libia*, and *Lycabas* the Prince of
Assur, was most hot, young *Admetus* being sent Ambassadour
into *Libia*, was so stroken in love with *Alcest*, onely Daughter
to his fathers foe, and she repaying his lyking with such loyaltie,
as death it selfe could never dissolve their amitie. If Madame,
these premisses may perswade you to take pittie of my passions,
or these examples induce you, not to let the hatred of our
parents, be a hinderaunce of our love, whether your father
reject mee as a foe, or accept me as a friend, I doubt not but
the destinies will drive the bargaine through, in despight of
them and fortune.

Sir (quoth she) I confesse *Progne* poore wench loved *Tereus*,
but how wretchedly dyd he reward her loyaltie? and *Scilla*
was enamored of *Minos* her fathers foe, but how tyrannouslie
dyd he repaie her love with trecherie? *Tar / peia* betrayed

the Tower of *Rome* to one of the *Sabynes* whome she most entirely loved, but the meede of her merite, was extreame miserie. Shall I then *Thersandro* see the traine and yet fall into the trappe? shall I spie the nettes and yet strike at the stale? shall I see the mishap, and yet wilfullie incurre the mischaunce? no, I meane not for an inch of joye, to reape an ell of annoy, for a moment of mirth, a month of miserie: for a dram of pleasure, a whole pound of paine, and by procuring mine owne delight, to purchase my fathers death and destruction. But let this suffice *Thersandro* to signifie how I pittie thy passions, and thinke well of thy person, that if my Fathers will might be framed to my wish, if he would condiscend as I would consent, thou onely arte the man who in the way of marriage should dispose of mee at thy pleasure. But sith the frowning state of Fortune denies our love to have suche happie successe, hope well, and rest uppon this point, that I wil alwaies like thee as a friend, though not love thee as my phere.

As *Thersandro* was readie to reply, and to seale up the bargaine of their love upon her sweete lippes, *Clerophontes* came in, who marred all their market, and tourned their sweete to sower, for he gave *Thersandro* his aunswere before *Lewcippa*, which was this. That he neither ment to accept of the conditions of peace, nor to receive the tribute, but to claime his due by the doubtfull event of battaile. That he shortly pretended in person, to visite *Orlanio*, and within the walles of *Alexandria* to demaund his debt, and that he would bestow his Fathers Dukedome upon a Lord of his called *Lucianus*, in dowrie with his Daughter *Lewcippa*.

Thersandro was nothing amazed with the first part of / the message, but when he heard how *Clerophontes* meant presumptuously both to deprave him of his living, and deprive him of his Love, he was so puffed up with wrath and choller, as hap what hap would, he fell into these tearmes.

I remember (quoth he) that *Caligula* the Emperour, providing a mightie armie to subdue great *Britaine*, when he was come to the Sea, readie to post over his Souldiours in his Navie, he left off his endlesse enterprise, and set them to gather Cockles. *Siphax* boldly boasting that he would bestow the kingdome of *Numidia* upon his second Sonne, was by *Massinissa* overthrowen, and sold as captive to the *Romanes*. I dare not sir inferre comparisons, because they be odious, nor apply the examples, sith time and place forbids mee: but this I say, that to fish before the net, is alwaies counted folly, and to vaunt before the victorie, is but vanitie. Yea, and if I hadde as good right to your Daughter *Lewcippa*, as I have to the supposed Dowrie which you assigne her, I would in despight of *Lucianus* and the divell him selfe, dispose her at my pleasure.

Clerophontes hearing the cholericke conclusion of *Thersandro*, could scarcely bridle his frantike furie from raging without reason against this young youth, yet somewhat mittigating his moode, he breathed out these cruell threatnings.

If the law of armes (quoth he) did not both safelie protect thee, and surely forbid mee to hurt thee in that thou art a messenger, I would with such severitie chastice these thy presumptuous speeches, as thou shouldest learn hereafter to answere with more reverence: yet I wish thee not to stande too stiffe upon this point, least if thou be / so recklesse as to breake the bondes of reason, I bee so forgetfull as to passe the limites of the lawe. Thou hast received a determinate answere for the Embassage, and there I charge thee this present to depart out of my Dominions.

Thersandro fearing the tyrannie of this cruell *Clerophontes*, presentlie passed out of the Chamber of Presence, taking his leave of Ladie *Lewcippa*, onelie with loving lookes, which shee requited with such glaunces of good will, that they were sufficient signes what insupportable sorrowe shee received by his so sodaine departure: yet knowing that her fancie was incountered with mutuall affection, she drove awaie the mystie clowdes of despaire, hoping that the Gods seeing their faithfull amitie, would take pittie of their passions, and in time redresse their miserie.

But *Thersandro* having with speede dispatcht his affaires (all his traine being set aboord, and they coasting the straights with a luckie gale) was so cumbered with care, and so overgrowen with griefe, that hee passed no houre, minute, nor moment, without wofull wailing, sorrowfull sobs, and far fetcht sighs, so that the Gentlemen his companions, supposing that he was thus painfullie perplexed for feare of *Clerophontes* puisance, began both to comfort and incourage him, not to doubt or dreade the force of the enimie, sith his Father was able to repulse him, without anie daunger to himselfe, or anie great damage to his subjects. But these their perswasions could no whit prevaile to asswage his passions, this their incouragement could not cure his care.

But as there is no greater bane to the bodie, than trouble

of the minde: so *Thersandro* so long continued in these pensive passions and carefull cogitations, concealing his griefe so covertlie, which so much the more furiouslie flamed within him, that hee was constrayned to / keepe his Cabbine till his arrivall at *Alexandria*. Where being set on shore, and presentlie convied to the Court, hee remained for the space of three dayes so strangelie perplexed, as he was not able to make reporte of his message: which so griped *Orlanio* with such inspeakable griefe, as he wished rather to have died valiantlie with the force of his enimie, then to put the death of his sonne in hazard by passing so perillous a journey. But *Thersandro* seeing that sorrow would not salve his sore, but rather increase his sicknesse: that mourning would not appease his maladie, but rather augment his miserie: began to take heart at grasse, and within few daies began to recover his former health. And then hee declared to his Father what he had in charge from *Clerophontes*, how he meant speedelie to wage warre against him, and by force of armes to drive him out of his Dukedome, which he had alreadie promised to one *Lucianus* in dowrie with his daughter.

Orlanio hearing this proude presumption of this bragging Duke, thought the greatest barkers were not alwayes the sorest biters, and that it was farre more easie with wordes to obtaine the victorie, then with deedes to attaine the Conquest. Yet, least hee might bee taken at unwares, hee made a generall muster thorought all his Dominions, providing in everie place necessarie munition for the defence of his Countrie. And assembling his Nobilitie to give their verdite, who were fittest to bee Captaines in this skirmishe: after some consultation hadde in this cause, they concluded, that since *Clerophontes* meant to joyne battayle in his owne person, that lykewise hee should bee Generall of the fielde, and *Gwydonius* who surpassed all the rest in martiall exploites, shoulde be Lieuetenant, and conduct the armie: which he no sooner heard but hee was tormented with inspeakable griefe: he beganne to pull / downe his Peacockes feathers, to hang his wings, and crie creake: everie man hoping to winne fame was merrie, but he alone mourning: everie man laughed, and he alone lowred: insomuch that hee was generallie suspected to be a fearefull coward, and that dreade of daunger drave him into these dolefull dumpes. But as they rashlie conjectured the cause of his sorrowe, so they mist the nature of his sicknesse: for *Gwydonius* seeing that of this cruell conflict his calamitie should insue, and that this bloudie broile woulde breede his bane, hee fell into such solitarie surmises, and such musing meditations, that *Valericus* his open friend, and yet his secrete foe, sought by sundrie meanes to search out the cause of his care, but not beeing able to wring out anie thing, either by flattering promises, or fained protestations, he ceased from his importunate sute. But frowarde Fortune brought it so to passe, that *Valericus* comming by the chamber of *Gwydonius*, heard him thus desperatlie discoursing with himselfe.

Alasse (quoth he) I see the Sun being at the highest declineth, the Sea being at the full tide ebbeth: calme continueth not long without a storme, neither is happinesse had long without heavinesse, blisse without bale, weale without wo, mirth without mourning. For who a late so floated in the flouds of felicitie as I, which now by the sinister meanes of frowning Fortune am sowsed in the seas of sorrow, exalted alate to the highest degree of happinesse, am now driven to the greatest extremitie of evill: alate puffed up with prosperitie, and now pushed downe with adversitie: yea, alate placed in Paradise, and now plunged in perplexitie.

Oh *Gwydonius*, if thy Fathers friendlie preceptes might / have perswaded thee, if his advice had beene thy advertisement, and thou hadst carefullie kept his counsaile, then by his fore-warning, thou hadst bene fore-armed against all mishap and miserie. The force of fickle fancie had not then given thee the foile, Love had not so lightlie procured thy losse, nor the painted shew of beautie had not so soone procured thy bane. My bane? Why fond foole, beautie hath bredde my blisse, fancie hath not given me the foile, but hath yeelded mee the forte: Love hath not wrought my losse, but requited mee with treble gaine!

Hath not *Castania* requited my love with loyaltie, and repayed my good will with mutuall affection? Is shee not my Saint, and I her servant? Are wee not contracted together by love, and shall continue together by lawe? May I not dispose of her in the waie of Marriage at my pleasure? Yes, but what then? The more is my griefe, and the greater my care. For if her presence procureth my delight, will not her absence breede my despight? If her consent preserved my life, will not her contempt inferre my death? Yes. For alasse, since the destinies meane to dissolve that fancie hath decreed, since the frowning fates seeke to unloose that which love hath linked, since froward fortune meanes to breake the bonds wherein beautie hath bound us, since these bloudie broiles will cause *Castania*, (where before shee accepted mee for a friend) now to reject mee for a foe: What better lucke can I looke for than a loathsome life, or what better happe can I hope for than horrour and heavinesse? Yea, which waie so ever I tourne mee, I see nothing but woe and wretchednesse. For if *Orlanio* perceived our liking, howe woulde hee storme at our love? If he knew my chaunce, how woulde hee fret at his Daughters choyce? Woulde hee ever consent, that / *Castania* should match with so meane a mate, that her princelie personage should be disgraced with my base parentage, that her calling should be crazed with my slender countenance? no, hee would no doubt first banish me out of all his dominions. Tush *Gwydonius*, would God this were the worst, and then thou mightest hope in time by some meanes to redresse this doubt. But if *Orlanio* shoulde knowe thou wert heire apparant to the Dukedome of *Metelyne*, and onelie sonne to *Clerophontes* his fatall foe, what torment were there so terrible, which thou shouldst not trie? What paine so pinching, which thou shouldest not passe? What hap so hard which thou shouldest not hazard? Yea, what death so direfull, which at his cruell handes thou shouldest not suffer? And what if *Castania* were privie to thy state, doest thou thinke her so constant as to consent to her fathers foe? Doest thou thinke she wold wish the sonnes weale, when the father wisheth her mishap? No, assure thy selfe if thy state be once knowen, that *Castania* will most deadlie detest thee, which will be more grievous to thee than death it selfe, be it never so terrible. Sith then *Gwydonius*, thou must shortlie either go in armes against thine owne father, or else loose both thy love and thy life, let not delaie breede daunger, but strike on the stith while the yron is hot: *Castania* hath promised to forsake both father, friends, and her owne Countrie, to passe where and when it pleaseth thee: she doubteth no daungers, she forceth of no misfortune, she careth for no calamitie, she passeth for no perils, so she injoy thy desired companie, and therefore as speedelie as may be, convey her closelie into the confines of *Meteline*, before either she know thy staie or thy state. And shall I so practise her with pollicies? Shall I so sift her with subtiltie? Shall I put so little trust in her troth, and so small confidence in her constancie, as to conceale from her anie secret? No, come woe, come wretchednesse, / come death, come daunger, hap what hap will, I will presentlie impart unto her my present state, and my pretended purpose.

Valericus hearing this doubtfull discourse of *Gwydonius*, was driven into an extasie for joy, to see that he had found such fit meanes, whereby hee might not onelie purchase the Dukes favour, aspire unto honour and dignitie, but also obtaine the love of *Castania*, for hee meant speedelie to prevent the pretence of *Gwydonius*, by unfolding to the Duke the sum of his secret purpose, assuring himselfe, that after *Orlanio* knew his parents and parentage, that he was sonne and heire to *Clerophontes*, no price though never so precious, no ransome though never so rich, might redeeme him from the most despightfull death that could be devised. And of these premises he inferd this conclusion, that if the cause be taken awaie the effect faileth: that *Gwydonius* being rejected, he should be received: that he being despighted with hate, he should be requited with love, and uppon this hope he went presentlie to bewray this matter to *Orlanio*, whom he found with his sonne *Thersandro*, and diverse other noble men consulting what course they had best take against *Clerophontes*, whom *Valericus* saluted in this wise.

Plato (right worthie Prince) that grave and wise Philosopher, whose sentences in all ages have bene holden as most divine Oracles, portrayeth out in his bookes of the Common wealth, the picture of a perfect Citizen, whose liniaments being first levelled, he tricketh up with these colours, that hee love his Prince loiallie, keepe the lawes carefullie, and defend his Countrie valiantlie, in which three pointes (saith he) consisteth the chiefest duetie of a trustie subject: This saying of *Plato* throughlie considered, and calling to minde the sundrie good / turnes which without desert your grace hath bestowed uppon mee, I thought if I shoulde not repaie your favour with faithfulnesse, and your trust you repose in mee with inviolable troth, I might bee counted a vicious vassall devoide of all vertues, a trecherous Citizen, rather then a trustie subject, a carelesse slave, than a carefull Gentleman: yea, a gracelesse monster, nusled with ingratitude. I am come (right worthie Sir) not to betraie my foe, but to bewraie my friend, not to discover the fault of my enimie, but to disclose his essence, which liveth with mee in perfect amitie, in whose companie hetherto hath beene all my joy, pleasure and delight: but since his presence is greatlie prejudiciall to your graces person, I thought to preferre your profite before mine owne pleasure, and the commoditie of my Countrie before mine owne private contentation. So it is, that *Gwydonius*, whome your Grace hath honoured and all the Court esteemed, is sonne and heire to *Clerophontes* the Duke of *Metelyne*, who by the peevish pollicie of his Father, under the pretence of service, is purposed to procure your fatall death,

and the finall destruction of your Dukedome. And the better
to performe this divelish practise, he hath contracted himselfe
to my Ladie *Castania,* who blinded with his beautie, and inveigled with his wit, hath consented not onelie to keepe his
counsaile to your confusion, but also closelie to convey her self
with him into his Countrie. Which pretence if your Grace
doth not speedely prevent you shal finde that delay breeds
daunger, and that procrastination in perils is but the mother
of mishap.

And have I (quoth *Orlanio*) brought up the Birde that will
picke out mine owne eies? Have I fostered up the Serpent in
my bosome that will breede my bane? Have I given her life,
that seekes to yeelde mee death? Have I cherisht her beeing
young, and will shee consume / me being older: Was there none
to choose but *Gwydonius,* nor none to love, but the sonne of her
fathers foe? Will she prefer her lust before my life, her private
pleasure before the safetie of my person? Wel, as she forgets
the dutie of a childe, so I will forget the naturall affection of a
father, and therefore *Valericus,* goe speedelie with these noble
men to *Gwydonius* chamber, and apprehend him, that I may
requite his hatefull trecherie with most hellish torments. And
Thersandro, see you that *Castania* be closelie kept untill we
have caught the traitor, least the understanding that their
devise is disclosed, shee save her selfe by flight.

Valericus having this Commission given him from the Duke,
made no delaie, but passed to *Gwydonius* lodging with as much
speede as might be: but fortune who after every chip of mischance, sendeth some lot of good lucke, and after everie storme
of adversitie, sendeth a quiet calme of prosperitie, so carefully
provided to free *Gwydonius* from mishap, that he was newlie
gone towards *Castania,* to impart unto her this his pretence,
but before he came to her chamber, he was incountered by
Thersandro, who stearnlie taking *Gwydonius* by the bosome,
pulling out his Rapier, commanded him as a traitour to stand,
or else without anie farther doome, he should feele the dint
of death.

Gwydonius amazed with this sodaine motion, stoode as one
in a traunce, neither being able to defend himselfe with word
or weapon, but yeelded himself into the hands of *Thersandro,*
who shakt him up with these bitter speeches.

Thou traiterous wretch (quoth he) as it is impossible for the
flame so closelie to bee covered, but it will bee spied, so it is
impossible, but that treason, though never so secret, should in

tract of time bee disclosed, which now by / experience is verified
in thee, for although thou hast hetherto falselie fained thyselfe
to be a straunger of a forraine nation, thou art now knowen
to be sonne and heire to *Clerophontes* that cruell tyrant my
Fathers foe, by whose peevish pollicie thou hadst not onely
brought the common wealth to confusion, but didst pretend
to be prejudiciall to my fathers person, if thy deadly practise
and divelish purpose had not by *Valericus* his meanes beene
prevented. Hast thou bene so trained up in trecherie, or is
thy minde so spotted with villanie, as to repaie my Fathers
good will with such barbarous ingratitude, and to devise his
destruction which simply foresought thy preferment? Yea, to
counsell my sister *Castania*, not onely to consent to thy desire,
but to my fathers death? Is this the manner of *Metelyne*, or
the custome of thy countrie, to be such coosoning counterfaits?
Well, since I have happelie attached thee as a traitour, and as
a villanous rebell, both transgressing humaine and divine lawes,
thou shalt abide the paine and punishment due to such divellish
offenders. Now let thy cruel sire *Clerophontes*, free thee from
those torments which thou art like to suffer for thy trecherie,
and let the Lords of *Metelyne* deliver thee from his hands, who
meanes in most miserable wise to martir thee. Yea, let thy
Concubine *Castania*, who is like for her gracelesse disobedience,
to sippe of the same sorrow, see, if her teares will now prevaile
to moove *Orlanio* to pittie. No, if *Jupiter* him selfe sent *Mer-
curie* to mittigate his moode, neither the authoritie of the one,
nor the eloquence of the other might prevaile to pacifie his furie.

Gwydonius seeing that not onely his purpose was prevented,
and his secrets disclosed, but that also *Valericus* most villanously
had accused him and *Castania* of that which they never so much
as once imagined, was so perplexed, and driven into such dumps,
as he seemed by silence / to averre that which *Thersandro* had
alleadged: yet at last he began thus to reply.

Thersandro (quoth hee) as I meane not to affirme that which
is false, so I will not denie that which is true, but come dolor,
come death, come miserie, come martirdome, come torture,
come torments, I wil neither accuse my selfe injustly, nor
excuse my selfe by perjurie. I confesse *Thersandro*, that I am
sonne and heire to the Duke of *Meteline*, and contracted to thy
sister *Castania*, that *Clerophontes* is my Father by the lawe of
nature, and *Castania* my wife by the league of love, but that I
either pretended or purposed to be prejudiciall to *Orlanios*

person, or that *Castania* was counsailed or ever consented to her fathers confusion, I not onely deny, but I will prove by combat, that *Valericus* most villanously doth accuse us of that whereof we are altogether sacklesse.

Why *Gwydonius*, (quoth he) wilt thou seeke to prove thy selfe loyall, when the hearers deeme thee a lyar, or to make a tryall of thy troth, when thy wordes can have no trust? Dost thou think my fathers furie wil suffer thee to fable? Dost thou think his wrathful rage wil abide thy reasons, or that he will be so patient as to heare thee pleade thine owne cause? No, if thou wert as cleere from these crimes alleadged against thee by *Valericus* as I am, yet in that thou art sonne to *Clerophontes*, the coine of *Crœsus*, and kingdomes of *Cæsar*, were not sufficient raunsome to redeeme thee from death. But *Gwydonius*, since thy health hangeth in my handes, and thy lyfe or death is in my power, I will neither bee so bloudie minded as to breede thy bane, nor so cruell as to be the cause of thy confusion. The guerdon *Gwydonius* I crave for this my good will, and the recompence I claime for this curtesie, is, that when thou commest to *Metelyne*, / thou certifie thy sister and my love and Ladie *Lewcippa*, that for her sake I have procured thy safetie, that her perfection hath preserved thee from perill, the love I beare her hath saved thy life, the duetifull devotion I owe unto her, hath redeemed thee from death and daunger. And in token of this my unfained affection, I will lift my hande against none that commeth from *Metelyne*, but against *Lucianus* onely.

Before *Thersandro* was able fullie to unfolde his minde, or that *Gwydonius* had time to yeeld him thanks for the safegarde of his lyfe, they heard a great noyse, which made *Gwydonius* flie, and *Thersandro* hie him hastely to *Castanias* lodging. Now the companie which came, was *Orlanio* himselfe, who certified by *Valericus* that *Gwydonius* could not be found, laid not onely watch and ward throughout all his Dukedome to attach him, but went in proper person with his Gard to apprehend *Castania*, and lay her in close prison: whome he found all blubbered with teares, for that she had understoode the cause before of her brother *Thersandro*: *Orlanio* no sooner spied her thus weeping, but he raged against her in this wise.

Hath the force of love, nay rather the furie of lust (vild wretch) so blinded thy understanding, that to accomplish it, thou passest not to pervert both humane and divine lawes? Doth lascivious affection and fleshly fancie so furiously frie within thee, as thou wouldest procure thy fathers death to purchase thy divellish desire? Could no rules of reason, no prick of conscience, no respect of honestie, no feare of God, nor dread of man, prohibit thee from pretending such a monstrous mischief, as to conclude with my mortal foe to worke my fatal confusion? The young Storkes so tender the old ones in their age, as they will not suffer them so much as to flie to get their owne living. The / Bird called *Apis Indica*, beeing young, seeing the olde ones through age growen so weake, as they are not able to wave their wings, carrie them continually from place to place on their backs: these savage creatures have but onely sence, and are obedient, thou hast both reason and sense, and art more unnatural: these brute beastes are most dutiful to their parents, and thou a reasonable creature art most disobedient to thy Father: yea, contrarie both to the lawes of Nature and nurture, thou seekest to bath thy hands in his guiltlesse bloud, and without care or conscience, to commit most cruell murther: which is hatefull to all things, as the sencelesse plants and stones most deadlie detest such villanie. The Olive tree so hatefully abhorreth a Parasite, that who so beeing guiltie of that crime, attempteth to plant it, doth not onely himselfe presently perish, but the tree forthwith wayneth and withereth. The stone *Epistrites*, so loatheth this offence, counting it a fact so repugnant to Nature, that it will not vouchsafe to be worne by a murtherer. And shall I then let thee live, whom the sencelesse creatures doe so deadly loath? No, this hand which cherisht thee beeing a childe, shall now chastise thee being such a cursed caitife. And with that he drew out his Faulcon readie to have slaine her. But that *Thersandro* kneeling downe, desired him that he would not so in his furie forget himselfe, as without the sentence of the law put her to death, but to commit her to warde, untill the warres betweene him and *Clerophontes* were happely ended, and then upon more straight examination, if she were found faultie, to assigne her a punishment due for such an offence. *Orlanio*, somewhat pacified with his sonnes perswasion, commaunded that presently she should be carried to prison, and the ladie *Melytta* with her, as an actor in this Tragedie. And that with all speede they shuld post the countrie for the attaching of the traytor *Gwydonius*. Who / after that he parted from *Thersandro*, seeing before his eyes the terrour of torments, and the hellish horrour of death, was driven forward so with the dread of danger, and feare of imminent perills, that knowing perfectly the coast of the

Countrey, he passed so secretlie and speedelie, as he was not so much as once descried by the Postes that pursued him, but scaped safely out of the Dukedome of *Alexandria*. Beeing now without the dint of the Dukes daunger, seeing that although he had escaped himselfe, yet he had left his Love and Ladie *Castania* in hazarde of her life, he began thus to exclaime against his owne follie.

Ah *Gwydonius* (quoth he) what folly hast thou committed by this fearefull flight, what carefull calamitie is like to insue of this thy cowardise, in avoiding *Scilla* thou art falne into *Charibdis*, in preventing one daunger, thou art like to be plagued with a thousand discommodities. Had it not bene better for thee to have died in *Alexandria* with honor, than to live heere with shame and reproch, to have suffered mishap with *Castania*, then to linger heere in miserie? Doest thou thinke that she will ever count of such a prating Parasite, as will love her in prosperitie, and leave her in adversitie, as preferreth his owne safetie before her securitie, his life before her love, and draweth himselfe out of daunger to leave her in distresse? No, she will contempne thee as a coward, more fit to be a mate to some countrie slut, than a match for such a courtly Princesse: she will think thy greatest faith was but fained ficklenesse, thy forged love was but filthie lust, thy promises was but perjuries, and that thy greatest amitie was but most dissembled enmitie: so that of a professed friend, she will become thy professed foe: her desire will tourne to despite, and her love to most hellish hate. /

Why alas, would my paine have pleased her, would my martir-dome have contented her minde, had my peril procured her profit, or my care her commoditie? Nay, rather would not my daunger have beene her death, my mishap her miserie, my torture her torments, and my fatall destinie her finall destruction? By saving my lyfe, in time we may enjoy our love, but by death no hope had bene left for obtaining our desire: so that I assure my self, *Castania* wil rather allow of my policie by preventing perills by flight, than mislike of my practise in procuring mine owne safetie. And upon this point I rest, hoping that the Gods seeing how unjustly *Valericus* hath accused us, will in tract of time ridde us from blame, and reward him with shame.

Gwydonius was not more distressed with dolour, than poore *Castania* was combred with care, to see so strange a chaunce, and so sodaine a chaunge, that she who of late was a royall

Princesse, was now a ruthfull prisoner, that her freedome was tourned to fetters, her dignitie to miserie, and her happie staie to a most hellish state: that after floudes of teares which fell from her Christal eyes, she burst foorth into these tearmes.

Alas (quoth she) what poore damosell was ever driven into such doubtfull distresse? What Princes was ever perplexed with such doleful passions? what maid was ever crossed with such mishap? nay, what creature ever was clogged with the like calamitie? Have the spightfull destinies decreed my destruction, or the perverse Planets conspired my bitter bane? Doeth froward fortune meane to make mee a mirrour of her mutabilitie, or is this the rewarde that *Cupid* bestowes uppon his Clyents? Is everie one that doth fancie, maimed with the / like misfortune, or is love alwaies accompanied with such haplesse lucke? Alas no, for their love is laufull, and mine lewde and lascivious: their fancie is fixed upon vertue, and mine upon vanitie, they make their matche with consent of their parents, and I my market without my Fathers counsaile: so that I am like in choosing such chaffre, to chop and chaunge and live by the losse: yea, to buy repentance at an unreasonable rate. Had it not bene better for thee *Castania*, to have condescended to the requests of *Valericus*, than consented to the sute of *Gwydonius*: to have liked thine owne Countrie man, than loved a straggeling stranger: to have satisfied thy selfe with assurance, than vainelie to fish for hope? Truth, but what then? Can the strawe resist the vertue of the pure Jet? Can the flaxe resist the force of the fire? Can a lover withstand the brunt of beautie? Freeze, if he stand by the flame: pervert the lawes of nature, or eschue that which is framed by the fates, or flie from the force of fancie? No, for who so escapeth the deadlie dartes of *Cupid*, shall be scorched with his fire, and she that with the dew of chastitie quencheth this flame, shall be overtaken with his wings, so that to seeke by flight to eschue affection is foolishlie to enterprise that which can never be atchieved.

But alas, if I must needes lende a listening eare to the allurements of love, was there none to like but thy Fathers foe? How fonde foole, couldest thou shew him courtesie, that intendes to repaye thee with crueltie? How couldest thou choose the sonne to thy mate, when the Father seekes thy miserie? It is not possible to mixe the bloud of a Bull and a Beare, together in one vessell. The Lions whelpes will never companie with the yong Wolves: the Fawlchons called *Pelagræ*, will never flye with the yong Lavarets, and if the Egges of a Crowe

and a Curlewe bee put in one nest, they both / forthwith burst
in sunder, because there is such ancient enmitie betweene the
olde ones. And wilt thou then bee so wilfull to love him
whome thy Father doth loath, or so perverse as to place thy
selfe in that parentage, where there is such mortall hatred
betweene the Parents? Wilt thou so farre forget the dutie of
a childe, as more to respect thy fatall enimie than regarde thy
naturall Father? But why vilde wretch doe I thus fondlie
fable, though *Clerophontes* be my Fathers foe, yet *Gwydonius*
is my faithfull frend: though the one seeke to procure my
paine, the other seekes to purchase my pleasure: though the
olde sire strives to subvert my Fathers state, yet the sonne
never sought to be prejudiciall to his person: although that
perjured Parasite *Valericus* hath most unjustlie accused him of
trecherie. Shall I then hate him who hath alwaies honored
me? Shall I worke his wo that wisheth my weale? Shal I
be his bane, who hath bred my blisse? Shal I detest him which
serveth me with most deepe devotion? No, I heere heartelie
powre out most pittifull plaintes to the gods to preserve my
Gwydonius from perill, and that Fortune may so favour him
as he may passe out of *Alexandria* without death or danger.
What though I heere in prison pine in paine? What
though I sinke in sorrow? What though I be distressed
with griefe and oppressed with miserie? What though I be
crossed with care, and cumbered with calamitie? Tush, let
my Father fret and fume in his furie, let my brother rage
and raile, let that traitor *Valericus* triumph, and all the Countrie most bitterlie curse me, yea, let them martyr mee most
miserablie, let them torment me most terriblie, yet direfull
death shall not feare me, as long as I know *Gwydonius* is devoide
of danger. For I hope though Fortune frowne, though the
destinies denie it, though the fates forsweare it, yea, though the
Gods themselves saie no, yet in time wee shall have such /
happie successe, as the loyaltie of our love, and the cleerenesse
of our conscience by the lawe of justice doe deserve. And
therefore *Gwydonius* shall bee the Planet whereby to direct my
doings, he shall be the starre shall guide my compasse, he shall
be the haven to harbour in, and the Saint at whose shrine I
meane to offer my devotion.

Castania having thus discoursed with her selfe, shee determined when the warres were ended, if shee coulde have no
hope to injoy the love of *Gwydonius*, to confesse her faults, and
to sue for mercie at the barre of her Fathers curtesie: not that

she meant to live without *Gwydonius*, or to love or like anie other, but to prolong her daies in dolour, that she might most rigorouslie revenge the villanie of *Valericus*, and by bathing in his bloude, she might both satisfie her selfe and signifie to *Gwydonius* how entirelie shee loved and liked him. But leaving her perplexed with these passions, againe to *Clerophontes*.

Who frying still in his frantike furie, was not anie whit per-swaded to conclude peace with *Orlanio*, but having mustered his men, as speedelie as might be, imbarkt them, and with a luckie gale arived at the coast of *Alexandria*, where the borderers not able to abide his force, were constrained to save themselves by flight. But hee as a man having exiled from his heart both pietie and pittie, bathed his handes in guiltlesse bloud, firing everie fort, battering downe everie bulwarke, sacking each Cittie, racing downe the walles to the ground, and commanding his souldiours upon paine of most grievous punishment, not to have anie respect of persons, neither to regard the hoarie haires of the aged Citizens, nor the tender yeeres of the sucking Infants, but to imbrue their blades with the bloud of all men, of what degree so ever./

Orlanio hearing how *Clerophontes* had invaded his dominions, and with what barbarous crueltie hee hadde murthered his subjects, having also intelligence by his Scowtes, that his armie was passing huge, the better to resist the furious force of his enimie, hired out of other Countries a great multitude of Mer-cenarie souldiours, so that he gathered a mervailous great hoast, wherein was an infinit number indued with great skill and long experience.

Furnished thus sufficientlie both with men and munition, like a wise and warie Captaine, seeing that he no waie else might resist the puisant power of so mightie a Prince, determined without further delaie to meete him and give him present battaile, having mervailous affiance in the approved manhoode and vertue of his souldiours.

Clerophontes likewise being of such a valiant and invincible courage, as he seemed from his infancie to be vowed to *Mars* and martiall affaires, manfullie marched forward to meete with his enimies, which he performed so speedelie, that within few daies, both the armies were within view: which *Clerophontes* seeing, hee began to incourage his souldiours on this sort.

Although most trustie subjects (quoth he) I neyther doubt of your prowesse, nor have cause to feare your manhood, as having mine armie fraught with the most couragious Captaines

and boldest blouds of *Metelyne*, yet I wish you to consider
how desperatlie wee have adventured uppon the conquest of
this Dukedome: which if we atchieve, we shall not onelie gaine
perpetuall fame and renowne, but reape such riches and treasure,
as shall sufficientlie countervaile our travaile. But to obtaine
this victorie wee must behave our selves valiantlie, neither
dreading anie daunger, though never so desperate, nor / doubting
anie perill though never so fearefull. Before our face we have
enimies, behinde our backes the surging seas, so that fight we
must, but flie we cannot: in being couragious we winne the
field and returne conquerours: in proving cowards, we both
loose our lives and the conquest: if we foile our foes, we returne
with triumph, if we faint and flie, we have no hope of safetie,
but death and desperation is imminent. Be then hardie to
hazard, and valiant to venture amiddest the prease of your
enimies, that daunted with your valour, they may bee forced
to flie, and wee both triumph and injoye the treasure.

Clerophontes having thus lovinglie incouraged his souldiours,
Orlanio on the other side seeing his men began to feare the
force of the enimie, and were amazed with such a monstrous
multitude, prickt them forward with this *parle*.

That mightie Monarch *Alexander* the great, who for his
martiall exploits was a mirrour to all his posteritie, whose
prowesse was such, as he danted *Darius*, and by his invincible
courage made a conquest of the whole world: hearing on a time
one of his captaines to demand what multitude was in their
enimies campe, answered, that it was not the point of a good
souldior, to inquire how many the enimies were, but where
they were: meaning that to feare the multitude is rather the
signe of cowardise, than a token of courage. Which saying
I wish you carefully to consider, that the huge armie of *Clerophontes* neither amaze your minds, nor abate your valor, sith
that the equitie of our cause doth more than countervaile his
companie. He invadeth our realme without reason, and we
defend but our owne right: he cruelly seeketh to deprive us of
freedome, and we lawfully doe maintain our own liberty. He /
tyrannouslie striveth to make us bondslaves, and we fight to
free our selves from captivitie. If hee prevaile let us looke
for no pittie, but that we shall be murthered without mercie:
wee shall see before our face our wives ravished, our daughters
deflowred, our parents put to death, our children slaine, our
goods spoiled, our Citie sacked, and our selves brought to
utter ruth and ruine. Sith then we are placed betweene two

extremities, either to possesse our owne with plentie, or to passe
our lives in penurie: let us valiantlie venter whatsoever we
gaine, let us fight without feare: for better it is to die with
honor, than to live with shame.

By that time *Orlanio* had ended his Oration, the armies met
in a Plaine, within thirty leagues of *Alexandria*. Where both
of them ordering (as became good Captaines) their people,
there began in the breake of the daie the most cruell and terrible
battaile that earst was heard of, considering the number on both
parties, their experience and pollicie, with the valiaunt prowesse
and courage of the Captaines. Thus continued they in fight
even almost untill even, with mervailous slaughter on both
sides, the victorie yet doubtfull, till in the end the *Alexandrians*
began to faint and flie, more oppressed with the excesse of the
multitude, than distressed for want of manhoode: for there
were two and fortie thousand slaine, but not one taken prisoner:
and of *Clerophontes* companie eight and twenty thousand slaine,
and sixe hundered mortallie wounded. This monstrous massacre,
and fearefull slaughter, so amazed the mindes of these two
Captaines, that for the better burying of the dead, and healing
of them which were hurt, they concluded a truce betweene
them for fifteene dayes, in which time *Orlanio* sent Ambassadors
to parle of peace with *Clerophontes*, but in vaine: for hee was
resolved either / valiantlie to die in the field with glorie, or to
injoye the Dukedome of *Alexandria* with renowme. Yet as
a worthie Prince, preferring the securitie of his souldiours before
the safetie of his owne person, he offered them the combat,
which *Orlanio*, to avoid the effusion of blood, most willinglie
accepted. Now it was agreed and concluded betweene them,
that two champions might be chosen, who by the dint of the
sword shuld stint the strife betweene these two armies. If he
of *Metelyne* remained victor, then *Orlanio* should not onelie
paie his former tribute, but deliver up his Dukedome into the
hands of *Clerophontes*. But if the *Alexandrians* obtained the
conquest, the Duke of *Meteline* should peaceably depart the
Countrie, release the tribute, and also resigne his state, and
become a subject to *Orlanio*. And for the better keeping and
confirming of these conditions, they presently despatcht Embassadours to *Fernandus* the king of *Bohemia*, to intreate his
majestie that he would vouchsafe to become judge in the
combat, who for that he wished wel to both these Dukes,
graunted to their requeste, and with as much speede as might
bee, came to *Alexandria*. But in the meane time there was

some difference about the champions, for *Clerophontes* sayd, that sith in loosing the field consisted the losse of living, life, and libertie, and in getting the victorie the gaine of a Dukedome, he woulde in proper person fight the combat, and trie the chance of Fortune: and therefore made a challenge to *Orlanio*. But hee finding himselfe farre unfit to resist his furious force, refused it. Yet promising, that none unlesse he were descended of Nobilitie, should enter the lists: wherewith *Clerophontes* was verie well contented. Nowe while this truce continued, which was prolonged for thirtie daies, it was lawfull for them of *Alexandria* to come and view the campe of *Metelyne*, and for the *Metelynes* to goe and see the Citie. Whereupon *Clerophontes* desirous to see *Orlanio* / and his Court, went onelie accompanied with his gard to *Alexandria*: where hee was most roiallie entertained, and sumptuouslie feasted by *Orlanio*, both of them remitting the rigour of their mallice, till it shoulde bee shewed in effect by reason of their manhood. But as soone as *Thersandro* and the other Lordes saw *Clerophontes*, that he was rather a monster than a man, having each lim so stronglie couched, ech part so proportioned, so huge of stature, and so fierce of countenance, they were so danted with the sight of his person, as they almost feared to come in his presence, saying: that three of the boldest blouds in *Alexandria* were not able to abide the force of *Clerophontes*. Who now peaceablie departing to his hoast, left *Orlanio* as greatlie perplexed: for assembling his nobilitie together, amongst whom he appointed the champion should be chosen. They not onelie with one consent withstood his command, but began to murmure and mutine against him, condemning him of follie that he would so unadvisedlie commit his own state and their staie to the doubtfull hazard of one mans hap. *Orlanio* seeing that it was now no time to chastise this their presumption, unlesse he meant to raise civill dissention in the citie, which were the next waie to confirme the enimie, and breed his owne confusion, he dissembled his cholar, and began to work a new waie. For first he freed *Castania* out of prison, then made general proclamation throughout the Dukedome, that what Lord so ever within his land would trie to combat with *Clerophontes*, if he remained victor in the conquest, he woulde not onelie give him his Daughter *Castania* to wife [and] let him possesse peaceablie the dukedome of *Meteline* as her dowrie, but be content to acknowledge him as his liege, and paie him tribute, as he was wont to *Clerophontes*.

While he lingred and listned how this proclamation would prevaile, *Castania* hearing this severe sentence, and dolefull doome pronounced, seeing that she should not onelie bee / forced to forsake *Gwydonius*, but be constrained to match in marriage with one whome she should neither love nor like, burst forth into these bitter complaints.

Alasse (quoth she) how pinching a paine is it to be perplexed with diverse passions, what a noisome care it is to be cumbered with sundrie cogitations, what a wo it is to hang betweene desire and despaire, and what a hell it is to hover betweene feare and hope. For as to him which is assured to die, death is no dolor, in that he perfectlie knowes there is no salve can cure his sorrow, so to him which feares to die, and yet hopes to live, death were thrice more welcome, than to linger in such doubt. In which cursed case alasse my care consisteth, for as out of the river *Cea* in *Sicillia* bursteth most fearefull flames, and yet the streame is passing colde, neither is the water able to quench the fire, nor the fire cause the water to bee hotte, so the heate of hope flameth out of the chilling fountaine of feare, and yet the force of the one is not able to asswage the vehemencie of the other, but still my heavie heart is diverslie assailed with them both. If my Father *Orlanio* win the conquest, I doubt my desire shall never have happie successe, if *Clerophontes* triumph as victor, I greatlie feare his crueltie is such, as I shall not escape most haplesse death. And yet againe I hope that then my owne *Gwydonius* will accept mee for his, and with triumphant armes embrace me. But alasse, will *Clerophontes* suffer him to match with his mortall foe, will he not rather prevent it by my perill? Yes no doubt, if he returne with triumph my father shall serve him as a subject, my brother shall become his vassall, my friends shal bee forlorne, my Cittie sackt, and my native Countrie brought to utter confusion. And shall I for the love of a straunger wish these straunge stratagems? Shall I to feede mine owne fancie, and content my lusting minde, / wish my Fathers death, my Brothers bane, my friends mishap, my Countries confusion, and perhappes my owne miserie? For though *Gwydonius* loved mee when our parents were friendes, hee will not now lyke me being foes: but to revenge the injuries my Father offered him, will subtillie seeke to sacke my honour and honestie, and so triumph of my shame and discredit. Had I not better praie my Father may win the combat, and then shall I bath in the streames of blisse, and flowe in the flouds of felicitie? then shall I dreade no

daunger, no feare, no perils: then shall I see my Father, friends,
and Countrie, flourish in most happie prosperitie: then shall I
injoy some jollie Gentleman, who will love me being young,
and cherish me being olde, and possesse the Dukedome of
Metelyne for my dowrie. And canst thou *Castania* bee so in-
gratefull, as to will his woe which wisheth thy weale, to desire
his destruction which praieth for thy prosperitie? Canst thou
be so covetous as to crave that for thy possession, which is thy
Gwydonius patrimonie, or so suspitious, as to accuse him of
trecherie, which hath ben but too trustie: to count him a
counterfait, which hath alwaies ben constant? No, come what
come will, let froward fortune favour whom she please, so I
may joy and safelie injoy my onelie joy *Gwydonius.*

As *Castania* had thus ended her complaint, *Gwydonius* who
all this while lurked about the borders of *Alexandria,* heard
what successe *Orlanios* affaires had with his Father *Clerophontes,*
how verie few or none at all durst trie the combat with him,
that his love and Ladie *Castania* was the prise that he should
get that gained the conquest. Which things considered, supposing that *Castania* had cast him off, and that she plaid, out
of sight, out of minde, by a secret and trustie messenger, he
presented her with this Letter./

Gwydonius to Castania, health

The fine spice *Castania,* the more it is pounded, the sweeter
smel it yeelds, the Camomil increaseth most being trodden on,
the Palme tree the greater waight it beareth, the straighter it
groweth: the stone *Terpistretes,* the more it is beaten, the harder
it is, and loyall love is not weakened by the storlines of adversitie, but rather far the more fortified by the froward state of
frowning fortune: which Madame I speake by proofe and
experience, for since I have sipped of the sower dregs of sorow,
and bene pestered with the bitter pills of penurie, since sinister
fortune hath crossed me with mishaps, and disaster fates have
driven mee downe to miserie, my fancie hath so furiously
assaulted my mynde, and affection hath so incessantly battered
the bulwarke of my breast, as that sparks of love which were
kindled in mee in prosperitie, are turned to fierce and firie
flames by adversitie. So that madame, your presence did not
before procure me such pleasure, as your absence doth paine,
neither was I so drowned in delight, in frequenting your companie, as I am drenched with despight, by leading my life in

sorrowfull calamitie. Alasse *Castania*, what unspeakable griefe
hath tormented mee? what direfull dolour hath distressed mee?
what hellish horrour hath haunted me? yea, what woe and
wretchednesse hath wracked my wittes, since thou hast bene
proclaimed a pray to him whosoever winneth the prise in the
combat. How ofte have I wished that I might bee the champion
to make the challenge, that I might venture my life to purchase
thy libertie, that my death might redeeme thee from daunger.

But alasse, I see to wish is in vaine, to crave of the Gods,/
that thy Father should vaunt of the victorie, is but to wish that
your love should have haplesse miserie: to pray that *Clerophontes*
should returne with conquest, thou wilt deeme I desire thy
friends misfortune: thus assailed with divers doubts, I drive of
my dayes in dolour: hoping howsoever fortune frowne, that
the fates will assigne us a perfect calme of permanent felicitie,
for this sturdie storme of pinching miserie.

Thine ever, exiled
Gwydonius.

Castania having received this Letter, seeing that no sinister
chaunce of fortune was able to change the fixed fancie of
Gwydonius, conceived such assured hope in his constancie, as
now she thought his troth was filed with no spot of trecherie,
that his faith was quite devoide of flatterie, and that whatsoever
chaunced, she might safely repose her staie and state in his
loyaltie. Insomuch that to drive out the evill opinion which she
thought her brother *Thersandro* hadde conceived of *Gwydonius*
conspiracie, shee secretylye showed him the Letter, / which
after he had read over, and carefully construed everie clause,
he began both to detect and detest the villanie of *Valericus*,
desiring his sister *Castania* that she would earnestly perswade
Gwydonius in disguised apparell speedelie to repaire to her
lodging, promising with solempne vowes and sacred oathes, not
to bee prejudiciall to his person: *Castania* affying greatly in
her brothers faith, and desiring to have a sight of her loving
Gwydonius, returned him these few lines./

Castania to Gwydonius, prosperitie

Who so tasteth *Gwydonius* of the hearbe *Mely Sophilos* is
never tormented with the sting of adversitie, and she that
weareth the stone *Mephites* about her, never sorroweth at
sinister fortune: who so fancieth without faining never proveth
fickle. and she that loveth loyallie may well be crossed with

calamitie, but never justly accused of inconstancie. Account
thy *Castania* good *Gwydonius* to be in the same predicament,
for let disaster mishap drive mee downe to most deadlie miserie,
lette the cruell fates compasse mee with cursed care, let fortune
and the destinies conclude my confusion, yet it shall not diminish
my fancie, but rather increase my affection. I wil still in weale,
in woe, in bale, in blisse, in mirth and miserie, say I love, and
it is onely *Gwydonius*. For shall our fancie bee such as it shal
be foiled with misfortune? no, but as *Thetis* chaunging into
manie shapes, at last returned into her owne forme, so into
what mishap I be driven by miserie, yet I will stand in mine
olde state in despight of the fates and fortune. Come therefore
Gwydonius to the Court in disguised apparell, but without care,
for thou shalt finde me so trustie, as my troth shall be without
spotte, and thy health without hazard. Thus wishing thy
curtesie to conster well of my constancie, I bid thee farewell.

> *Thine or not her owne,*
> *constant Castania.*

Gwydonius having carefully construed over the contents of
this loving letter, although the rigor of *Orlanio* might have given
him sufficient cause of suspition, yet the cleerenes of his own
conscience, and the love he bare to *Castania*, would not /
suffer him either to suspect any treason, or to doubt of any
deceit, but determined without any delay to put the safetie of
his person and the safegarde of his life into her handes. But
leaving him to bring his purpose luckely to passe, againe to
Orlanio.

Who seeing that his proclamation could not prevaile, and
that his nobles preferred their owne safetie before his securitie,
was perplexed with such hellish passions, and griped with such
pinching griefe, as the Ghoasts tormented with grisly fiends,
felt no such haplesse furie. To fight with *Clerophontes*, he felt
his strength farre unfit to resist his force: to denie the combat,
he neither could nor would, although he brought himselfe to
confusion, and his children to captivitie, so that howsoever he
tourned himselfe, he saw before his face death and despaire, woe
and wretchednesse, mishap and miserie. Combred thus with
this curelesse care, and sitting solitarily in sorrow, seeing the
dismall day drew on, and hearing that *Fernandus* the king of
Bohemia was lately landed, he fell into more furious passions,
untill he was driven out of his dumps by his sonne *Thersandro*:
who perceiving his father thus dolefully daunted, he began most

lovingly to comfort him, promising that since none durst venter to deale with *Clerophontes*, hee himselfe would fight the combat, and either worthelie winne the conquest with renowme, or manfully dye on the field with honour.

Orlanio hearing the bold courage of this new champion, felt his sorrow somewhat salved by this profer, perswading himselfe that his sonne was better able to abide the brunt then hee, and hoping that the Gods would favour the equitie of the cause, and assuredly by justice graunt him the victorie. Resting I saye, upon this hope, and thanking *Thersandro* for his naturall affection, and praysing him for his noble courage, hee presently went to meete *Fernandus*, whom he most princely entertained, con/ducting him very royally into *Alexandria*, where hee most sumptuously feasted him and all his traine. But as they passed away the time in pastime and pleasure, so poore *Thersandro* spent the daye in dolour and the night in sorrow. For although to comfort his Father he made light of the combat, and valiantly offered himselfe to trye the chaunce of Fortune, yet seeing his enimies force far to exceed his feeble strength, he began to faint, although like a worthie Gentleman he covered his dreadfull courage with a desperate countenance, raunging up and downe the fieldes to drive away his melancholy: wher by chance in disguised apparaile he met *Gwydonius*, to whom after some *parle* past between them, he bewraied the whole state of the matter: how he was to enter combat with *Clerophontes*, and that he doubted greatlie of the event of the victorie, fearing the force of his Father, and fainting at his owne imbecilitie. Which *Gwydonius* hearing, he made this short aunswere.

Thersandro (quoth hee) it is vaine with long talke to passe awaye the time when delaye breedes daunger, and follye to hope for faire weather when the Aire is overcast with clowdes: leaving off therefore all oathes to confirme my faith, thus much to the purpose. If it please thee to trust mee without tryall, and to give any confidence to my wordes, I heere promise both to make manifest my loyall love to *Castania*, and to repay thy courtesie, that I will, resembling thy person, and disguised in thy armour, enter combat with my Father *Clerophontes*, either intending by winning the victorie to obtaine my will, or by loosing the conquest to want my wish: if this my profer please thee, I will passe privelie to the Court, if not, good *Thersandro*, let me goe as I came. /

Thersandro commending the subtill devise of *Gwydonius* caried him as covertly as could be to *Castania*, to whome he was farre more welcome than soone come, remaining closely in her closet till the next morning: *Castania* notwithstanding knowing nothing of their pretence.

Fernandus king of *Bohemia*, the next day being gone with all his nobilitie to the place appointed for the combat, *Orlanio*, *Castania*, and all the Lords of *Alexandria*, clad in mourning attire followed him, thinking this dismall day should be the date of their destruction. And *Clerophontes* as a balefull wretch thirsting after bloud, and glorying in the hope of his supposed conquest, stoode in the listes, expecting his fatall foe. To whome *Gwydonius* his sonne furnished with the armour of *Thersandro*, presented himselfe. Who seeing, that forced by the fond allurements of love, he was to fight, not with his mortall foe, but with his naturall father, he fell into these doubtfull dumps.

Alas poore *Gwydonius* (quoth he) how art thou combred with divers cogitations, what a cruell conflict dost thou finde in thy minde betweene love and loyaltie, nature and necessitie? who ever was so wilfull as willingly to wage battaile against his owne father? who so cruell as to enter combat with his owne sire? Alas, duetie perswades mee not to practise so monstrous a mischiefe: but the devotion I owe to *Castania*, drives mee to performe the deede, were it thrice more daungerous or desperate. The honour I owe to my Father, makes mee faint for feare but once to imagine so brutish a fact: the love I owe to *Castania*, constraineth mee to defend the combat if *Jupiter* himselfe made the challenge. And is not (fond foole) necessitie above nature, is not the law of love above King or Keysar, Father or friend, God or the divell? Yes. And so I meane to take it: for either I will valiantly win the conquest and my *Castania*, or lose the / victorie, and so by death ende my miseries.

With that the Trumpets sounded, and *Gwydonius* lustely leaping into the lystes, fell presently into furious fight with his Father, driving not onely *Fernandus* and *Orlanio*, but also both the armies into a great doubt, for although *Clerophontes* most cruelly prosecuted him, yet he alwaies received the strokes, but never so much as once returned one blow: till at last looking aloft, and spying *Castania*, his courage increased, that all feare set aside, he carelessly flung away his sword and shield and ranne upon his Father, not onely tearing from him his Target, but violentlie casting him uppon the ground, and speedely unlacing his Helmet, offered to cut of his head with his owne sword: but *Clerophontes* crying out confessed himselfe captive, and graunted his enimie the conquest. Whereupon they of *Alex-andria*, gave a mightie shout, and *Fernandus* and *Orlanio* came downe readie to carrie *Clerophontes* captive to the Citie. But *Gwydonius* first demanded of *Orlanio* if he was content to performe that which he promised by proclamation, to whome *Fernandus* aunswered, that he would and should, or else as he was his friend, so he should be his foe. *Gwydonius* hearing this faithfull assertion of the king, pulling down his beaver, began to speake in this maner.

I let thee *Orlanio* (quoth he) and the worthie king of *Bohemia* to know, that I am *Gwydonius*, sonne and heire to this conquered *Clerophontes*, who for the love of thy Daughter *Castania*, have not spared contrarie to the law of nature, to fight with mine owne Father, hoping the destinies by my meanes have decreed, not onely of fatall foes to make you faithfull friends, but to finish uppe our love which otherwise could not have bene per-fourmed./ I have wonne *Orlanio* my Fathers Dukedome by victorie, and thy daughter by conquest, the one I had before by inheritaunce, and the other by love, yet I would willingly have thy good will: which if thou graunt, I hope my father will both pardon my offence, and thinke well of my proffer.

Clerophontes kissing and imbracing *Gwydonius*, tolde him his care was halfe cured, in that such a good Captaine had wonne the Conquest. *Fernandus* and *Orlanio* stood astonished at this straunge Tragedie, doubting whether they dreamt of such a rare device, or saw it in effect. At last *Orlanio* as one wakened out of a trance, with trickling teares, imbraced *Clerophontes*, honouring him as his Soveraigne, and promising not onelye to give *Castania* to *Gwydonius*, but also halfe his Dukedome in dowrie. *Clerophontes* thanking him for his courtesie, consented most willingly to this motion, so that before *Fernandus* departed, the marriage betweene *Gwydonius* and *Castania*, *Thersandro* and *Lewcippa*: was most sumptuously solempnized.

FINIS. /

THE
VNFORTV-
nate Traueller.

OR,

The life of Iacke Wilton.

Newly corrected and aug-
mented.

Qui audiunt audita dicunt.

THO. NASHE.

LONDON,
Imprinted by Thomas Scarlet
for Cuthbert Burby.

1594.

To the right Honorable Lord Henrie Wriothsley, Earle of South-hampton, and Baron of Tichfeeld.

INGENUOUS honorable Lord, I know not what blinde custome methodicall antiquity hath thrust upon us, to dedicate such books as we publish, to one great man or other; In which respect, least anie man should challenge these my papers as goods uncustomd, and so extend uppon them as forfeite to contempt, to the seale of your excellent censure loe here I present them to bee seene and allowed. Prize them as high or as low as you list: if you set anie price on them, I hold my labor well satisfide. Long have I desired to approove my wit unto you. My reverent duetifull thoughts (even from their infancie) have been retayners to your glorie. Now at last I have enforst an opportunitie to plead my devoted minde. All that in this phantasticall Treatise I can promise, is some reasonable conveyance of historie, and varietie of mirth. By divers of my good frends have I been dealt with to employ my dul pen in this kinde, it being a cleane different vaine from other my former courses of writing. How wel or ill I have done in it, I am ignorant: the eye that sees round about it selfe, sees not into it selfe): only your Honours applauding encouragement hath power to make mee arrogant. Incomprehensible is the heighth of your spirit both in heroical resolution and matters of conceit. Unprepriveably perisheth that booke whatsoever to wast paper, which on the diamond rocke of your judgement disasterly chanceth to be shipwrackt. A dere lover and cherisher you are, as well of the lovers of Poets, as of Poets themselves. Amongst their sacred number I dare not ascribe my selfe, though now and then I speak English: that smal braine I have, to no further use I convert, save to be kinde to my frends, and fatall to my enemies. A new brain, a new wit, a new stile, a new soule will I get mee, to canonise your name to posteritie, if in this my first attempt I be not taxed of presumption. Of your gracious favour I despaire not, for I am not altogether Fames out-cast. This handfull of leaves I offer to your view, to the leaves on trees I compare, which as they cannot grow of themselves except they have some branches or boughes to cleave too, and with whose juice and sap they be evermore recreated and nourisht: so except these unpolisht leaves of mine have some braunch of Nobilitie whereon to depend and cleave, and with the vigorous nutriment of whose authorised commendation they may be continually fosterd and refresht, never wil they grow to the worlds good liking, but forthwith fade and die on the first houre of their birth.   Your Lordship is the large spreading branch of renown, from whence these my idle leaves seeke to derive their whole nourishing: it resteth you either scornfully shake them off, as worm-eaten and worthles, or in pity preserve them and cherish them, for some litle summer frute you hope to finde amongst them.

Your Honors in all humble service:

Tho: Nashe.

The Induction to the dapper Mounsier Pages of the Court.

GALLANT Squires, have amongst you: at Mumchaunce I meane not, for so I might chaunce come to short commons, but at *novus, nova, novum*, which is in English, newes of the maker. A proper fellow Page of yours called *Jack Wilton*, by me commends him unto you, and hath bequeathed for wast paper here amongst you certaine pages of his misfortunes. In anie case keepe them preciously as a *privie* token of his good will towardes you. If there bee some better than other, he craves you would honor them in theyr death so much, as to drie and kindle Tobacco with them: for a need he permits you to wrap velvet pantofles in them also; so they bee not woe begone at the heeles, or weather-beaten lyke a blacke head with graie hayres, or mangie at the toes, lyke an Ape about the mouth. But as you love good fellowship and ames ace, rather turne them to stop mustard-pottes, than the Grocers should have one patch of them to wrap mace in: a strong hot costly spice it is, which above all things he hates. To anie use about meat and drinke put them to and spare not, for they cannot doe theyr countrie better service. Printers are madde whoorsons, allowe them some of them for napkins. Jost a little neerer to the matter and the purpose. *Memorandum*, everie one of you after the perusing of this pamphlet, is to provide him a case of ponyardes, that if you come in companie with anie man which shall dispraise it or speak against it, you may straight crie *Sic respondeo*, and give him the stackado. It standes not with your honours (I assure ye) to have a gentleman and a page abusde in his absence. Secondly, whereas you were wont to swere men on a pantofle to be true to your puisant order, you shall sweare them on nothing but this Chronicle of the king of Pages hence forward. Thirdly, it shall be lawfull for anie whatsoever, to play with false dice in a corner on the cover of this foresayd Acts and Monuments. None of the fraternitie of the minorities shall refuse it for a pawne in the times of famine and necessitie.

Everie Stationers stall they passe by, whether by daie or by night, they shall put off theyr hats too and make a low legge, in regard their grand printed Capitano is there entombd. It shalbe flat treason for anie of this fore-mentioned catalogue of the point trussers, once to name him within fortie foote of an alehouse, mary the taverne is honorable. Many speciall grave articles more had I to give you in charge, which your wisdomes waiting together at the bottom of the great chamber staires, or sitting in a porch (your parliament house) may better consider off than I can deliver: onely let this suffice for a tast to the text, and a bitte to pull on a good wit with, as a rasher on the coles is to pull on a cup of Wine.

> Heigh passe, come alofte: everie man of you take
> your places, and heare *Jacke Wilton*
> tell his owne Tale.

The Unfortunate Traveller.

I

ABOUT that time that the terror of the world, and feaver quartane of the French, *Henrie* the eight (the onely true subject of Chronicles), advanced his standard against the two hundred and fifty towers of *Turney* and *Turwin*, and had the Emperour and all the nobilitie of *Flanders*, *Holand*, and *Brabant* as mercenarie attendants on his ful-sayld fortune, I, *Jacke Wilton*, (a Gentleman at least) was a certain kind of an appendix or page, belonging or appertaining in or unto the confines of the English court, where what my credit was, a number of my creditors that I cosned can testifie, *Cœlum petimus stultitia*, which of us al is not a sinner. Bee it knowen to as many as will paie mony inough to peruse my storie, that I folowed the court or the camp, or the campe and the court, when *Turwin* lost her maidenhead, and opened her gates to more than *Jane Trosse* did. There did I, (soft let me drinke before I go anie further) raigne sole king of the cans and blacke jackes, prince of the pigmeis, countie palatine or cleane straw and provant, and, to conclude, Lord high regent of rashers of the coles and red herring cobs. *Paulo majora canamus*. Well, to the purpose. What stratagemicall acts and monuments doo you thinke an ingenious infant of my yeeres might enact? you will say it were sufficient if he slur a die, pawn his master to the utmost peny, and minister the oath of the pantofle artefcially. These are signes of good education, I must confesse, and arguments of In grace and vertue to proceed. Oh but *Aliquid latet quod non patet*, theres a further path I must trace: examples confirme, list lordings to my proceedings. Who so ever is acquainted with the state of a campe, understandes that in it be many quarters, and yet not so many as on *London* bridge. In those quarters are many companies: Much companie, much knavery, as true as that olde adage, Much curtesie, much subtiltie. Those companies, lyke a greate deale of corne, do yeeld some chaffe, the corne are cormorants, the chaffe are good fellowes, which are quickly blowen to nothing, wyth bearing a light heart in a lyght purse. Amongest this chaffe was I winnowing my wittes to live merrily, and by my troth as I did: the prince could but command men spend their bloud in his service, I could make them spend al the mony they had for my pleasure. But povertie in the end partes friends, though I was prince of their purses, and exacted of my unthrifte subjects as much liquid alleageance as any keisar in the world could doe, yet where it is not to bee had the king must loose his right, want cannot bee withstoode, men can doe no more than they can doe, what remained then, but the foxes case must help, when the lions skin is out at the elbowes.

There was a Lord in the campe, let him be a Lord of misrule if you will, for he kept a plaine alehouse without welt or gard of anie ivybush, and sold syder and cheese by pint and by pound to all that came (at the verie name of sider I can but sigh, there is so much of it in renish wine now a daies.) Well, *Tendit ad sydera virtus*, thers great vertue belongs (I can tel you) to a cup of sider, and very good men have sold it, and at sea it is *Aqua cœlestis*, but thats neither here nor there, if it had no other patrone but this peere of quart pottes to authorize it, it were sufficient. This great Lord, this worthie Lord, this noble Lord, thought no scorne (Lord have mercie upon us) to have his great velvet breeches larded with the droppinges of this daintie liquor, and yet he was an old servitor, a cavelier of an ancient house, as might appeare by the armes of his ancestors, drawen verie amiably in chalke on the in side of his tent dore.

He and no other was the man I chose out to damne with a lewd monilesse device, for comming to him on a day as he was counting his barels and setting the price in chalke on the head of them, I did my dutie very devoutly, and tolde his *alie* honor I had matters of some secrecy to impart unto him, if it pleased him to grant me private audience. With me yong *Wilton* qd. he, mary and shalt: bring us a pint of syder of a fresh tap into the three cups here, wash the pot, so into a backe roome hee lead me, where after he had spitte on his finger, and pickt of two or three moats of his olde moth eaten velvet cap, and spunged and wrong all the rumatike drivell from his ill favored goats beard, he bad me declare my minde, and thereupon hee dranke to mee on the same. I up with a long circumstaunce, alias, a cunning shift of the seventeenes, and discourst unto him what entire affection I had borne him time out of minde, partly for the high descent and linage from whence hee sprong, and partly for the tender care and provident respect he had of pore souldiers, that whereas the vastitie of that place, (which afforded them no indifferent supply of drink or of victuals) might humble them to some extremitie, and so weaken their handes, he vouchsafed in his owne person to be a victualler to the campe (a rare example of magnifisence and honorable curtesy) and diligently provided that without farre travell, everie man might for his money have syder and cheese his belly full, nor did hee sell his cheese by the way onely, or his syder by the great, but abast himself with his owne hands to take a shoomakers knife, (a homely instrument for such a high personage to touch) and cut it out equally lyke a true justiciarie, in little pennyworths, that it would doo a man good for to looke upon. So likewise of his syder, the pore man might have his moderate draught of it, (as there is a moderation in all things) as well for his doit or his dandiprat, as the rich man for his half souse or his denier. Not so much quoth I, but this Tapsters linnen apron which you weare to protect your apparell from the imperfections of the spigot, most amply bewrais your lowly minde, I speake it with teares, too few such noble men have wee that will drawe drinke in linnen aprons. Why you are everie childes fellow, anie man that comes under the name of a souldier and a good fellowe, you will sit and beare companie to the last pot, yea, and you take in as good part the homely phrase of mine host heeres to you, as if one saluted you by all the titles of your baronie. These considerations I saie, which the world suffers to slip by in the channell of forgetfulness, have moved me in ardent zeale of your welfare, to forewarne you of some dangers that have beset you and your barrels. At the name of dangers hee start up and bounst with his fist on the boord so hard, that his tapster over-hearing him, cried, anone anone sir, by and by, and came and made a low legge and askt him what he lackt. Hee was readie to have striken his tapster, for interrupting him in attention of this his so much desired relation, but for feare of displeasing mee hee moderated his furie, and onely sending for the other fresh pint, wild him looke to the barre, and come when he is cald with a devils name. Well, at his earnest importunitie, after I had moistned my lippes, to make my lie run glibbe to his journeies end, forward I went as followeth. It chanced me the other night, amongst other pages, to attend where the King with his Lordes and many chiefe leaders sate in counsell, there amongst sundrie serious matters that were debated, and intelligences from the

enemy given up, it was privily informed (no villains to these
privie informers) that you, even you that I nowe speake to,
had (O would I had no tong to tell the rest by this drinke it
grieves me so I am not able to repeate it.) Nowe was my
dronken Lord readie to hang himselfe for the ende of the full
point, and over my necke he throwes himself verie lubberly,
and intreated me as I was a proper young Gentleman, and ever
lookt for pleasure at his handes, soone to rid him out of this
hell of suspence, and resolve him of the rest, then fell hee on
his knees, wrong his handes, and I thinke on my conscience,
wepte out all the syder that he had dronke in a weeke before,
to move mee to have pittie on him, he rose and put his rustie
ring on my finger, gave mee his greasie purse with that single
mony that was in it, promised to make mee his heire, and a
thousand more favours, if I woulde expire the miserie of his
unspeakable tormenting uncertaintie. I beeing by nature
inclined to *Mercie* (for in deede I knew two or three good wenches
of that name), bad him harden his eares, and not make his eies
abortive before theyr time, and he should have the inside of
my brest turned outward, heare such a tale as would tempt the
utmost strength of lyfe to attend it, and not die in the midst
of it. Why (quoth I,) my selfe that am but a poore childish
well-willer of yours, with the verie thought, that a man of your
deserte and state, by a number of pesants and varlets shoulde
be so injuriously abused in hugger mugger, have wepte all my
urine upwarde. The wheele under our citie bridge, carries not
so much water over the citie, as my braine hath welled forth
gushing streames of sorrow, I have wepte so immoderately and
lavishly, that I thought verily my palat had bin turned to
pissing Conduit in *London*. My eyes have bin dronke, outragiously dronke, wyth giving but ordinarie entercourse through
their sea-circled Ilands to my distilling dreriment. What shal
I say? that which malice hath saide is the meere overthrow
and murther of these daies. Change not your colour, none
can slander a cleere conscience to it self, receive al your fraught
of misfortune in at once.

It is buzzed in the Kings head that you are a secret frend
to the Enemie, and under pretence of getting a License to
furnish the Campe with syder and such like provant, you have
furnisht the Enemie, and in emptie barrels sent letters of
discoverie, and corne innumerable.

I might wel have left here, for by this time his white liver
had mixt it selfe with the white of his eye, and both were

turned upwards, as if they had offered themselves a faire white for death to shoote at. The troth was, I was verie loath mine hoste and I should part with drye lips: wherefore the best meanes that I could imagine to wake hym out of his traunce, was to crie loud in his eare, Hoe hoste, whats to pay? will no man looke to the reckoning here? And in plaine veritie it tooke expected effect, for with the noyse he started and bustled, lyke a man that had beene scarde with fire out of his sleepe, and ran hastely to his Tapster, and all to belaboured him about the eares, for letting Gentlemen call so long, and not looke in to them. Presently he remembred himselfe, and had like to fall into his memento againe, but that I met him halfe waies, and askt his Lordship what hee meant to slip his necke out of the collar so sodainly, and being revived stryke hys Tapster so hastely?

Oh (quoth he), I am bought and sold for dooing my Countrey such good service as I have done. They are afraid of me, because my good deedes have brought me into such estimation with the Comminaltie. I see, I see, it is not for the lambe to live with the wolfe.

The world is well amended (thought I) with your Sidership; such another fortie yeares nap together as *Epimenides* had, would make you a perfect wise man. Answere me (quoth he) my wise yong *Wilton*, is it true that I am thus underhand dead and buried by these bad tongues?

Nay (quoth I) you shall pardon me, for I have spoken too much alreadie, no definitive sentence of death shall march out of my well meaning lips: they have but lately suckt milke, and shall they so sodainly change their food and seeke after bloud?

Oh, but (quoth he) a mans friend is his friend, fill the other pint Tapster: what said the King, did he beleeve it when he heard it? I pray thee say, I sweare by my Nobilitie; none in the world shall ever be made privie, that I received anie light of this matter by thee.

That firme affiance (quoth I) had I in you before, or else I wold never have gone so farre over the shooes, to plucke you out of the myre. Not to make manie words (since you will needs knowe) the King saies flatly; you are a myser and a snudge, and he never hoped better of you. Nay, then (quoth he) questionles some Planet that loves not Syder hath conspired against me. Moreover, which is worse, the King hath vowed to give *Turwin* one hot breakfast, onely with the bungs that he will plucke out of your barrells. I cannot stay at thys time to report each circumstaunce that passed, but the onely counsell that my long cherished kinde inclination can possibly contrive, is now in your old daies to be liberall, such victualls or provision as you have, presently distribute it frankely amongst poore Souldiers, I would let them burst their bellies with Syder, and bathe in it, before I would run into my Princes ill opinion for a whole sea of it. The hunter pursuing the Beaver for his stones, he bites them off, and leaves them behinde for him to gather up, whereby he lives quiet. If greedy hunters and hungrie tale-tellers pursue you, it is for a litle pelfe that you have, cast it behinde you, neglect it, let them have it, least it breede a farther inconvenience. Credit my advice, you shall finde it propheticall: and thus have I discharged the part of a poore frend. With some few like phrases of ceremonie, your Honors poore supliant, and so forth, and farewell my good youth, I thanke thee, and wil remember thee, we parted. But the next day I thinke we had a doale of syder, syder in bowles, in scuppets, in helmets: and to conclude, if a man wold have fild his boots full, ther he might have had it: provant thrust it selfe into poore souldiers pockets whether they would or no. Wee made five peales of shot into the towne together, of nothing but spiggots and faucets of discarded emptie barrels: everie under-foot souldior had a distenanted tun, as *Diogenes* had his tub to sleepe in. I my selfe got as manie confiscated Tapsters aprons as made me a Tent, as big as anie ordinarie Commaunders in the field. But in conclusion, my welbeloved Baron of double beere got him humbly on hys mary-bones to the King, and complained he was old and striken in yeares, and had never an heire to cast at a dogge, wherfore if it might please his Majestie to take his lands into his hands, and allowe hym some reasonable pension to live, he shuld be mervailously wel pleased: as for warres he was weary of them, yet as long as his highnes ventred his owne person, he would not flinch a foot, but make his wythered bodie a buckler to beare off any blow advanced against him.

The King mervailing at this alteration of his syder-merchant (for so he often pleasantly tearmd him) with a litle farther talk bolted out the the whole complotment. Then was I pitifully whipt for my holiday lye, though they made themselves merrie with it manie a Winters evening after. For all this, his good asse-headed-honor, mine host, persevered in his former request to the King to accept his lands, and allow him a beadsmanrie or our-brothershippe of brachet: which through his vehement instancie tooke effect, and the King jestingly said, since he would needs have it so, he would distraine one part of his land for impost of syder, which he was behinde with.

This was one of my famous atchievements, insomuch as I never light upon the like famous Foole, but I have done a thousand better jests, if they had been bookt in order as they were begotten. It is pittie posteritie should be deprived of such precious Records: and yet there is no remedie, and yet there is too, for when all failes, welfare a good memorie. Gentle Readers (looke you be gentle now since I have cald you so), as freely as my knaverie was mine owne, it shall be yours to use in the way of honestie.

Even in this expedition of *Turwin* (for the King stood not long a thrumming of buttons there) it hapned me fall in (I would it had faln out otherwise for his sake) with an ugly mechanichall Captain. You must thinke in an Armie, where trunchions are in their state-house, it is a flat stab once to name a Captaine without cap in hand. Well, suppose he was a Captaine, and had never a good cap of his owne, but I was faine to lend him one of my Lords cast velvet caps, and a weather-beaten feather, wherewith he threatned his soldiers a far off, as *Jupiter* is said, with the shaking of his haire to make heaven and earth to quake. Suppose out of the parings of a paire of false dice, I apparelled both him and my selfe manie a time and oft: and surely, not to slander the divell, if anie man ever deserved the golden dice the King of the *Parthians* sent to *Demetrius* it was I. I had the right vayne of sucking up a die twixt the dints of my fingers, not a crevise in my hand but could swallow a quater trey for a neede: in the line of life manie a dead lift did there lurke, but it was nothing towards the maintenance of a familie. This Monsieur Capitano eate up the creame of my earnings, and *Crede mihi, res est ingeniosa dare,* any man is a fine fellow as long as he hath any money in his purse. That money is like the Marigold, which opens and shuts with the Sunne: if fortune smileth or one bee in favour, it floweth; if the evening of Age comes on, or he falls into disgrace, it fadeth and is not to be found. I was my crafts-master though I were but yong, and could as soone decline *Nominativo hic Asinus,* as a greater Clearke, wherefore I thought it not convenient my Soldado should have my purs any longer for his drum to play uppon, but I would give him Jacke Drums entertainment, and send him packing.

This was my plot: I knewe a peece of service of Intelligence, which was presently to be done, that required a man with all his five senses to effect it, and would overthrow anie foole that should undertake it: to this service did I animate and egge my foresaid costs and charges, alias, Senior velvet-cap, whose head was not encombred with too much forcast; and comming to him in his cabbin about dinner time, where I found him very devoutly paring of his nayles for want of other repast, I entertained him with this solemne oration.

Captaine, you perceive how nere both of us are driven, the dice of late are growen as melancholy as a dog, high men and low men both prosper alike, langrets, fullams, and all the whole fellowshippe of them, will not affoord a man his dinner, some other meanes must be invented to prevent imminent extremitie. My state, you are not ignorant, depends on trencher service, your advancement must be derived from the valour of your arme. In the delaies of Siege, desert hardly gets a day of hearing: tis gowns must direct and guns enact all the warres that is to be made against walls. Resteth no way for you to clime sodenly, but by doing some rare stratageme, the like not before heard of: and fitlie at this time occasion is offered.

There is a feate the King is desirous to have wrought on some great Man of the Enemies side: marrie it requireth not so much resolution as discretion to bring it to passe; and yet resolution inough should be showne in it too, being so ful of hazardous jeopardie as it is, harke in your eare, thus it is: without more drumbling or pawsing, if you will undertake it, and worke it through stitch (as you maye, ere the King hath determined which waie to goe about it) I warrant you are made while you live, you need not care which way your staffe falls, if it prove not so, then cut off my head.

Oh my Auditors, had you seene him how he stretcht out his lims, scratcht his scabd elbowes at this speach, how hee set his cap over his ey-browes like a polititian, and then folded his armes one in another, and nodded with the head, as who would say, let the French beware for they shall finde me a divell: if (I say) you had seene but halfe the action that he used, of shrucking up his shoulders, smiling scornfully, playing with his fingers on his buttons, and biting the lip; you wold have laught your face and your knees together. The yron being hot, I thought to lay on load, for in anie case I would not have his humor coole. As before I laid open unto him the briefe summe of the service, so now I began to urge the honorableness of it, and what a rare thing it was to be a right polititian, how much esteemd of Kings and princes, and how diverse of meane

Parentage have come to bee Monarchs by it. Then I discourst of the quallities and properties of him in every respect, how like the Woolfe he must drawe the breath from a man long before he bee seene, how like a Hare he must sleepe with his eyes open, how as the Eagle in his flying casts dust in the eyes of Crowes and other Fowles, for to blinde them, so hee must cast dust in the eyes of his enemies, delude their sight by one meanes or other that they dive not into his subtleties: howe hee must be familiar with all and trust none, drinke, carouse, and lecher with him out of whom he hopes to wring any matter, sweare and forsweare, rather than be suspected, and in a word, have the Art of dissembling at his fingers ends as perfect as any Courtier.

Perhaps (quoth I) you may have some fewe greasie Cavailiers that will seeke to disswade you from it, and they will not sticke to stand on their three halfe penny honour, swearing and staring that a man were better be a hangman than an Intelligencer, and call him a sneaking Eavesdropper, a scraping hedgecreeper, and a piperly pickethanke, but you must not be discouraged by their talke, for the most part of these beggarly contemners of wit, are huge burly-bond Butchers like *Aiax*, good for nothing but to strike right downe blowes on a wedge with a cleaving beetle, or stand hammering all day upon barres of yron. The whelpes of a Beare never growe but sleeping, and these Beare-wards having bigge lims shall be preferd though they doo nothing. You have read stories, (Ile be sworne he never lookt in booke in his life) howe many of the Romaine worthies were there that have gone as Spialls into their Enemies Campe? *Ulysses, Nestor, Diomed*, went as spies together in the night into the Tents of *Rhœsus*, and intercepted *Dolon* the spie of the Trojans: never any discredited the trade of Intelligencers but *Judas*, and he hanged himselfe. Danger will put wit into any man. *Archytas* made a woodden Dove to flie; by which pro-portion I see no reason that the veryest blocke in the worlde shoulde dispayre of any thing. Though nature be contrary inclined, it may be altred, yet usually those whom shee denies her ordinary gifts in one thing, shee doubles them in another. That which the Asse wants in wit, hee hath in honesty, who ever sawe him kicke or winch, or use any jades tricks? though he live an hundred yeares you shall never heare that he breaks pasture. Amongst men, he that hath not a good wit, lightly hath a good yron memory, and he that hath neither of both, hath some bones to carry burthens. Blinde men have better

noses than other men: the buls hornes serve him as well as hands
to fight withall, the Lyons pawes are as good to him as a pol-
axe to knocke downe anye that resist him, the bores tushes
serve him in better steed than a sword and buckler: what neede
the snaile care for eyes, when hee feeles the way with his two
hornes, as well as if he were as quicke sighted as a decypherer.
There is a fish, that having no wings supports herselfe in the
aire with her finnes. Admit that you had neither wit nor
capacitie, as sure in my judgement there is none equall unto
you in idiotisme, yet if you have simplicitie and secrecie, serpents themselves wil thinke you a serpent, for what serpent is
there but hydes his sting: and yet whatsoever be wanting, a
good plausible tongue in such a man of imployment, can hardly
be sparde, which as the fore-named serpent, with his winding
taile fetcheth in those that come nere him, so with a ravishing
tale it gathers al mens harts unto him: which if he have not let
him never looke to ingender by the mouth as ravens and doves
do, that is, mount or be great by undermining. Sir, I am
ascertained that all these imperfections I speak of in you have
their naturall resiance. I see in your face, that you wer born
with the swallow to feed flying, to get much tresure and honor
by travell. None so fit as you for so important an enterprise:
our vulgar polititians are but flies swimming on the streame of
subtilitie superficially in comparison of your singularitie, their
blinde narrow eyes cannot pierce into the profundity of hypocrisie, you alone with *Palamed*, can pry into *Ulysses* mad
counterfeting, you can discerne *Achilles* from a chamber maide,
though he be deckt with his spindle and distaffe: as *Jove* dining
with *Licaon* could not bee beguiled with humane fleshe drest
like meate, so no humane braine may goe beyond you, none
beguile you, you gull all, all feare you, love you, stoup to you.
Therefore good sir be ruld by me, stoup your fortune so low,
as to bequeath your selfe wholy to this busines.

This silver-sounding tale made such sugred harmonie in his
eares, that with the sweete meditation, what a more than
myraculous polititian he should be, and what kingly promotion
shuld come tumbling on him thereby, he could have found in
his hart to have packt up his pipes, and to have gone to heaven
without a bait: yea, hee was more inflamed and ravishte with
it, than a yong man called *Taurimontanus* was with the *Phrigian*
melodie, who was so incensed and fired therwith, that he would
needs run presently upon it, and set a Curtizans house on fire
that had angred him.

No remedie there was, but I must help to furnish him with mony. I did so, as who will not make his enemie a bridge of gold to flie by. Verie earnestly he conjurde me to make no man living privie to hys departure, in regard of his place and charge, and on his honor assured me, his returne should be verie short and successfull. I, I, shorter by the necke (thought I) in the meane time let this be thy posie, *I live in hope to scape the rope.*

Gone he is, God send him good shipping to Wapping, and by this time if you will, let him be a pitiful poore fellow, and undone for ever: for mine own part, if he had bin mine own brother, I could have done no more for him than I did, for straight after his back was turnd I went in all love and kindnes to the Marshall generall of the field, and certifide him that such a man was lately fled to the Enemie, and got his place begd for another immediately: what became of him after you shall heare. To the Enemie he went and offred his service, rayling egregiously against the King of *England,* he swore, as he was a Gentleman and a souldier, he would be revenged on him: and let but the King of *France* follow his counsel, he would drive him from *Turwin* wals yet ere three daies to an end. All these were good humors, but the tragedie followeth. The French King hearing of such a prating fellow that was come, desired to see him, but yet he feared treson, willing one of his Minions to take upon him his person, and he wold stand by as a private person while he was examined. Why should I use anie idle delaies? In was Captaine gogs wounds brought, after hee was throughly searched, not a louse in his doublet was let passe, but was askt *Quevela,* and chargd to stand in the Kings name, the molds of his buttons they turnd out, to see if they were not bullets covered over with thred, the cod-piece in his divels breeches (for they wer then in fashion) they said plainly was a case for a pistol: if he had had ever a hob-naile in his shooes it had hangd him, and hee should never have known who had harmd him, but as lucke was, he had no myte of any mettall about him, he tooke part with none of the foure Ages, neyther the golden Age, the silver Age, the brazen nor the yron Age, onely his purse was aged in emptines, and I think verily a puritane, for it kept it selfe from any pollution of crosses. Standing before the supposed King, he was askt what he was, and wherefore he came? To which, in a glorious bragging humor he answered, that he was a gentleman a capten commander, a chiefe leader, that came from the King of *England* upon discontentment. Questiond of the perticular cause, he had not a word to blesse himselfe with, yet faine he would have patcht out a polt-foot tale, but (God knowes) it had not one true leg to stand on.

Then began he to smell on the villaine so rammishly, that none there but was ready to rent him in pieces, yet the Minion King kept in his cholar, and propounded unto him further, what of the King of Englands secrets (so advantageable) he was privy to, as might remoove him from the siege of Turwin in three daies. He said diverse, diverse matters, which askt longer conference, but in good honesty they were lies, which he had not yet stampt. Hereat the true King stept forth, and commaunded to lay hande on the Lozell, and that he should be tortured to confesse the truth, for he was a spie and nothing else.

He no sooner sawe the wheele and the torments set before him, but he cryde out like a Rascall, and said he was a poore Captaine in the English Campe, suborned by one *Jacke Wilton* (a Noble mans Page) and no other, to come and kill the French King in a braverie and returne, and that he had no other intention in the world.

This confession could not choose but moove them all to laughter, in that he made it as light a matter to kill their King and come backe, as to goe to Islington and eate a messe of Creame, and come home againe, nay, and besides he protested that he had no other intention, as if that were not inough to hang him.

Adam never fell till God made fooles, all this could not keepe his joynts from ransacking on the Wheele, for they vowed either to make him a Confessor or a Martyr with a trice: when still he sung all one song, they told the King he was a foole, and that some shrewd head had knavishly wrought on him, wherefore it should stand with his honour to whip him out of the Campe and send him home. That perswasion tooke place, and soundly was he lasht out of their liberties, and sent home by a Herrald with this message, that so the King his Master hoped to whip home all the English fooles very shortly: answere was returned, that that shortly, was a long-lie, and they were shrewd fooles that should drive the French-man out of his Kingdome, and make him glad with Corinthian *Dionisius* to play the Schoolemaster.

The Herrald being dismist, our afflicted Intelligencer was calde *coram nobis*, how he sped judge you, but something he was adjudged too. The sparrow for his lechery liveth but a yeare, he for his trechery was turnd on the toe, *Plura dolor prohibet.*

II

Here let me triumph a while, and ruminate a line or two on the excellence of my wit, but I will not breath neither till I have disfraughted all my knaverie.

Another Switzer Captaine that was farre gone for want of the wench, I lead astray most notoriously, for he being a monstrous unthrift of battle-axes (as one that cared not in his anger to bid flye out scuttels to five score of them) and a notable emboweler of quart pots, I came disguised unto him in the forme of a halfe crowne wench, my gowne and attyre according to the custome then in request. Iwis I had my curtsies in cue or in quart pot rather, for they dyvide into the verie entrailes of the dust, and I sympered with my countenance like a porredge pot on the fire when it first begins to seethe. The sobriety of the circumstance is, that after hee had courted mee and all, and given me the earnest-penie of impietie, some sixe Crownes at the least for an antipast to iniquitie, I fained an impregnable excuse to be gone and never came at him after.

Yet left I not here, but committed a little more scutcherie. A companie of coystrell Clearkes (who were in band with Sathan, and not of anie Souldiers collar nor hat-band) pincht a number of good mindes to God-ward of their provant. They would not let a dram of dead-pay over-slip them, they would not lend a groat of the weeke to come, to him that had spent his money before this weeke was done. They out-faced the greatest and most magnanimious Servitors in their sincere and finigraphicall cleane shirts and cuffes. A Lowce (that was anie Gentlemans companion) they thought scorne of, their nere bitten beards must in a devills name bee dewed everye day with Rose-water, Hogges could have nere a haire on their backs for making them rubbing-brushes to rouse their Crab-lice. They would in no wise permit that the moates in the Sunbeames should be full mouthd beholders of their cleane phinifide apparel, their shooes shined as bright as a slikestone, their hands troubled and soyled more water with washing, than the Cammell doth, that never drinkes till the whole streame be troubled. Summarily, never anie were so fantasticall the one halfe as they.

My masters, you may conceave of me what you list, but I thinke confidently I was ordained Gods scourge from above for their daintie finicalitie. The houre of their punishment could no longer be proroged, but vengeance must have at them, at all a ventures. So it was, that the most of these above-named goose-quill Braggadoches, were mere cowards and cravens, and durst not so much as throwe a pen-full of inke into the Enemies face, if proofe were made: wherefore on the experience of their pusillanimitie I thought to raise the foundation of my roguerie.

What did I now but one day made a false alarum in the quarter where they lay, to try how they would stand to their tackling, and with a pittifull out-crie warned them to flie, for there was treason a foote, they were invironed and beset. Upon the first watch worde of treason that was given, I thinke they betooke them to their heeles verie stoutly, left their penne and inke-hornes and paper behinde them, for spoile resigned their deskes, with the money that was in them to the mercie of the vanquisher, and in fine, left me and my fellowes (their foole-catchers) Lordes of the field: How wee dealt with them, their disburdened deskes canne best tell, but this I am assured, we fared the better for it a fortnight of fasting dayes after.

I must not place a volume in the precincts of a pamphlet: sleepe an houre or two, and dreame that Turney and Turwin is wonne, that the King is shipt againe into England, and that I am close at harde meate at Windsore or at Hampton Court. What will you in your indifferent opinions allow me for my travell, no more signiorie over the Pages than I had before? yes, whether you will part with so much probable friendly suppose or no, Ile have it in spite of your hearts. For your instruction and godly consolation, bee informed, that at that time I was no common squire, no undertrodden torch-bearer, I had my feather in my cap as big as a flag in the fore-top, my French dublet gelte in the bellie as though (like a pig readie to be spitted) all my guts had bin pluckt out, a paire of side paned hose that hung downe like two scales filled with Holland cheeses, my longe stock that sate close to my docke, and smoothered not a scab or a leacherous hairie sinew on the calfe of the legge, my rapier pendant like a round sticke fastned in the tacklings for skippers the better to climbe by, my cape cloake of blacke cloth, overspreading my backe like a thorne-backe, or an Elephantes eare, that hanges on his shoulders like a countrie huswives banskin, which she thirles hir spindle on, and in consummation of my curiositie, my hands without glooves, all a more French, and a blacke budge edging of a beard on the upper lip, and the like sable auglet of excrements in the rising

of the anckle of my chinne. I was the first that brought in the
order of passing into the Court which I derived from the common
word *Qui passa*, and the Heralds phrase of armes *Passant*,
thinking in sinceritie, he was not a Gentleman, nor his armes
currant, who was not first past by the Pages. If anie Prentise
or other came into the Court that was not a Gentleman, I
thought it was an indignitie to the preheminence of the Court
to include such a one, and could not bee salvde except wee gave
him Armes Passant, to make him a Gentleman.

Besides, in Spaine, none passe anie farre way but he must be
examined what he is, and give three pence for his passe.

In which regard it was considered of by the common table
of the cupbearers, what a perilsome thing it was to let anie
stranger or out dweller approch so neare the precincts of the
Prince, as the greate Chamber, without examining what hee
was, and giving him his passe, whereupon we established the like
order, but tooke no mony of them as they did, onely for a signe
that he had not past our hands unexamined, we set a red marke
on their eares, and so let them walke as authenticall.

I must not discover what ungodlie dealing we had with the
blacke jackes, or how oft I was crowned King of the drunkardes
with a Court cuppe, let mee quietly descend to the waining
of my youthfull daies, and tell a little of the sweating sicknes,
that made me in a cold sweate take my heeles and runne out
of England.

This sweating sicknes, was a disease that a man then might
catch and never goe to a hot-house. Manie Masters desire to have
such servants as would worke till they sweate againe, but in
those dayes hee that sweate never wrought againe. That
Scripture then was not thought so necessarie, which sayes,
Earne thy living with the sweat of thy browes, for then they
earnd their dying with the sweat of their browes. It was
inough if a fat man did but trusse his points, to turne him over
the pearch: Mother *Cornelius* tub why it was like hell, he that
came into it, never came out of it.

Cookes that stand continually basting their faces before the
fire, were now all cashierd with this sweat into kitchin stuffe:
their hall fell into the Kings hands for want of one of the trade
to uphold it.

Felt makers and Furriers, what the one with the hot steame
of their wooll new taken out of the pan, and the other with the
contagious heat of their slaughter budge and connie-skinnes,
died more thicke than of the pestelence: I have seene an old

woman at that season having three chins, wipe them all away one after another, as they melted to water, and left hir selfe nothing of a mouth but an upper chap. Looke how in May or the heat of Summer we lay butter in water for feare it should melt away, so then were men faine to wet their clothes in water as Diers doo, and hide themselves in welles from the heat of the Sunne.

Then happie was he that was an asse, for nothing will kill an asse but colde, and none dide but with extreame heate. The fishes called Sea-starres, that burne one another by excessive heate, were not so contagious as one man that had the Sweate was to another. Masons paid nothing for haire to mixe their lyme, nor Glovers to stuffe their balls with, for then they had it for nothing, it dropped off mens heads and beards faster than anie Barber could shave it. O, if haire breeches had then been in fashion, what a fine world had it beene for Tailers, and so it was a fine world for Tailers neverthelesse, for he that could make a garment sleightest and thinnest carried it awaie: Cutters I can tell you then stood upon it to have their Trade one of the twelve Companies, for who was it then that would not have his dublet cut to the skin, and his shirt cut into it too, to make it more cold. It was as much as a mans life was worth ones to name a freeze jerkin, it was hye treason for a fat grosse man to come within five miles of the Court. I heard where they dyde up all in one Familie, and not a mothers childe escapde, insomuch as they had but an Irish rugge lockt up in a presse, and not laid upon anie bed neither, if those that were sicke of this maladie slept of it, they never wakde more. Phisitions with their simples, in this case wext simple fellowes, and knew not which way to bestirre them.

Galen might goe shooe the Gander for any good he could doo, his Secretaries had so long called him Divine, that now he had lost all his vertue upon earth. *Hippocrates* might well helpe Almanacke-makers, but here he had not a word to say: a man might sooner catch the sweate with plodding over him to no end, than cure the sweate with anie of his impotent principles. *Paracelsus* with his Spirite of the Butterie and his spirites of Mineralls, could not so much as saye, God amend him to the matter. *Plus erat in artifice quam arte,* there was more infection in the Phisition himselfe than his arte could cure. This Mortalitie first began amongst old men, for they taking a pride to have their breasts loose basted with tedious beards, kept their houses so hot with their hayry excrements, that not so much but their verie walls sweat out salt-peeter, with the smothering perplexitie: nay a number of them had mervailous hot breaths, which sticking in the briers of their bushie beards, could not choose, but (as close aire long imprisoned) ingender corruption.

Wiser was our Brother *Bankes* of these latter daies, who made his jugling horse a Cut, for feare if at anie time hee should foyst, the stinke sticking in his thicke bushie taile might be noysome to his Auditors. Should I tell you how manie Pursevants with red noses, and Sergeants with precious faces shrunke away in this Sweate, you would not beleeve me. Even as the Salamander with his very sight blasteth apples on the trees: so a Pursevant or a Sergeant at this present, with the verie reflexe of his fierie facies, was able to spoyle a man a farre of. In some places of the world there is no shaddowe of the Sunne, *Diebus illis* if it had been so in *England,* the generation of *Brute* had died all and some. To knit up this description in a pursnet, so fervent and scorching was the burning aire which inclosed them, that the most blessed man then alive, would have thought that God had done fairly by him, if hee had turnd him to a Goate, for Goates take breath not at the mouth or nose onely, but at the eares also.

Take breath how they would, I vowd to tarrie no longer among them. As at *Turwin* I was a demy souldier in jest: so now I became a Martialist in earnest. Over Sea with my implements I got mee, where hearing the King of *France* and the *Switzers* were together by the eares, I made towards them as fast as I could, thinking to thrust my selfe into that Faction that was strongest. It was my good lucke or my ill (I know not which) to come just to the fighting of the Battell: where I saw a wonderfull spectacle of blood-shed on both sides, here unweeldie *Switzers* wallowing in their gore, like an Oxe in his dung, there the sprightly *French* sprawling and turning on the stained grasse, like a Roach new taken out of the streame: all the ground was strewed as thicke with Battle-axes, as the Carpenters yard with chips, the Plaine appeared like a quagmyre, overspred as it were with trampled dead bodies. In one place might you behold a heape of dead murthered men overwhelmed with a falling Steede, in stead of a toombe stone: in another place, a bundell of bodies fettered together in their owne bowells: and as the tyrant Romane Emperours used to tye condemned living caytives face to face to dead corses, so were the halfe living here mixt with squeazed carcases long putrifide. Anie man might give Armes that was an actor in that Battell, for there were more armes and legs scattered in the Field that day, than will be gathered up till Doomes-day: the French King himselfe in this Conflict was much distressed, the braines of his owne men sprinkled in his face, thrice was his Courser slaine under him, and thrice was he strucke on the brest with a speare: but in the end, by the helpe of the *Venetians*, the *Helvetians* or *Switzers* were subdude, and he crowned a Victor, a peace concluded, and the Citie of *Millaine* surrendred unto him, as a pledge of reconciliation.

III

That Warre thus blowen over, and the severall Bands dissolved, like a Crowe that still followes aloofe where there is carrion, I flew me over to *Munster* in *Germanie*, which an Anabaptisticall Brother named *John Leiden*, kept at that instant against the Emperour and the Duke of *Saxonie*. Here I was in good hope to set upp my staffe for some reasonable time, deeming that no Citie would drive it to a siedge, except they were able to hold out: and pretely well had these *Munsterians* held out, for they kept the Emperour and the Duke of *Saxonie* play for the space of a yere, and longer would have done, but that Dame Famine came amongst them: whereuppon they were forst by Messengers to agree upon a day of Fight, when according to their Anabaptisticall errour they might al be new christened in their owne blood.

That day come, flourishing entred *John Leiden* the Botcher into the field, with a scarffe made of lysts like a bow-case, a crosse on hys breast like a thred bottome, a round twilted Taylors cushion, buckled like a Tankard-bearers device to his shoulders for a target, the pyke whereof was a pack-needle, a tough prentisse club for his spear, a great Bruers cow on his backe for a corslet, and on his head for a helmet a huge high shooe with the bottome turnd upwards, embossed as full of hob-nayles as ever it might sticke: his men were all base handicrafts, as coblers, and curriers and tinkers, whereof some had barres of yron, some hatchets, some coole-staves, some dungforkes, some spades, some mattockes, some wood-knives, some, addises for their weapons: he that was best provided, had but a peece of a rustie browne bill bravely fringed with cop-webs to fight for him. Perchance here and there you might see a felow that had a canker-eaten scull on his head, which served him and his ancestors, for a chamber pot two hundred yeeres, and another that had bent a couple of yron dripping pans armour-wise, to fence his back and his belly, another that had thrust a paire of dire olde bootes as a breast-plate before his belly of his dublet, because he would not be dangerously hurt: an other that had twilted all his trusse full of counters, thinking if the Enemie should take him, he would mistake them for gold, and so save his life for his money. Verie devout Asses they were, for all they were so dunstically set forth, and such as thought they knew as much of Gods minde as richer men: why inspiration was their ordinarie familiar, and buzd in their eares like a Bee in a boxe everie hower what newes from heaven, hell, and the land of whipperginnie, displease them who durst, he should have his mittimus to damnation *ex tempore*, they would vaunt there was not a pease difference betwixt them and the Apostles, they were as poore as they, of as base trades as they, and no more inspired than they, and with God there is no respect of persons, onely herein may seeme some little diversitie to lurk, that *Peter* wore a sword, and they count it flat hel fire for anie man to weare a dagger: nay, so grounded and gravelled were they in this opinion, that now when they should come to Battell, theres never a one of them would bring a blade (no, not an onion blade) about hym to dye for it. It was not lawfull said they, for anie man to draw the sword but the Magistrate: and in fidelitie (which I had welnigh forgot) *Jacke Leiden* their Magistrate had the Image or likenes of a peece of a rustie sword like a lustie lad by his side: now I remember mee, it was but a foyle neither, and he wore it, to shewe that hee should have the foyle of his Enemies, which might have been an oracle for his two-hand Interpretation. *Quid plura?* His Battell is pitcht: by pitcht, I doo not meane set in order, for that was farre from their order, onely as Sailers doo pitch their apparell to make it storm proofe, so had most of them pitcht their patcht clothes to make them impearceable: a neerer way than to be at the charges of armour by halfe. And in another sort he might be said to have pitcht the Field, for he had pitcht or rather set up his rest whither to flie if they were discomfited.

Peace, peace there in the belfrie, service begins, upon their knees before they joine fals *John Leiden* and his fraternitie verie devoutly, they pray, they howle, they expostulate with God to grant them victorie, and use such unspeakable vehemence, a man wold thinke them the onely wel bent men under heaven. Wherin let me dilate a litle more gravely, than the nature of this historie requires, or wilbe expected of so yong a practitioner in divinity: that not those that intermissively cry *Lord open unto us, Lord open unto us* enter first into the kingdom, that not the greatest professors have the greatest portion in grace, that all is not gold that glisters.   When Christ said, *the king-dome of heaven must suffer violence,* hee meant not the violence of long babling praiers, nor the violence of tedious invective Sermons without wit, but the violence of faith, the violence of good works, the violence of patient suffering. The ignorant snatch the kingdome of heaven to themselves with greedines, when we with all our learning sinke into hell.

Where did *Peter* and *John* in the third of the Acts, finde the lame cripple but in the gate of the temple called beautifull, in the beautifullest gates of our temple, in the forefront of professors, are many lame cripples, lame in life, lame in good workes, lame in everie thing, yet will they alwaies sit at the gates of the temple, none be more forwarde then they to enter into matters of reformation, yet none more behinde hand to enter into the true Temple of the Lord by the gates of good life.

You may object, that those which I speake against, are more diligent in reading the Scriptures, more carefull to resort unto Sermons, more sober in their lookes, more modest in their attire, than anie else.   But I pray you let me answere you, Doth not Christ say, that before the Latter day the Sunne shall be turned into darknesse, and the Moone into bloud: whereof what may be the meaning bee, but that the glorious Sunne of the Gospell shall be eclipsed with the dim clowd of dissimulation, that that which is the brightest Planet of salva-tion, shall be a meanes of error and darknes: and the Moone shall be turned into blood, those that shine fairest, make the simplest shewe, seeme most to favour Religion, shal rent out the bowels of the church, be turned into blood, and all this shall come to passe before the notable day of the Lord, whereof this Age is the Eve.

Let me use a more familiar example, since the heate of a great number outraged so excessively.   Did not the Divell lead Christ to the pinacle or highest place of the Temple to tempt him?   If he led Christ, he will lead a whole Armie of hypocrites to the top or highest part of the Temple, the highest step of Religion and Holines, to seduce them and subvert them.   I say unto you that which this our tempted Saviour with manie other words besought his Disciples, *Save your selves from this froward generation. Verily, verily, the servant is not greater than his master:* Verily, verily, sinfull men are not holier than holy Jesus their maker. That holy Jesus again repeates this holy sentence, *Remember the words I said unto you, the servaunt is not holier nor greater than his Master:* as if he should say, Remember then, imprint in your memorie, your pride and singularitie wyll make you forget them, the effects of them manie yeeres hence will come to passe. *Whosoever will seeke to save his soule shall loose it:* whosoever seekes by headlong meanes to enter into Heaven, and disanull Gods ordinance, shall with the Gyaunts that thought to scale heaven in contempt of *Jupiter,* be over-whelmed with Mount *Ossa* and *Peleon,* and dwell with the divell in eternall desolation.

Though the High Priests office was expired, when *Paul* said unto one of them, God rebuke thee thou painted sepulcher: yet when a stander by reprooved him, saying: Revilest thou the High Priest? he repented and askt forgivenes.

That which I suppose I doe not grant, the lawfulnes of the authoritie they oppose themselves against is sufficiently proved: farre be it my under-age arguments should intrude themselves as a greene weake prop to support so high a Building: let it suffice, If you know Christ, you know his Father also: if you know Christianitie, you know the Fathers of the Church also. But a great number of you with *Philip* have beene long with Christ, and have not knowen him, have long professed your selves Christians and have not knowen his true Ministers: you follow the French and Scottish fashion and faction, and in all poynts are like the Switzers, *Qui quærunt, cum qua Gente cadant,* that seeke with what Nation they may first miscarrie.

In the dayes of *Nero* there was an odde Fellowe that had found out an exquisite way to make glasse as hammer-proofe as golde: shall I say, that the like experiment he made upon glasse, wee have practised on the Gospell? I, confidently will I: Wee have found out a sleight to hammer it to anie Heresie whatsoever. But those furnaces of Falshood, and hammerheads of Heresie must bee dissolved and broken as his was, or els I feare mee the false glittering glasse of Innovation will bee better esteemed of, than the auncient golde of the Gospell.

The fault of faults is this, that your dead borne faith is begotten by too-too infant Fathers. *Cato* one of the wisest men in Romane Histories canonised, was not borne till his father was foure score yeres olde: none can be a perfect father

of faith and beget men aright unto God, but those that are
aged in experience, have manie yeres imprinted in their milde
conversation, and have with *Zacheus* solde all their possessions
of vanities to enjoy the sweet fellowship, not of the humane
but spirituall *Messias*.

Ministers and Pastors, sell away your sects and schismes to
the decrepite Churches in contention beyond sea, they have
been so long inured to warre, both about matters of Religion
and Regiment, that now they have no peace of minde, but in
troubling all other mens peace. Because the povertie of their
Provinces will allow them no proportionable maintenance for
higher callings of ecclesiasticall Magistrates, they wold reduce
us to the president of their rebellious persecuted beggerie: much
like the sect of Philosophers called Cynikes, who when they
saw they were born to no lands or possessions, nor had any
possible meanes to support their estates, but they must live
despised and in misery doo what they could, they plotted and
consulted with themselves how to make their povertie better
esteemed of than rich dominion and sovereigntie. The upshot
of their plotting and consultation was this, that they would
live to themselves, scorning the very breath or companie of
all men, they profest (according to the rate of their lands)
voluntarie povertie, thin fare and lying hard, contemning and
inveighing against all those as brute beasts whatsoever whome
the world had given anie reputation for riches or prosperitie.
Diogenes was one of the first and formost of the ring-leaders of
this rustie morositie, and he for all his nice dogged disposition,
and blunt deriding of worldly drosse, and the grosse felicitie
of fooles, was taken notwithstanding a little after verie fairely
a coyning monie in his cell: so fares it upp and downe with our
cinicall reformed forraine Churches, they will disgest no grapes
of great Bishoprikes forsooth, because they cannot tell how
to come by them, they must shape their cotes good men according to their cloath and doe as they may, not as they wold, yet
they must give us leave here in England that are their honest
neighbours, if wee have more cloth than they, to make our
garment some what larger.

What was the foundation or ground-worke of this dismall
declining of Munster, but the banishing of their Bishop, their
confiscating and casting lots for Church livinges, as the souldiers
cast lottes for Christes garments, and in short tearmes, their
making the house of God a den of theeves. The house of God
a number of hungrie Church robbers in these dayes have made

a den of theeves. Theeves spend looselie what they have gotten lightly, sacriledge is no sure inheritance, *Dionisius* was nere the richer for robbing of *Jupiter* of his golden coate, hee was driven in the end to play the Schoolemaster at Corinth. The name of Religion, bee it good or bad that is ruinated, God never suffers unrevenged, Ile say of it as *Ovid* said of Eunuchs:

> *Qui primus pueris genitalia membra recidit,*
> *Vulnera quæ fecit debuit ipse pati.*

> Who first deprivde yong boies of their best part,
> With self seame wounds he gave he ought to smart.

So would he that first gelt religion or Church-livings had bin first gelt himselfe or never lived; Cardinall *Wolsey* is the man I aim at, *Qui in suas pœnas ingeniosus erat,* first gave others a light to his own overthrow. How it prospered with him and his instrumentes that after wrought for themselves, Chronicles largely report, though not applie, and some parcell of their punishment yet unpaid, I doe not doubt but will be required of their posteritie.

To goe forward with my storie of the overthrow of that usurper *John Leiden,* he and all his armie (as I saide before), falling prostrate on their faces, and fervently given over to praier, determined never to cease, or leave soliciting of God, till he had showed them from heaven some manifest miracle of successe.

Note that it was a generall received tradition both with *John Leiden* and all the crue of Cnipperdolings and Muncers, if God at any time at their vehement outcries and clamours did not condiscend to their requests, to raile on him and curse him to his face, to dispute with him, and argue him of injustice, for not beeing so good as his word with them, and to urge his manie promises in the Scripture against him: so that they did not serve God simplie, but that he should serve their turnes, and after that tenure are many content to serve as bondmen to save the danger of hanging: but hee that serves God aright, whose upright conscience hath for his mot, *Amor est mihi causa sequendi,* I serve because I love: he saies, *Ego te potius Domine quam tua dona sequar,* Ile rather follow thee O Lord, for thine own sake, than for anië covetous respect of that thou canst doe for mee.

Christ would have no followers, but such as forsooke all and followed him, such as forsake all their owne desires, such as abandon all expectations of reward in this world, such as neglected and contemned their lives, their wives and children in comparison of him, and were content to take up their crosse and follow him.

These Anabaptists had not yet forsooke all and followed Christ, they had not forsooke their owne desires of revenge and innovation, they had not abandoned their expectation of the spoile of their enimies, they regarded their lives, they lookt after their wives and children, they tooke not up their Crosses of humilitie and followed him, but would crosse him, upbraid him, and set him at nought, if he assured not by some signe their prayers and supplications. *Deteriora sequntur* they followed God as daring him. God heard their praiers, *Quod petitur pœna est,* It was their speedie punishment that they prayde for. Lo according to the summe of their impudent supplications, a signe in the heavens appeard the glorious signe of the rainebowe, which agreed just with the signe of their ensigne that was a rainbow likewise.

Whereupon, assuring themselves of victorie (*Miseri quod volunt, facile credunt*) that which wretches would have they easely beleeve. With showtes and clamors they presently ranne headlong on theyr well deserved confusion.

Pittifull and lamentable was their unpittied and well perfourmed slaughter. To see even a Beare, (which is the most cruellest of all beasts) too-too bloudily over-matcht, and deformedly rent in peeces by an unconscionable number of curres, it would moove compassion against kinde, and make those that (beholding him at the stake yet uncoapt with) wisht him a sutable death to his ugly shape, now to recall their hard-harted wishes, and moane him suffering as a milde beast, in comparison of the fowle mouthd Mastives, his butchers: even such compassion did those over-matcht ungracious *Munsterians* obtaine of manie indifferent eyes, who now thought them (suffering) to bee sheepe brought innocent to the shambles, when as before they deemed them as a number of wolves up in armes against the shepheards.

The Emperialls themselves that were their Executioners (like a father that weepes when he beates his childe, yet still weepes and stil beates) not without much ruth and sorrow prosecuted that lamentable massacre, yet drums and trumpets sounding nothing but stearne revenge in their eares, made them so eager, that their handes had no leasure to aske counsell of their effeminate eyes, their swordes, theyr pikes, their bills, their bowes, their caleevers slew, empierced, knockt downe, shot through and overthrew as manie men everie minute of the battell, as there falls eares of corne before the sythe at one blow: yet all their weapons so slaying, empiercing, knocking downe, shooting through, over-throwing, dissoule-joyned not halfe so manie, as the hailing thunder of the great Ordinance: so ordinarie at everie foot-step was the imbrument of yron in bloud, that one could hardly discern heads from bullets, or clottred haire from mangled flesh hung with goare.

This tale must at one time or other give up the ghost, and as good now as stay longer, I would gladly rid my handes of it cleanly, if I could tell how, for what with talking of coblers, tinkers, roape-makers, botchers and durt-daubers, the mark is clean out of my Muses mouth, and I am as it were more than duncified twixt divinity and poetrie. What is there more as touching this tragedie that you would be resolved of? say quickly, for now is my pen on foote againe. How *John Leyden* dyed, is that it? He dyde like a dogge, he was hangd and the halter paid for. For his companions, doe they trouble you? I can tell you they troubled some men before, for they were all kild, and none escapt, no not so much as one to tell the tale of the rainebow. Heare what it is to be Anabaptists, to be Puritans, to be villaines, you may bee counted illuminate botchers for a while, but your end will bee Good people pray for us.

With the tragicall catastrophe of this Munsterian conflict, did I cashier the new vocation of my cavaliership. There was no more honorable wars in christendome then towards, where-fore after I had learned to be halfe an houre in bidding a man *bonjure* in Germane synonimas, I travelled along the countrie towards England as fast as I could.

What with wagons and bare tentoes having attained to Middleborough (good Lord see the changing chances of us knights arrant infants) I met with the right honorable Lord *Henrie Howard* Earle of Surrey my late master, Jesu I was perswaded I should not bee more glad to see heaven than I was to see him, O it was a right noble Lord, liberalitie it selfe, (if in this yron age there were any such creature as liberalitie left on the earth) a Prince in content because a Poet without peere.

Destinie never defames hir selfe but when shee lets an excellent Poet die, if there bee anie sparke of Adams Paradized perfection yet emberd up in the breastes of mortall men, certainelie God hath bestowed that his perfectest image on Poets. None come so neere to God in wit, none more contemne the world, *vatis avarus non temere est animus,* sayth *Horace, versus amat, hoc studet unum,* Seldom have you seene anie Poet possessed with avarice, only verses he loves, nothing else he delights in: and as they contemne the world, so contrarilie of the mechanicall world are none more contemned. Despised they are of the worlde, because they are not of the world: their thoughts are exalted above the worlde of ignorance and all earthly conceits.

As sweet Angelicall queristers they are continually conversant in the heaven of Arts, heaven it selfe is but the highest height of knowledge, he that knowes himselfe and all things else, knowes the meanes to be happie: happie, thrice happie are they whom God hath doubled his spirite uppon, and given a double soule unto to be Poets.

My Heroicall Master exceeded in this supernaturall kinde of wit, he entertained no grosse earthly spirite of avarice, nor weake womanly spirite of pusillanimitie and feare that are fained to bee of the water, but admirable, airie, and firie spirites, full of freedome, magnanimitie and bountihood. Let me not speake anie more of his accomplishments, for feare I spend all my spirits in praising him and leave my selfe no vigor of wit, or effects of a soule to goe forward with my historie.

Having thus met him I so much adored, no interpleading was there of opposite occasions, but backe I must returne and beare halfe stakes with him in the lotterie of travell. I was not altogether unwilling to walke a long with such a good purse-bearer, yet musing what changeable humor had so soddainely seduced him from his native soyle to seeke out needlesse perils in those parts beyond sea, one night verie boldly I demaunded of him the reason that mooved him thereto.

Ah quoth he, my little Page, full little canst thou perceive howe farre Metamorphozed I am from my selfe, since I last saw thee. There is a little God called Love, that will not bee worshipt of anie leaden braines, one that proclaimes himselfe sole King and Emperour of pearcing eyes, and cheefe Soveraigne of soft hearts, hee it is that exercising his Empire in my eyes, hath exorsized and cleane conjured me from my content.

Thou knowst statelie *Geraldine,* too stately I feare for mee to doe homage to her statue or shrine, she it is that is come out of Italie to bewitch all the wise men of England, uppon Queene *Katherine Dowager* she waites, that hath a dowrie of beautie sufficient to make hir wooed of the greatest Kinges in Christendome. Her high exalted sunne beames have set the Phenix neast of my breast on fire, and I my selfe have brought Arabian spiceries of sweet passions and praises, to furnish out the funerall flame of my follie. Those who were condemned to be smothered to death by sincking downe into the softe bottome of an high built bedde of Roses, never dide so sweet a death as I shoulde die, if hir Rose coloured disdaine were my deathesman.

Oh thrice Emperiall Hampton Court, *Cupids* inchaunted Castle, the place where I first sawe the perfecte omnipotence of the Almightie expressed in mortalitie, tis thou alone, that tithing all other men solace in thy pleasant scituation, affoordest mee nothinge but an excellent begotten sorrow out of the cheefe treasurie of all thy recreations.

Deare *Wilton* understand that there it was where I first set eie on my more than celestiall *Geraldine*. Seeing her I admired her, all the whole receptacle of my sight was unhabited with hir rare worth. Long sute and uncessant protestations got me the grace to be entertained. Did never unloving servant so prentiselike obey his never pleased Mistris, as I did her. My life, my wealth, my friendes, had all their destinie depending on hir command.

Uppon a time I was determined to travell, the fame of Italy, and an especiall affection I had unto Poetrie my second Mistris, for which Italy was so famous, had wholy ravisht me unto it. There was no dehortment from it, but needs thether I would, wherefore comming to my Mistris as she was then walking with other Ladies of estate in paradice at Hampton Court, I most humbly besought her of favour, that she would give mee so much gratious leave to absent my selfe from her service, as to travell a yeare or two into Italy. She verie discreetly answered me that if my love were so hot as I had often avouched, I did verie well to applie the plaister of absence unto it, for absence as they say, causeth forgetfulnesse: yet neverthelesse since it is Italy my native countrie you are so desirous to see, I am the more willing to make my will yours. *I pete Italiam*, goe and seeke Italie with *Aenæas*, but bee more true than *Aenæas*, I hope that kinde wit-cherishing climate will worke no change in so wittie a breast. No Countrie of mine shall it be more, if it conspire with thee, in any new love against mee. One charge I will give thee and let it bee rather a request than a charge: When thou commest to Florence (the faire Cittie from whence I fetcht the pride of my birth) by an open challenge defende my beautie against all commers.

Thou hast that honourable carryage in Armes, that it shall bee no discredite for me to bequeath all the glorie of my beautie to thy well governed Arme. Faine would I bee knowne where I was borne, faine would I have thee knowen where fame sits in her chiefest Theater. Farewell, forget me not, continued deserts wil eternize me unto thee, thy wishes shall be expired when they travell shall bee once ended.

Here did teares step out before words, and intercepted the course of my kinde conceived speech, even as winde is allayed with raine: with heart scalding sighes I confirmed her parting request, and vowed my selfe hers, while living heate allowed mee to bee mine owne, *Hinc illæ lachrimæ*, heere hence proceedeth the whole cause of my peregrination.

Not a little was I delighted with this unexpected love storie, especially from a mouth out of which was nought wont to march but sterne precepts of gravetie and modestie. I sweare unto you I thought his companie the better by a thousand crownes, because hee had discarded those nice tearmes of chastitie and continencie. Now I beseech God love me so well as I love a plaine dealing man, earth is earth, flesh is flesh, earth wil to earth, and flesh unto flesh, fraile earth, fraile flesh, who can keepe you from the worke of your creation.

Dismissing this fruitles annotation *pro et contra*, towards Venice we progrest, and tooke Roterdam in our waie, that was cleane out of our waie, there we met with aged learnings chiefe ornament, that abundant and superingenious clarke *Erasmus*, as also with merrie Sir *Thomas Moore* our Countriman, who was come purposelie over a little before us, to visite the said grave father *Erasmus*: what talke, what conference wee had then, it were here superfluous to rehearse, but this I can assure you, *Erasmus* in all his speeches seemed so much to mislike the indiscretion of Princes in preferring of parasites and fooles, that he decreed with himselfe to swim with the stream, and write a booke forthwith in commendation of follie. Quick witted Sir *Thomas Moore* traveld in a cleane contrarie province, for he seeing most common-wealths corrupted by ill custome, and that principalities were nothing but great piracies, which gotten by violence and murther, were maintained by private undermining and bloudshed, that in the cheefest flourishing kingdomes there was no equall or well devided weale one with an other, but a manifest conspiracie of rich men against poore men, procuring their owne unlawfull commodities under the name and interest of the common-wealth: hee concluded with himselfe to lay downe a perfect plot of a common-wealth or government, which he would intitle his *Utopia*.

So left we them to prosecute their discontented studies, and make our next journey to Wittenberg.

IV

At the verie pointe of our enterance into Wittenberg, we were spectators of a verie solemne scholasticall entertainment of the Duke of Saxonie thether. Whome because hee was the chiefe Patrone of their Universitie, and had tooke *Luthers* parte in banishing the Masse and all like papal jurisdiction out of their towne, they croucht unto extreamely. The chiefe ceremonies of their intertainment were these: first, the heads of their universitie (they were great heads of certaintie) met him in their hooded hypocrisie and doctorly accoustrements, *secundum formam statuti*, where by the orator of the universitie, whose pickerdevant was verie plentifully besprinkled with rose water, a very learned or rather ruthfull oration was delivered (for it raind all the while) signifieng thus much, that it was all, by patch and by peecemeale stolne out of *Tully*, and he must pardon them, though in emptying their phrase bookes the world emptied his intrailes, for they dyd it not in any ostentation of wit (which God knowes they had not) but to shew the extra-ordinarie good will they bare the Duke, (to have him stand in the raine till he was through wet) a thousand *quemadmodums* and *quapropters* he came over him with, every sentence he concluded with *Esse posse videatur*; through all the nine worthies he ran with praising and comparing him, *Nestors* yeeres he assured him off under the broade seale of their supplications, and with that crowe troden verse in Virgil, *Dum juga montis aper*, hee packt up his pipes and cride *dixi*.

That pageant overpast, there rusht upon him a miserable rablement of junior graduats, that all cride uppon him mightily in their gibrige lyke a companie of beggers, God save your grace, God save your grace, Jesus preserve your Highnesse, though it be but for an houre. Some three halfe penyworth of Latine here also had he throwen at his face, but it was choise stuffe I can tell you, as there is a choise even amongst ragges gathered up from the dunghill. At the townes end met him the burgers and dunsticall incorporationers of *Wittenberg* in their distinguished liveries, their distinguished liverie faces I meane,

for they were most of them hot livered dronkards, and had all
the coate colours of sanguine, purple, crimson, copper, carna-
tion, that were to be had, in their countenances. Filthie knaves,
no cost had they bestowed on the towne for his welcome, saving
new painted their houghs and bousing houses, which commonly
are fairer than their churches, and over their gates set the towne
armes carousing a whole health to the Dukes armes, which
sounded gulping after this sorte, *Vanhotten, slotten, irk bloshen
glotten gelderslike*: what ever the wordes were, the sense was this,
Good drinke is a medicine for all diseases.

A bursten belly inkhorne orator called *Vanderhulke*, they
pickt out to present him with an oration, one that had a
sulpherous big swolne large face, like a Saracen, eyes lyke two
kentish oysters, a mouth that opened as wide every time he
spake, as one of those old knit trap doores, a beard as though
it had ben made of a birds neast pluckt in peeces, which consisteth of strawe, haire, and durt mixt together. He was
apparelled in blacke leather new licourd, and a short gowne
without anie gathering in the backe, faced before and behinde
with a boistrous beare skin, and a red night-cap on his head.
To this purport and effect was this broccing duble beere oration.
Right noble Duke (*ideo nobilis quasi no bilis*) for you have no
bile or colar in you, know that our present incorporation of
Wittenberg, by me the tongue man of their thankfulnes, a
townesman by birth, a free Germane by nature, an oratour by
arte, and a scrivener by education, in all obedience and chastity,
most bountifully bid you welcome to Witenberg: welcome,
sayd I, O orificiall rethorike wipe thy everlasting mouth, and
affoord me a more Indian metaphor than that for the brave
princely bloud of a Saxon. Oratorie uncaske the bard hutch
of thy complements, and with the triumphantest troupe in thy
treasurie doe trewage unto him. What impotent speech with
his eight partes may not specifie this unestimable gift holding
his peace, shall as it were (with teares I speak it) do wherby as
it may seeme or appeare, to manifest or declare, and yet it is,
and yet it is not, and yet it may be a diminitive oblation meritorious to your high pusillanimitie and indignitie. Why should
I goe gadding and fisgigging after firking flantado amfibologies,
wit is wit, and good will is good will. With all the wit I have, I
here according to the premises, offer up unto you the cities
generall good will, which is a gilded Can, in manner and forme
folowing, for you and the heirs of your bodie lawfully begotten,
to drinke healths in. The scholasticall squitter bookes clout

you up cannopies and foot-clothes of verses. We that are good fellowes, and live as merry as cup and can, will not verse upon you as they doe, but must do as we can, and entertaine you if it bee but with a plaine emptie Canne. He hath learning inough, that hath learnde to drinke to his first man.

Gentle Duke, without paradox bee it spoken, thy horses at our owne proper costes and charges shall kneed up to the knees all the while thou art heere in spruce beere and lubecke licour. Not a dogge thou bringest with thee but shall bee banketted with rhenish wine and sturgion. On our shoulders we weare no lambe skinne or miniver like these academikes, yet wee can drinke to the confusion of thy enemies. Good lambs wooll have we for their lambe skins, and for their miniver, large minerals in our coffers. Mechanicall men they call us, and not amisse, for most of us being *Mœchi*, that is cuckoldes and whoore-masters, fetch our antiquitie from the temple of *Mœcha*, where Mahomet was hung up. Three partes of the worlde America, Affrike and Asia, are of this our mechanike religion. *Nero* when he crid *O quantus artifex pereo*, profest himselfe of our freedome. Insomuch as *Artifex* is a citizen or craftes man, as well as *Carnifex* a scholler or hangman. Passe on by leave into the precincts of our abhomination. Bonie Duke frolike in our boure, and perswade thy selfe, that even as garlike hath three properties, to make a man winke, drinke, and stinke, so we wil winke on thy imperfections, drinke to thy favorites, and al thy foes shall stinke before us. So be it. Farewell.

The Duke laught not a little at this ridiculous oration, but that verie night as great an ironicall occasion was ministred, for he was bidden to one of the chiefe schooles to a Comedie handled by scollers. *Acolastus* the prodigal child was the name of it, which was so filthily acted, so leathernly set forth, as would have moved laughter in *Heraclitus*. One as if he had ben playn-ing a clay floore stampingly trode the stage so harde with his feete, that I thought verily he had resolved to do the Carpenter that set it up some utter shame. Another flong his armes lyke cudgels at a peare tree, insomuch as it was mightily dreaded that he wold strike the candles that hung above their heades out of their sockettes, and leave them all darke. Another did nothing but winke and make faces. There was a parasite, and he with clapping his handes and thripping his fingers seemed to dance an antike to and fro. The onely thing they did well, was the prodigall childs hunger, most of their schollers being hungerly kept, and surely you would have sayd they had bin

brought up in hogs academie to learne to eate acornes, if you
had seene how sedulously they fell to them. Not a jeast had
they to keepe their auditors from sleeping but of swill and
draffe, yes nowe and then the servant put his hand into the dish
before his master, and almost chokt himselfe, eating slovenly
and ravenously to cause sport.

The next daie they had solempne disputations, where *Luther*
and *Carolostadius* scolded levell coyle. A masse of wordes I
wote well they heapte up agaynst the masse and the Pope,
but farther particulars of their disputations I remember not.
I thought verily they woulde have worried one another with
wordes, they were so earnest and vehement. *Luther* had the
louder voyce, *Carolostadius* went beyond him in beating and
bounsing with his fists, *Quæ supra nos nihil ad nos.* They
uttered nothing to make a man laugh, therefore I will leave
them. Mary their outwarde jestures would now and then afford
a man a morsel of mirth: of those two I meane not so much, as
of all the other traine of opponents and respondents. One
peckt with his fore-finger at everie halfe sillable hee brought
forth, and nodded with his nose like an olde singing man, teaching
a yong querister to keepe time. Another woulde be sure to
wipe his mouth with his handkercher at the ende of every ful
point, and ever when he thought he had cast a figure so curiously,
as he dived over head and eares into his auditors admiration,
hee woulde take occasion to stroke up his haire, and twine up
his mustachios twice or thrice over while they might have
leasure to applaud him. A third wavered and wagled his head,
like a proud horse playing with his bridle, or as I have seene
some fantasticall swimmer, at everie stroke train his chin side-
long over his left shoulder. A fourth swet and foamed at the
mouth, for verie anger his adversarie had denied that part of
the sillogisme which he was not prepared to answere. A fifth
spread his armes, like an usher that goes before to make rome,
and thript with his finger and his thumbe when he thought he
had tickled it with a conclusion. A sixt hung downe his countenaunce like a sheepe, and stutted and slavered very pittifully
when his invention was stept aside out of the way. A seventh
gaspt for winde, and groned in his pronunciation as if hee were
hard bound with some bad argument. Grosse plodders they
were all, that had some learning and reading, but no wit to make
use of it. They imagined the Duke tooke the greatest pleasure
and contentment under heaven to heare them speake Latine,
and as long as they talkt nothing but *Tully* he was bound to

attend them. A most vaine thing it is in many universities at this daie, that they count him excellent eloquent who stealeth not whole phrases but whole pages out of *Tully*. If of a number of shreds of his sentences he can shape an oration from all the world he carries it awaie, although in truth it be no more than a fooles coat of many colours. No invention or matter have they of theyr owne, but tack up a stile of his stale galymafries. The leaden headed Germanes first began this, and wee Englishmen have surfetted of their absurd imitation. I pitie *Nizolius* that had nothing to do but picke thrids ends out of an olde over-worne garment.

This is but by the waie, we must looke back to our disputants. One amongest the rest thinking to bee more conceited than his fellowes, seeing the Duke have a dog he loved well, which sate by him on the tarras, converted al his oration to him, and not a haire of his tayle but he kembd out with comparisons: so to have courted him if he were a bitch had bin verie suspitious. Another commented and descanted on the Dukes staffe, new tipping it with many queint epithites. Some cast his nativitie, and promised him hee shoulde not die untill the day of judgement. Omitting further superfluityes of this stampe, in this generall assembly we found intermixed that abundant scholler *Cornelius Agrippa*. At that time he bare the fame to be the greatest conjurer in christendome. *Scoto* that dyd the jugling tricks before the Queene, never came neere him one quarter in magicke reputation. The Doctors of *Wittenberg* doting on the rumor that went of him, desired him before the Duke and them to doe some thing extraordinarie memorable.

One requested to see pleasant *Plautus*, and that hee would shewe them in what habit he went, and with what counten-aunce he lookt when he ground corne in the mil. Another had halfe a months mind to *Ovid* and his hooke nose. *Erasmus* who was not wanting in that honorable meeting, requested to see *Tully* in that same grace and majestie he pleaded his oration *pro Roscio Amerino*. Affirming, that til in person he beheld his importunitie of pleading, hee woulde in no wise bee per-swaded that anie man coulde carrie awaye a manifest case with rethorike so strangely. To *Erasmus* petition he easily con-descended, and willing the doctors at such an houre to hold their convocation, and every one to keepe him in his place without moving: at the time prefixed in entered *Tullie*, ascended his pleading place, and declaimed verbatim the forenamed oration, but with such astonishing amazement, with such fervent

exaltation of spirit, with such soule-stirring jestures, that all his
auditours were readie to install his guiltie client for a God.

Great was the concourse of glorie *Agrippa* drewe to him wyth
this one feate.   And in deede hee was so cloyed with men which
came to beholde him, that he was fayne sooner than he would,
to returne to the Emperours court from whence he came, and
leave *Wittenberg* before he woulde.   With him we travelled
along, having purchast his acquaintance a litle before.   By
the waie as we went, my master and I agreed to change names.
It was concluded betwixte us, that I should be the Earle of
Surrie, and he my man, onely because in his owne person,
which hee woulde not have reproched, hee meant to take more
liberty of behavior: as for my cariage, he knew hee was to tune
it at a key, either high or low, as he list.

To the Emperours court wee came, where our entertainment
was every way plentiful, carouses we had in whole galons in
sted of quart pots.   Not a health was given us but contained
well neere a hogshead.   The customes of the countrie we were
eager to bee instructed in, but nothing wee coulde learne but
this, that ever at the Emperours coronation there is an oxe
roasted with a stag in the belly, and that stag in his belly hath
a kid, and that kid is stufte full of birds.   Some courtiers to
wearie out time, would tell us further tales of *Cornelius Agrippa*,
and howe when sir *Thomas Moore* our countryman was there,
he shewed him the whole destruction of Troy in a dreame.
How the Lord *Cromwell* being the kings Embassador there, in
like case in a perspective glasse hee set before his eyes king
Henrie the eight, with all his Lordes on hunting in his forrest
at Windsore, and when he came into his studie, and was verie
urgent to be partaker of some rare experiment, that he might
reporte when he came into England, he wild him amongst two
thousande great bookes to take downe which hee list, and begin
to reade one line in anie place, and without booke he woulde
rehearse twentie leaves following.   *Cromwel* did so, and in
many bookes tride him, when in every thing he exceeded his
promise and conquered his expectation.   To *Charles* the fift
then Emperour, they reported how he shewed the nine worthies,
David, Salomon, Gedeon, and the rest in that similitude and
likenes that they lived upon earth.   My master and I having
by the high waie side gotten some reasonable familiaritie with
him, upon this accesse of myracles imputed to him, resolved to
request him somthing in our owne behalfes.   I because I was
his suborned Lorde and master, desired him to see the lively

image of *Geraldine* his love in the glasse, and what at that instant she did, and with whome she was talking. He shewed her us with out anie more adoe, sicke weeping on her bed, and resolved all into devout religion for the absence of her Lord. At the sight thereof he could in no wise refrain, though he had tooke upon him the condition of a servant, but he must forthwith frame this extemporal dity.

> All soule, no earthly flesh, why dost thou fade,
> All gold, no worthlesse drosse, why lookst thou pale,
> Sicknesse how darst thou one so faire invade,
> Too base infirmitie to worke hir bale.
> > Heaven be distemperd since she grieved pines,
> > Never be drie these my sad plaintive lines.
>
> Pearch thou my spirit on hir silver breasts,
> And with their paine redoubled musike beatings,
> Let them tosse thee to world where all toile rests,
> Where blisse is subject to no feares defeatings,
> > Her praise I tune whose tongue doth tune the sphears,
> > And gets new muses in hir hearers eares.
>
> Starres fall to fetch fresh light from hir rich eyes,
> Her bright brow drives the Sunne to cloudes beneath,
> Hir haires reflex with red strakes paints the skies,
> Sweet morne and evening deaw flowes from her breath,
> > Phœbe rules tides, she my teares tides forth drawes,
> > In her sicke bed love sits and maketh lawes.
>
> Hir daintie lims tinsill hir silke soft sheets,
> Hir rose-crownd cheekes eclipse my dazeled sight,
> O glasse with too much joy my thoughts thou greets,
> And yet thou shewest me day but by twy-light.
> > Ile kisse thee for the kindnes I have felt,
> > Hir lips one kisse would unto Nectar melt.

Though the Emperours court, and the extraordinarie edyfiing companie of *Cornelius Agrippa* might have bin argumentes of waight to have arested us a little longer there, yet Italy still stuck as a great moate in my masters eie, he thought he had travelled no farther than Wales, till he had tooke survey of that countrie which was such a curious molder of wits.

V

To cut off blind ambages by the high way side, we made a long stride and got to Venice in short time, where having scarce lookt about us, a precious supernaturall pandor apparelled in all points like a gentleman, and having halfe a dosen several languages in his purse, entertained us in our owne tongue very paraphrastically and eloquently, and maugre all other pretended acquaintance, would have us in a violent kinde of curtesie to be the guestes of his appointment. His name was *Petro de campo Frego,* a notable practitioner in the pollicie of baudrie. The place whether he brought us was a pernicious curtizans house named *Tabitha* the Temptresses, a wench that could set as civill a face on it as chastities first martyr *Lucrecia.* What will you conceit to be in any saints house that was there to seeke? Bookes, pictures, beades, crucifixes, why there was a haberdashers shop of them in everie chamber. I warrant you should not see one set of her neckercher perverted or turned awrie, not a piece of a haire displast. On her beds there was not a wrinkle of any wallowing to be found, her pillows bare out as smooth as a groning wives belly, and yet she was a Turke and an infidel, and had more dooings then all her neighbours besides. Us for our money they used like Emperours. I was master as you heard before, and my master the Earle was but as my chief man whome I made my companion. So it happened (as iniquitie will out at one time or other) that she perceiving my expence had no more vents, then it should have, fel in with my supposed servant my man, and gave him half a promise of mariage, if he would help to make me away, that shee and he might enjoy the jewels and wealth that I had.

The indifficultie of the condition thus she explained unto him, her house stood uppon vaultes, which in two hundred yeeres togither were never searcht, who came into her house none tooke notice of, his fellow servants that knew of his masters abode there, shoulde be all dispatcht by him as from his master, into sundry parts of the citie about busines, and when they returned, aunswere should be made that he lay not there anye more, but had removed to Padua since their departure, and thither they must follow him. Now (quoth she) if you be disposed to make him away in their absence, you shall have my house at commaund. Stab, poyson or shoote him through with a pistol all is one, into the vault he shalbe throwen when the deed is doone. On my bare honestie it was a craftie queane, for shee had enacted with her self if he had bin my legitimate servant, as he was one that served and supplied my necessities, when he had murthered me, to have accused him of the murther, and made all that I had hirs (as I carried all my masters wealth, monie, jewels, rings, or bils of exchange, continually about me.) He verie subtilly consented to her stratageme at the first motion, kill me hee would, that heavens could not withstand, and a pistoll was the predestinate engine which must deliver the parting blow. God wot I was a rawe yong squier, and my master dealt judasly with me, for he tolde me but everie thing that she and he agreed of. Wherefore I coulde not possibly prevent it, but as a man would saie avoide it. The execution day aspired to his utmost devolution, into my chamber came my honorable attendant with his pistoll charged by his side very suspitiouslie and sullenly, ladie *Tabitha* and *Petro de campo Frego* her pandor folowed him at the hard heeles.

At their enterance I saluted them all very familiarly and merily, and began to impart unto them what disquiet dreams had disturbed mee the last night. I dreamt, quoth I, that my man *Brunquell* here (for no better name got he of me) came into my chamber with a pistol charged under his arme to kill me, and that he was suborned by you mistres *Tabitha*, and my verie good friende *Petro de campo Frego*, God send it turne to good, for it hath affrighted mee above measure. As they were readie to enter into a coulourable common place of the deceitfull frivolousnes of dreames, my trustie servant *Brunquel* stoode quivering and quaking everye joynt of him, and as it was before compacted betweene us, let his pistoll droppe from him on the sodaine, wherewith I started out of my bed, and drew my rapier, and cryde murther, murther, which made good wife *Tabitha* redie to bepis her.

My servant, or my master, which you will, I tooke roughlie by the coller, and threatned to run him through incontinent if he confest not the truth. He as it were striken with remorse of conscience, (God be with him, for he could counterfeit most daintily) downe on his knees, askt me forgivenesse, and impeached *Tabitha* and *Petro de campo Frego* as guiltie of subornation. I very mildly and gravely, gave him audience, raile on them I dyd not after his tale was ended, but sayde I would trie what the lawe could doe. Conspiracy by the custome of their countrie was a capitall offence, and what custome or justice might affoorde, they should bee all sure to feele. I could, quoth I, acquite my selfe otherwise, but it is not for a straunger to be his owne carver in revenge. Not a word more with *Tabitha*, but die she would before God or the devill would have her, shee sounded and revived, and then sounded again, and after she revived againe, sighed heavily, spoke faintly and pittifully, yea, and so pittifully, as if a man had not knowen the prankes of harlots before, he would have melted into commiseration. Tears, sighs, and dolefull tuned wordes could not make anie forcible claime to my stonie eares, it was the glittering crownes that I hungred and thirsted after, and with them for all her mocke holy daie jestures she was faine to come off, before I condescended to anie bargaine of silence. So it fortuned (fie uppon that unfortunate worde of Fortune) that this whoore, this queane, this curtizan, this common of ten thousand, so bribing me not to bewray her, had given me a great deal of counterfeit gold, which she had received of a coyner to make awaie a little before. Amongst the grosse summe of my briberie, I silly milkesop mistrusting no deceit, under an angell of light tooke what shee gave me, nere turnd it over, for which (O falsehood in faire shewe) my master and I had lyke to have bin turnd over. He that is a knight arrant, exercised in the affaires of Ladies and Gentlewomen, hath more places to send mony to than the devil hath to send his spirits to. There was a delicate wench named *Flavia Aemilia* lodging in saint Markes street at a goldsmiths, which I would faine have had to the grand test, to trie whether she were cunning in Alcumie or no. Aie me, she was but a counterfet slip, for she not onely gave me the slip, but had welnigh made me a slipstring. To her I sent my golde to beg an houre of grace, ah gracelesse fornicatres, my hostesse and shee were confederate, who having gotten but one peece of my ill golde in their handes, devised the meanes to make me immortall. I could drinke for anger till my head akt, to thinke howe I was abused. Shall I shame the devill and speak the truth? To prison was I sent as principal, and my master as accessarie, nor was it to a prison neither, but to the master of the mintes house, who though partlie our judge, and a most severe upright justice in his own nature, extremely seemed to condole our ignorant estate, and without all peradventure a present redresse he had ministred, if certaine of our countrymen hearing an English Earle was apprehended for coyning, had not come to visite us. An ill planet brought them thether, for at the first glance they knew the servant of my secrecies to be the Earle of Surrie, and I (not worthy to be named I) an outcast of his cuppe or pantofles. Thence, thence sprong the full period of our infelicity. The master of the mint our whilom refresher and consolation, now tooke part against us, he thought we had a mint in our heads of mischivous conspiracies against their state. Heavens bare witnes with us it was not so (heavens will not alwayes come to witnes when they are cald). To a straiter ward were we committed: that which we have imputatively transgressed must be answered. O the heathen heigh passe, and the intrinsecall legerdemaine of

our special approved good pandor *Petro de Campo Frego*. He
although he dipt in the same dish with us everie daie, seeming
to labour our cause verie importunatly, and had interpreted
for us to the state from the beginning, yet was one of those
trecherous brother *Trulies*, and abused us most clarkly. He
interpreted to us with a pestilence, for whereas we stood obstin-
atly upon it, we were wrongfully deteined, and that it was
naught but a malicious practise of sinfull *Tabitha* our late
hostes, he by a fine cunny-catching corrupt translation, made
us plainly to confesse, and crie *Miserere*, ere we had need of our
necke-verse. Detestable, detestable, that the flesh and the
devill shoulde deale by their factors, Ile stand to it, there is
not a pandor but hath vowed paganisme. The devel himselfe
is not such a devil as he, so be he perform his function aright.
He must have the backe of an asse, the snout of an elephant,
the wit of a foxe, and the teeth of a wolfe, he must faune like a
spaniell, crouch like a Jew, liere like a sheepbiter. If he be
halfe a puritan, and have scripture continually in his mouth,
hee speeds the better. I can tell you it is a trade of great promotion, and let none ever thinke to mount by service in forain
courts, or creep neere to some magnifique Lords, if they be
not seene in this science. O it is the art of arts, and ten thousand
times goes beyond the intelligencer. None but a staid grave
civill man is capable of it, he must have exquisite courtship
in him or else he is not old who, he wants the best point in his
tables. God be mercifull to our pandor (and that were for God
to worke a miracle) he was seene in all the seven liberall deadly
sciences, not a sinne but he was as absolute in as sathan himselfe. Sathan could never have supplanted us so as hee did.
I may saie to you, he planted in us the first Italionate wit that
we had. During the time we lay close and tooke phisick in this
castle of contemplation, there was a magnificos wife of good
calling sent to beare us companie. Her husbands name was
Castaldo, she hight *Diamante*, the cause of her committing,
was an ungrounded jelous suspition which her doting husband
had conceived of her chastitie. One *Isaac Medicus* a bergo-
mast was the man he chose to make him a monster, who being
a courtier, and repairing to his house very often, neither for
love of him nor his wife, but only with a drift to borrow mony
of a paune of wax and parchment, when he sawe his expectation
deluded, and that *Castaldo* was too charie for him to close with,
hee privily with purpose of revenge, gave out amongst his
copesmates, that he resorted to *Castaldos* house for no other

end but to cuckolde him, and doubtfully he talkt that he had and he had not obtained his sute. Rings which he borrowed of a light curtizan that hee used to, he would faine to be taken from her fingers, and in summe, so handled the matter, that *Castaldo* exclaimed, Out, whore, strumpet, six penie hackster, away with her to prison.

As glad were we almost as if they had given us libertie, that fortune lent us such a sweete pue-fellow. A pretie rounde faced wench was it, with blacke eie browes, a high forehead, a little mouth, and a sharpe nose, as fat and plum everie part of her as a plover, a skin as slike and soft as the backe of a swan, it doth me good when I remember her. Like a bird she tript on the grounde, and bare out her belly as majesticall as an Estrich. With a licorous rouling eie fixt piercing on the earth, and sometimes scornfully darted on the tone side, she figured forth a high discontented disdaine, much like a prince puffing and storming at the treason of some mightie subject fled lately out of his power. Her very countenaunce repiningly wrathfull, and yet cleere and unwrinkled, would have confirmed the cleernes of her conscience to the austerest judge in the worlde. If in anie thing shee were culpable, it was in beeing too melancholy chast, and shewing her self as covetous of her beautie as hir husband was of his bags. Many are honest, because they know not howe to bee dishonest: shee thought there was no pleasure in stolne bread, because there was no pleasure in an olde mans bed. It is almost impossible that any woman should be excellently wittie, and not make the utmost pennie of her beautie. This age and this countrie of ours admits of some miraculous exceptions, but former times are my constant informers. Those that have quicke motions of wit have quicke motions in everie thing, yron onely needs many strokes, only yron wits are not wonne without a long siege of intreatie. Gold easily bends, the most ingenious mindes are easiest mooved, *Ingenium nobis molle Thalia dedit*, sayth *Psapho* to *Phao*. Who hath no mercifull milde mistres, I will maintaine, hath no wittie, but a clownish dull flegmatike puppie to his mistres.

This magnificos wife was a good loving soule, that had mettall inough in her to make a good wit of, but being never removed from under her mother and her husbands wing, it was not molded and fashioned as it ought. Causeles distrust is able to drive deceit into a simple womans head. I durst pawne the credite of a page, which is worth ams ace at all times, that she was immaculate honest till she met with us in prison. Mary what temptations she had then, when fire and flax were put together, conceit with your selves, but hold my master excusable. Alacke he was too vertuous to make her vicious, he stood upon religion and conscience, what a hainous thing it was to subvert Gods ordinance. This was all the injurie he would offer her, sometimes he would imagine her in a melancholy humor to bee his *Geraldine*, and court her in tearmes correspondent, nay he would sweare she was his *Geraldine*, and take her white hand and wipe his eyes with it, as though the verie touch of her might staunch his anguish. Now would he kneele and kisse the ground as holy ground which she vouchsafed to blesse from barrennes by her steppes. Who would have learned to write an excellent passion, might have bin a perfect tragick poet, had he but attended halfe the extremitie of his lament. Passion upon passion would throng one on anothers necke, he wold praise her beyond the moone and starres, and that so sweetly and ravishingly, as I perswade my self he was more in love with his own curious forming fancie than her face, and truth it is, many become passionate lovers, onely to winne praise to theyr wits.

He praised, he praied, he desired and besought her to pittie him that perisht for her. From this his intranced mistaking extasie could no man remove him. Who loveth resolutely, wil include every thing under the name of his love. From prose hee would leape into verse and with these or such like rimes assault her.

> If I must die, O let me choose my death,
> Sucke out my soule with kisses cruell maide,
> In thy breasts christall bals enbalme my breath,
> Dole it all out in sighs when I am laide.
> Thy lips on mine like cupping glasses claspe,
> Let our tongs meete and strive as they would sting,
> Crush out my winde with one strait girting graspe,
> Stabs on my heart keepe time whilest thou doest sing.
> Thy eyes lyke searing yrons burne out mine,
> In thy faire tresses stifle me outright,
> Like Circes change me to a loathsome swine,
> So I may live for ever in thy sight.
>> Into heavens joyes none can profoundly see,
>> Except that first they meditate on thee.

Sadly and verily, if my master sayde true, I shoulde if I were a wench make many men quickly immortall. What ist, what ist for a maide fayre and fresh to spend a little lip-salve on a hungrie lover. My master beate the bush and kepte a coyle and a pratling, but I caught the birde, simplicitie and plainnesse shall carrie it away in another world. God wot he was *Petro Desperato*, when I stepping to her with a dunstable tale made up my market. A holy requiem to their soules that thinke to wooe a woman with riddles. I hadde some cunning plot you must suppose, to bring this about. Hir husband had abused her, and it was verie necessarie she should be revenged: seldome doe they proove patient martyrs who are punisht unjustly, one waie or other they will crie quittance whatsoever it cost them. No other apt meanes had this poore shee captived *Cicely*, to worke her hoddie peake husband a proportionable plague for his jealousie, but to give his head his full loading of infamie. Shee thought shee would make him complaine for some thing, that now was so harde bound with an hereticall opinion. How I dealt with her, gesse gentle reader, *subaudi* that I was in prison, and she my silly Jaylor.

VI

Meanes there was made after a moneths or two durance by M. *John Russell*, a Gentleman of king *Henrie* the eights chamber, who then laie lieger at *Venice* for England, that our cause should be favorably heard. At that time was Monsieur *Petro Aretino* searcher and chiefe Inquisiter to the colledge of curtizans. Diverse and sundrie waies was this *Aretine* beholding to the king of England, especially for by this foresayd master *John Russell*, a little before he had sent him a pension of foure hundred crownes yerely during his life. Verie forcibly was he dealt withall, to straine the utmost of his credit for our deliverie out of prison. Nothing at his hands we sought, but that the curtizan might bee more narrowly sifted and examined. Such and so extraordinarie was his care and industrie herein, that, within few dayes after mistres *Tabitha* and her pandor cride *Peccavi confiteor*, and we were presently discharged, they for example sake executed. Most honorably after our inlargement of the state were we used, and had sufficient recompence for all our troubles and wrongs.

Before I goe anie further, let me speake a word or two of this *Aretine*. It was one of the wittiest knaves that ever God made. If out of so base a thing as inke, there may bee extracted a spirite, hee writ with nought but the spirite of inke, and his stile was the spiritualitie of artes, and nothing else, whereas all others of his age were but the lay temporaltie of inkehorne tearmes. For indeede they were mere temporizers and no better. His pen was sharp pointed lyke a poinyard, no leafe he wrote on, but was lyke a burning glasse to set on fire all his readers. With more than musket shot did he charge his quill, where hee meant to inveigh. No houre but hee sent a whole legion of devils into some heard of swine or other. If *Martiall* had ten Muses (as he saith of himselfe) when he but tasted a cup of wine, he had ten score when he determined to tyrannize, nere a line of his but was able to make a man dronken with admiration. His sight pearst like lightning into the entrailes of all abuses. This I must needes saie, that most of his learning hee got by hearing the lectures at Florence. It is sufficient that learning he had, and a conceit exceeding all learning, to quintescence everie thing which hee heard. He was no timerous servile flatterer of the commonwealth wherein he lived, his tongue and his invention were foreborne, what they thought they would confidently utter. Princes hee spard not, that in the least point transgrest. His lyfe he contemned in comparison of the libertie of speech. Whereas some dull braine maligners of his, accuse him of that Treatise, *de tribus impostoribus Mundi*, which was never contrived without a generall counsell of devils, I am verily perswaded it was none of his, and of my minde are a number of the most judicial Italians. One reason is this, because it was published fortie yeres after his death, and hee never in his lyfe time wrote anie thing in Latine. Certainly I have heard that one of *Machivels* followers and disciples was the author of that booke, who to avoyde discredit, filcht it forth under *Aretines* name, a great while after he had sealed up his eloquent spirit in the grave. Too much gall dyd that wormwood of Gibeline wittes put in his inke, who ingraved that rubarbe Epitaph on this excellent poets tombstone. Quite forsaken of all good Angels was he, and utterly given over to artlesse envie. Foure universities honoured *Aretine* wyth these rich titles, *Il flagello de principi, Il veritiero, Il devino, and L'unico Aretino.* The French king *Frances* the first he kept in such awe, that to chaine his tongue he sent him a huge chaine of golde, in the forme of tongues fashioned. Singularly hath he commented of the humanitie of Christ. Besides, as Moses set forth his Genesis, so hath hee set forth his Genesis also, including the contents of the whole Bible. A notable Treatise hath he compiled called, *I sette Psalmi pœnetentiarii.* All the *Thomasos* have cause to love him, because hee hath dilated so magnificently of the lyfe of Saint *Thomas*. There is a good thing that hee hath sette foorth *La vita della virgine Maria*, though it somewhat smell of superstition, with a number more, which here for tediousness I suppresse. If lascivious he were, he may answer with *Ovid*, *Vita verecunda est, musa jocosa mea est*, My lyfe is chast though wanton be my verse. Tell mee who is travelled in histories, what good poet is, or ever was there, who hath not hadde a lyttle spice of wantonnesse in his dayes? Even *Beza* himselfe by your leave. *Aretine* as long as the world lives shalt thou live. *Tully*, *Virgil*, *Ovid*, *Seneca* were never such ornaments to Italy as thou hast bin. I never thought of Italy more religiously than England till I heard of thee. Peace to thy Ghost, and yet me thinkes so indefinite a spirit should have no peace or intermission of paines, but be penning ditties to the archangels in another world. Puritans spue forth the venome of your dull inventions. A toade swels with thicke troubled poison, you swell with poisonous perturbations, your malice hath not a cleere dram of anie inspired disposition.

My principall subject pluckes me by the elbowe, *Diamante Castaldos* the magnificos wife, after my enlargement proved to be with child, at which instant there grew an unsatiable famine in Venice, wherein, whether it were for meere niggardise, or that *Castaldo* stil eate out his heart with jealousie, saint *Anne* be our record, he turned up the heels verie devoutly. To master *Aretine* after this, once more verie dutifully I appeald, requested him of favour, acknowledged former gratuities, he made no more humming or halting, but in despite of her husbands kinsfolkes, gave her her *Nunc dimittis*, and so establisht her free of my companie.

Being out, and fully possest of her husbands goods, she invested me in the state of a monarch. Because the time of child-birth drew nigh, and she could not remaine in Venice but discredited, shee decreed to travell whether so ever I would conduct her. To see Italy throughout was my proposed scope, and that waie if she would travell, have with her, I had where-withall to releeve her.

From my master by her ful-hand provokement I parted with-out leave, the state of an Earle he had thrust upon me before, and now I would not bate him an ace of it. Through all the cities past I by no other name but the yong Earle of Surry, my pomp, my apparel, traine, and expence, was nothing inferior to his, my looks were as loftie, my wordes as magnificall.

Memorandum, that Florence being the principall scope of my masters course, missing mee hee journeyed thether without interruption. By the waie as hee went, hee heard of another Earle of Surry besides himselfe, which caused him make more hast to fetch me in, whom hee little dreamed off had such arte in my budget, to separate the shadow from the bodie. Overtake me at Florence he did, where sitting in my pontificalibus with my curtizan at supper, lyke *Anthonie* and *Cleopatra,* when they quafte standing boules of Wine spiced with pearle together, he stole in ere we sent for him, and bad much good it us, and askt us whether wee wanted anie gests. If he had askt me whether I would have hanged my selfe, his question had bin more acceptable. Hee that had then ungartered me, might have pluckt out my heart at my heeles.

My soule which was made to soare upward, now sought for passage downward, my bloud as the blushing Sabine maids surprised on the sodaine by the souldiers of *Romulus,* ranne to the noblest of bloud amongst them for succour, that were in no lesse (if not greater danger) so did it runne for refuge to the noblest of his bloude about my hart assembled, that stood in more need it selfe of comfort and refuge. A trembling earthquake or shaking feaver assailed either of us, and I thinke unfainedly, if he seeing our faint heart agonie, had not soone cheered and refreshed us, the dogs had gone together by the eares under the table for our feare-dropped lims.

In sted of menacing or afrighting me with his swoorde or his frounes for my superlative presumption, he burst out into laughter above Ela, to thinke how bravely napping he had tooke us, and how notably we were dampt and stroke dead in the neast, with the unexpected view of his presence.

Ah, quoth he, my noble Lord (after his tongue had borrowed a little leave of his laughter) is it my lucke to visite you thus unlookt for, I am sure you will bidde mee welcome, if it bee but for the names sake. It is a wonder to see two English Earles of one house at one time together in Italy. I hearing him so pleasant, began to gather up my spirites, and replid as boldly as I durst: Sir, you are welcome, your name which I borrowed I have not abused, some large summes of monie this my sweet mistres *Diamante* hath made me master of, which I knew not how better to imploy for the honor of my country, than by spending it munificently under your name. No English-man would I have renowmed for bountie, magnificence and curtesie but you, under your colours all my meritorious workes I was desirous to shroud. Deeme it no insolence to adde increase to your fame. Had I basely and beggarly, wanting abilitie to support anie part of your roialtie, undertooke the estimation of this high calling, your alleadgement of injurie had bin the greater, and my defence lesse authorised. It will be thought but a policie of yours thus to send one before you, who being a follower of yours, shall keepe and upholde the estate and port of an Earle. I have knowen many Earles my selfe that in their owne persons would go verie plaine, but delighted to have one that belonged to them (being loden with jewels, apparelled in cloth of golde, and al the rich imbroderie that might be) to stand bare headed unto him, arguing thus much, that if the greatest men went not more sumptuous, how more great than the greatest was he that could command one going so sumptuous. A noble mans glory appeareth in nothing so much as in the pompe of his attendants. What is the glory of the Sunne, but that the Moone and so many millions of starres borrow their lights from him? If you can reprehend me of anie one illiberall licentious action I have disparaged your name with, heape shame on me prodigally, I beg no pardon or pittie.

Non veniunt in idem pudor et amor, he was loth to detract from one that he loved so. Beholding with his eyes that I clipte not the wings of his honour, but rather increast them with additions of expence, he intreated me as if I had bin an Embassadour, he gave mee his hand and swore he had no more heartes but one, and I shoulde have halfe of it, in that I so inhanced his obscured reputation. One thing, quoth he, my sweet *Jacke* I will intreate thee (it shall bee but one) that though I am well pleased thou shouldest bee the ape of my birthright, (as what noble man hath not his ape and his foole) yet that thou be an ape without a clog, not carrie thy curtizan with thee. I tolde him that a king could doe nothing without his treasurie, this curtizan was my purs-bearer, my countenance and supporter. My Earledome I would sooner resigne, than parte with such a specyall benefactor. Resigne it I will how ever, since I am thus challenged of stolne goods by the true owner: Lo, into my former state I return agayne; poore *Jacke Wilton* and your servant am I, as I was at the beginning, and so wil I persever to my lives ending.

That theame was quickly cut off, and other talke entered in place, of what I have forgot, but talke it was, and talke let it be, and talke it shall be, for I do not meane here to remember it. Wee supt, we got to bed, rose in the morning, on my master

I waited, and the first thing he did after he was up, he went and visited the house where his *Geraldine* was borne, at sight whereof hee was so impassioned that in the open street but for me, he would have made an oration in prayse of it. Into it we were conducted, and shewed eache severall roome thereto appertaining. O but when hee came to the chamber where his *Geraldines* cleere Sunbeames first thrust themselves into this cloud of flesh, and acquainted mortalitie with the purity of Angels, then did his mouth overflow with magnificats, his tong thrust the starres out of heaven, and eclipsed the Sun and Moone with comparisons; *Geraldine* was the soule of heaven, sole daughter and heir to *primus motor*. The alcumie of his eloquence out of the incomprehensible drossie matter of cloudes and aire, distilled no more quintescence than would make his *Geraldine* compleat faire. In prayse of the chamber that was so illuminatively honored with her radiant conception, he penned this sonet.

> Faire roome the presence of sweet beauties pride,
> The place the Sunne upon the earth did hold,
> When Phaeton his chariot did misguide,
> The towre where Jove raind downe himselfe in golde,
> Prostrate as holy ground Ile worship thee,
> Our Ladies chappell henceforth be thou namd,
> Here first loves Queene put on mortalitie,
> And with her beautie all the world inflamd.
>   Heavens chambers harbering fierie cherubines,
> Are not with thee in glorie to compare;
> Lightning it is not light which in thee shines,
> None enter thee but straight intranced are.
>   O, if Elizium be above the ground,
>   Then here it is, where nought but joy is found.

Many other poems and epigrams in that chambers patient alablaster inclosure (which her melting eies long sithence had softned) were curiously ingraved. Diamonds thought themselves *Dii mundi*, if they might but carve her name on the naked glasse. With them on it did he anatomize these body-wanting mots, *Dulce puella malum est. Quod fugit ipse sequor. Amor est mihi causa sequendi. O infœlix ego. Cur vidi, cur perii. Non patienter amo. Tantum patiatur amari.* After the view of these veneriall monuments, he published a proud challenge in the Duke of Florence court against all commers (whether Christians, Turkes, Jewes, or Saracens), in defence of his *Geraldines* beautie. More mildly was it accepted, in that she whom he defended, was a towne borne child of that citie, or else the pride of the Italian would have prevented him ere he should have come to performe it. The Duke of Florence neverthelesse sent for him, and demaunded him of his estate, and the reason that drew him thereto, which when hee was advertised of to the full, hee graunted all Countryes whatsoever, as well enemies and outlawes, as friends and confederates, free accesse and regresse into his dominions unmolested, untill that insolent triall were ended.

The right honorable and ever renowmed Lord *Henrie Howard* earle of Surrie my singular good Lord and master, entered the lists after this order. His armour was all intermixed with lillyes and roses, and the bases thereof bordered with nettles and weeds, signifieng stings, crosses, and overgrowing incumberances in his love, his helmet round proportioned lyke a gardners water-pot, from which seemed to issue forth small thrids of water, like citterne strings, that not onely did moisten the lyllyes and roses, but did fructifie as well the nettles and weeds, and made them overgrow theyr liege Lords. Whereby he did import thus much, that the teares that issued from his braines, as those arteficiall distillations issued from the well counterfeit water-pot on his head, watered and gave lyfe as well to his mistres disdaine (resembled to nettles and weeds) as increase of glorie to her care-causing beauty (comprehended under the lillies and roses.) The simbole thereto annexed was this, *Ex lachrimis lachrimæ*. The trappings of his horse were pounced and bolstered out with rough plumed silver plush, in full proportion and shape of an Estrich. On the breast of the horse were the fore-parts of this greedie bird advanced, whence as his manner is, hee reacht out his long necke to the raines of the bridle, thinking they had bin yron, and styll seemed to gape after the golden bit, and ever as the courser did raise or corvet, to have swallowed it halfe in. His wings, which he never useth but running, beeing spread full saile, made his lustie stead as proud under him as he had bin some other *Pegasus*, and so quiveringly and tenderly were these his broade winges bounde to either side of him, that as he paced up and downe the tilt-yard in his majesty ere the knights were entered, they seemed wantonly to fan in his face, and make a flickering sound, such as Eagles doe, swiftly pursuing their praie in the ayre. On either of his wings, as the Estrich hath a sharpe goad or pricke wherewith he spurreth himselfe forward in his saile-assisted race, so this arteficiall Estrich on the inbent knuckle of the pinion of either wing had embossed christall eyes affixed, wherein wheelewise were circularly ingrafted sharpe pointed diamonds,

as rayes from those eyes derived, that like the rowell of a spur
ran deep into his horse sides, and made him more eager in his
course. Such a fine dim shine did these christall eies and these
round enranked diamonds make through their bolne swelling
bowres of feathers, as if it had bin a candle in a paper lanterne,
or a gloworme in a bush by night glistering through the leaves
and briers. The taile of the estrich being short and thicke,
served verie fitly for a plume to tricke up his horse taile with,
so that every parte of him was as naturally coapted as might
be. The worde to this device was *Aculeo alatus*, I spread my
wings onely spurd with her eyes. The morall of the whole is
this, that as the estrich, the most burning sighted bird of all
others, insomuch as the female of them hatcheth not her egs
by covering them, but by the effectuall rayes of her eyes, as he,
I say, outstrippeth the nimblest trippers of his feathered condition in footmanship, onely spurd on with the needle quickning
goad under his side: so he no lesse burning sighted than the
estrich, spurde on to the race of honor by the sweet rayes of
his mistres eyes, perswaded himselfe he should outstrip all other
in running to the goale of glorie, onely animated and incited
by hir excellence. And as the estrich will eate yron, swallow
anie hard mettall whatsoever, so woulde he refuse no iron
adventure, no hard taske whatsoever, to sit in the grace of so
fayre a commander. The order of his shielde was this, it was
framed lyke a burning glasse beset rounde with flame coloured
feathers, on the outside whereof was his mistres picture adorned
as beautiful as arte could portrature, on the inside a naked
sword tyed in a true love knot, the mot, *Militat omnis amans*.
Signifieng that in a true love knot his sword was tried to defend
and maintaine the features of his mistres.

Next him entered the blacke knight, whose bever was pointed
all torne and bloudie, as though he had new come from com-
batting with a Beare, his head piece seemed to bee a little oven
fraught full with smoothering flames, for nothing but sulphur
and smoake voided out at the clefts of his bever. His bases
were all imbrodred with snakes and adders, ingendered of the
aboundance of innocent bloud that was shed. His horses
trappinges were throughout bespangled with hunnie spottes,
which are no blemishes, but ornaments. On his shield hee
bare the Sunne full shining on a diall at his going downe, the
word *sufficit tandem*.

After him followed the knight of the Owle, whose armor
was a stubd tree overgrowne with ivie, his helmet fashioned

lyke an owle sitting on the top of this ivie, on his bases were
wrought all kinde of birdes as on the grounde wondering about
him; the word, *Ideo mirum quia monstrum*, his horses furniture
was framed like a carte, scattering whole sheaves of corne
amongst hogs, the word, *Liberalitas liberalitate perit*. On his
shield a Bee intangled in sheepes wool, the mot, *Fronti nulla
fides*. The fourth that succeeded was a wel proportioned knight
in an armor imitating rust, whose head peece was prefigured
lyke flowers growing in a narrow pot, where they had not anie
space to spread their roots or disperse their flourishing. His
bases embelisht with open armed hands scatring gold amongst
trunchions, the word, *Cura futuri est*. His horse was harnessed
with leaden chaines, having the out-side guilt, or at least saffrond
in sted of gilt, to decypher a holy or golden pretence of a covetous
purpose, the sentence, *Cani capilli mei compedes*, on his target
he had a number of crawling wormes kept under by a blocke,
the faburthen *Speramus lucem*. The fift was the forsaken
knight, whose helmet was crowned with nothing but cipresse
and willow garlandes, over his armour he had *Himens* nuptiali
robe died in a duskie yelowe, and all to be defaced and dis-
coloured with spots and staines. The enigma, *Nos quoque
florimus*, as who should say, we have bin in fashion, his sted was
adorned with orenge tawnie eies, such as those have that have
the yellow jandies, that make all things yellow they looke
uppon, with this briefe, *Qui invident egent*, those that envy are
hungry. The sixt was the knight of the stormes, whose helmet
was rounde molded lyke the moone, and all his armor like
waves, whereon the shine of the moone slightly silverd, perfectly represented moone-shine in the water, his bases were the
bankes or shores that bounded in the streames. The spoke
was this, *Frustra pius*,—as much to saye as fruitlesse service.
On his shield hee set foorth a lion driven from his praie by a
dunghill cock. The word, *Non vi sed voce*, not by violence but
by voyce. The seventh had lyke the giants that sought to
scale heaven in despight of *Jupiter*, a mount overwhelming his
head and whole bodie. His bases out-laid with armes and
legges, which the skirtes of that mountaine left uncovered,
under this did he characterise a man desirous to climbe to the
heaven of honour, kept under with the mountaine of his princes
command, and yet had he armes and legs exempted from the
suppression of that mountain. The word *Tu mihi criminis
author* (alluding to his Princes command) thou art the occasion
of my imputed cowardise. His horse was trapt in the earthie

strings of tree rootes, which though theyr increase was stubbed downe to the ground, yet were they not utterly deaded, but hoped for an after resurrection. The worde *Spe alor*, I hope for a spring. Upon his shield he bare a ball striken downe with a mans hand that it might mount   The worde, *Ferior ut efferar*, I suffer my selfe to be contemned because I will climbe. The eight had all his armor throughout engrailed like a crabbed brierie hawthorne bush, out of which notwithstanding sprong (as a good child of an il father) fragrant blossomes of delightfull may flowers, that made (according to the nature of may) a most odoriferous smell. In midst of this his snowie curled top, round wrapped together, on the ascending of his creast sate a solitarie nightingale close encaged, with a thorne at her breast, having this mot in her mouth, *Luctus monumenta manebunt*. At the foot of this bush represented on his bases, laye a number of blacke swolne Toads gasping for winde, and Summer livde gras-hoppers gaping after deaw, both which were choakt with excessive drouth for want of shade. The worde, *Non sine vulnere viresco*, I spring not without impedimentes, alluding to the Toads and such lyke that earst lay sucking at his rootes, but nowe were turnd out, and neere choakt with drought.   His horse was suted in blacke sandy earth (as adjacent to this bush) which was here and there patched with short burnt grasse, and as thicke inke dropped with toiling ants and emets as ever it might crall, who in the full of the summer moone, (ruddie garnished on his horses forehead) hoorded up theyr provision of graine against winter. The worde, *Victrix fortunæ sapientia*, providence prevents misfortune. On his shield he set foorth the picture of death doing almes deeds to a number of poore desolate children. The word, *Nemo alius explicat*. No other man takes pittie upon us. What his meaning was herein I cannot imagine, except death had done him and his brethren some great good turne in ridding them of some untoward parent or kinsman that would have beene their confusion, for else I cannot see howe death shoulde have bin sayd to doe almes deedes, except hee had deprived them sodainly of their lives, to deliver them out of some further miserie, which could not in anie wise bee because they were yet lyving.

The ninth was the infant knight, who on his armour hadde ennameld a poore young infant put into a shippe without tackling, masts, furniture or anie thing. This weather-beaten or ill apparelled ship was shadowed on his bases, and the slender compasse of his bodie set forth the right picture of an infant.

The waves wherein the ship was tossed were fretted on his steads trappinges so movingly, that ever as he offered to bound or stir, they seemed to bounce and tosse, and sparkle brine out of their hoarie silver billowes, the mot, *Inopem me copia fecit*, as much to saye, as the rich pray makes the theefe.

On his shield he expressed an olde goate that made a yong tree to wither onely with biting it, the word thereto, *Primo extinguor in ævo*. I am frost-bitten ere I come out of the blade.

VII

It were here too tedious to manifest all the discontented or amorous devises that were used in this turnament, the shields onely of some fewe I wyl touch to make short worke. One bare for his impresse the eyes of young swallowes comming againe after they were pluckt out, with this mot, *Et addit et adimit*, your beautie both bereaves and restores my sight. Another a syren smiling when the sea rageth and ships are overwhelmed, including a cruell woman, that laughs, sings, and scornes at her lovers teares, and the tempestes of his despayre, the word, *Cuncta pereunt*, all my labor is ill imploide. A third being troubled with a curst, a trecherous and wanton wife, used this similitude. On his shield he caused to be limmed *Pompeies* ordinance for paracides, as namely a man put into a sacke with a cocke, a serpent, and an ape, interpreting that his wife was a cocke for her crowing, a serpent for her stinging, and an ape for her unconstant wantonnes, with which ill qualities he was so beset, that therby he was throwen into a sea of griefe, the word *Extremum malorum mulier*, the utmost of evils is a woman. A fourth, who being a person of suspected religion, was continually haunted with intellygencers and spies, that thought to praie upon him for that he had, he could not devise which waie to shake them off, but by making away that he had. To obscure this, he used no other fansie but a number of blinde flyes, whose eyes the colde had inclosed, the word *Aurum reddit acutissimum*, Gold is the onely phisicke for the eie-sight. A fifth, whose mistres was fallen into a consumption, and yet woulde condescend to no treatie of love, emblazoned for his complaint, grapes that withered for want of pressing. The dittie to the mot, *Quid regna sine usu*. I will rehearse no more, but I have an hundred other, let this bee the upshot of those shewes, they were the admirablest that ever Florence yelded. To particularize their manner of encounter were to describe the whole art of tilting. Some had like to have fallen over their horse neckes, and so breake theyr neckes in breaking theyr staves. Others ranne at a buckle in sted of a button, and peradventure whetted theyr speares pointes, idlely gliding on theyr enemies sides, but did no other harme. Others ranne a crosse at their adversaryes left elbow, yea, and by your leave sometimes let not the lists scape scot-free they were so eager. Others because they woulde be sure not to be unsadled with the shocke, when they came to the speares utmost proofe, they threwe it over the right shoulder, and so tilted backward, for forward they durst not. Another had a monstrous spite at the pommel of his rivals saddle, and thought to have thrust his speare twixt his legs without rasing anie skin, and carried him clean awaie on it as a coolestaffe. Another held his speare to his nose, or his nose to his speare, as though he had bin discharging his caliver, and ranne at the right foote of his fellowes stead. Onely the Earle of Surrie my master observed the true measures of honour, and made all his encounterers new scoure their armor in the dust: so great was his glory that day, as *Geraldine* was therby eternally glorifid. Never such a bountiful master came amongst the heralds (not that he did inrich them with anie plentifull purse largesse) but that by his sterne assaults he tithed them more rich offals of bases, of helmets, of armor, than the rent of their offices came to in ten yeres before.

What would you have more, the trumpets proclaimed him master of the field, the trumpets proclaimed *Geraldine* the exceptionlesse fayrest of women. Everie one strived to magnifie him more than other. The Duke of Florence, whose name (as my memorie serveth me) was *Paschal de Medicis*, offered him such large proffers to stay with him, as it were incredible to report. He would not, his desire was as he had done in Florence, so to proceed throughout all the chiefe cities in Italy. If you aske why hee began not this at Venice first. It was because he would let Florence, his mistres native citie have the maidenhead of his chivalrie. As he came backe agayne he thought to have enacted some thing there worthie the Annals of posteritie, but he was debard both of that and all his other determinations, for continuing in feasting and banketting with the Duke of Florence and the Princes of Italy there assembled post-hast letters came to him from the king his master, to returne as speedily as he could possible into *England*, whereby his fame was quit cut off by the shins, and there was no reprive but

Bazelus manus, hee must into England, and I with my curtizan
travelled forward in Italy. What adventures happened him
after we parted, I am ignorant, but Florence we both forsooke,
and I having a wonderfull ardent inclination to see Rome,
the Queen of the world, and metropolitane mistres of all other cities,
made thether with my bag and baggage as fast as I could.

Attained thether, I was lodged at the house of one *Johannes
de Imola* a Roman cavaliero. Who being acquainted with
my curtisans deceased doting husband, for his sake usd us with
all the familiaritie that might be, he shewed us all the monu-
mentes that were to bee seene, which are as manye as there
have beene Emperours, Consulles, Oratours, Conquerours,
famous painters or plaiers in *Rome.* Tyll this daie not a Romane
(if he be a right Romane indeed) will kill a rat, but he will have
some registred remembraunce of it.

There was a poore fellowe during my remainder there, that
for a newe tricke that hee had invented of killing *Cymeses* and
scorpions, had his montebanke banner hung up on a high piller,
with an inscription about it longer than the king of Spaines
stile. I thought these *Cymesses* lyke the Cimbrians, hadde
beene some straunge Nation hee hadde brought under, and they
were no more but thinges lyke lice, which alive have the most
venimous sting that maye bee, and beeing dead, doe stinke
out of measure, Saint Austen compareth heretikes unto them.
The chiefest thing that my eyes delighted in, was the church
of the seven *Sibels,* which is a most miraculous thing. All
their prophesies and oracles being there inrolde, as also the
beginning and ending of theyr whole catalogue of the heathen
Gods, with theyr manner of worship. There are a number of
other shrines and statues dedicated to the Emperours, and
withall some statues of idolatrie reserved for detestation.

I was at *Pontius Pilates* house and pist against it. The name
of the place I remember not, but it is as one goes to Saint Paules
Church not farre from the jemmes *Piazza.* There is the prison
yet packt up together (an olde rotten thing) wher the man that
was condemned to death, and coulde have no bodie come to
him and succour him but was searcht, was kepte alive a long
space by sucking his daughters breasts. These are but the
shoppe dust of the sights that I sawe, and in truth I did not
beholde with anie care hereafter to report, but contented my
eie for the present, and so let them passe: should I memorize
halfe the miracles which they there tolde mee had beene done
about martyrs tombes, or the operations of the earth of the

sepulchre, and other relikes brought from Jerusalem, I shoulde bee counted the monstrous lyer that ever came in print. The ruines of *Pompeies* theater, reputed one of the nine wonders of the world, *Gregori* the sixths tombe, *Priscillas* grate, or the thousands of pillers arrered amongst the raced foundations of olde Rome, it were frivolous to specifie, since he that hath but once dronke with a traveller talks of them. Let me be a historiographer of my owne misfortunes, and not meddle with the continued Trophees of so olde a triumphing Citie.

At my first comming to Rome, I being a youth of the English cut, ware my haire long, went apparelled in light colours, and imitated foure or five sundry nations in my attire at once: which no sooner was noted, but I had all the boies of the citie in a swarme wondering about me.

I hadde not gone a little farther, but certaine officers croste the waie of mee, and demaunded to see my rapier: which when they found (as also my dagger) with his point unblunted, they wold have halde me headlong to the Strappado, but that with money I appeased them: and my fault was more pardonable in that I was a stranger, altogether ignorant of their customes. Note by the waye that it is the use in *Rome*, for all men whatsoever to weare their haire short: which they doe not so much for conscience sake, or any religion they place in it, but because the extremitie of the heate is such there, that if they should not doe so, they should not have a haire left on their heads to stand upright when they were scard with sprights. And hee is counted no Gentleman amongest them that goes not in blacke: they dresse theyr jesters and fooles only in fresh colours, and saie variable garments doe argue unstaiednes and unconstancie of affections.

The reason of theyr straight ordinaunce for carrying weapons without points is this: The Bandettos, which are certayne outlawes that lie betwixt *Rome* and *Naples*, and besiege the passage that none can travell that waie without robbing. Nowe and then hired for some few crownes, they will steale to *Rome* and do a murther, and betake them to their heeles againe. Disguised as they goe, they are not knowen from strangers, sometimes they will shroude themselves under the habite of grave citizens. In this consideration neither citizen or stranger, gentleman, knight, marques, or anie may weare anie weapon endamageable upon paine of the Strappado. I bought it out, let others buy experience of mee better cheape.

To tell you of the rare pleasures of their gardens, theyr bathes, theyr vineyardes, theyr galleries, were to write a seconde part of the gorgeous Gallerie of gallant devices. Why, you should not come into anie mannes house of account, but hee hadde fish-pondes and little orchardes on the toppe of his leads. If by raine or any other meanes those ponds were so full they need to be slust or let out, even of their superfluities they made melodious use, for they had great winde instruments in stead of leaden spoutes, that went duly on consort, onely with this waters rumbling discent. I sawe a summer banketting house belonging to a merchaunt, that was the mervaile of the world, and could not be matcht except God should make another paradise. It was builte round of greene marble, like a Theater with-out: within there was a heaven and earth comprehended both under one roofe, the heaven was a cleere overhanging vault of christall, wherein the Sunne and Moone, and each visible Starre had his true similitude, shine, scituation, and motion, and by what enwrapped arte I cannot conceive, these spheares in their proper orbes observed their circular wheelinges and turnings, making a certaine kinde of soft angelical murmering musicke in their often windings and going about, which musick the philosophers say in the true heaven by reason of the grosenes of our senses we are not capable of. For the earth it was counterfeited in that liknes that Adam lorded out it before his fall. A wide vast spacious roome it was, such as we would conceit prince Arthurs hall to be, where he feasted all his knights of the round table together everie penticost. The flore was painted with the beautifullest flowers that ever mans eie admired which so linealy were delineated, that he that viewd them a farre off and had not directly stood poaringly over them, would have sworne they had lived in deede. The wals round about were hedgde with Olives and palme trees, and all other odoriferous fruit-bearing plants, which at anie solemne intertainment dropt mirrhe and frankensence. Other trees that bare no fruit, were set in just order one against another, and divided the roome into a number of shadie lanes, leaving but one over spreading pine tree arbor, where wee sate and banketted. On the wel clothed boughs of this conspiracie of pine trees against the resembled Sun beames, were pearcht as many sortes of shrill breasted birdes as the Summer hath allowed for singing men in hir silvane chappels. Who though there were bodies without soules, and sweete resembled substances without sense, yet by the mathematicall experimentes of long silver pipes secretlye inrinded in the intrailes of the boughs whereon they sate, and

undiscerneablie convaid under their bellies into their small
throats sloaping, they whistled and freely carold theyr naturall
field note. Neyther went those silver pipes straight, but by
many edged unsundred writhings, and crankled wanderinges
aside strayed from bough to bough into an hundred throats.
But into this silver pipe so writhed and wandering aside, if anie
demand how the wind was breathed. Forsoth the tail of the
silver pipe stretcht it selfe into the mouth of a great paire of
belowes, where it was close soldered, and bailde a bout with
yron, it coulde not stirre or have anie vent betwixt. Those
bellowes with the rising and falling of leaden plummets wounde
up on a wheele, dyd beate up and downe uncessantly, and so
gathered in wind, serving with one blast all the snarled pipes
to and fro of one tree at once. But so closely were all those
organising implements obscured in the corpulent trunks of the
trees, that everie man there present renounst conjectures of art,
and sayd it was done by inchantment.

One tree for his fruit bare nothing but inchained chirping
birdes, whose throates beeing conduit pipt with squared narrowe
shels, and charged siring-wise with searching sweet water,
driven in by a little wheele for the nonce, that fed it a farre of,
made a spirting sound, such as chirping is in bubling upwards
through the rough crannies of their closed bills. Under tuition
of the shade of everie tree that I have signified to be in this
round hedge, on delightful levie cloisters lay a wylde tyranous
beast asleepe all prostrate: under some two together, as the
Dogge nusling his nose under the necke of the Deare, the Wolfe
glad to let the Lambe lye upon hym to keepe him warme, the
Lyon suffering the Asse to cast hys legge over him: preferring
one honest unmannerly friende, before a number of croutching
picke-thankes. No poysonous beast there reposed, (poyson
was not before our parent *Adam* transgressed). There were no
sweete-breathing Panthers, that would hyde their terrifying
heads to betray: no men imitating *Hyænaes*, that chaunged their
sexe to seeke after bloud. Wolves as now when they are hungrie
eate earth, so then did they feed on earth only, and abstained
from innocent flesh. The Unicorne did not put his horne into
the streame to chase awaye venome before hee dronke, for then
there was no suche thing extant in the water or on the earth.
Serpents were as harmlesse to mankinde, as they are still one
to another: the rose had no cankers, the leves no caterpillers,
the sea no *Syrens*, the earth no usurers. Goats then bare wooll,
as it is recorded in *Sicily* they doo yet. The torride Zone was

habitable: only Jayes loved to steale gold and silver to build their nests withall, and none cared for covetous clientrie, or runing to the Indies. As the Elephant understands his countrey speach, so everie beast understood what man spoke. The ant did not hoord up against winter, for there was no winter but a perpetuall spring, as *Ovid* sayth. No frosts to make the greene almound tree counted rash and improvident, in budding soonest of all other: or the mulberie tree a strange polititian, in blooming late and ripening early. The peach tree at the first planting was fruitfull and wholsome, whereas now till it be transplanted, it is poisonous and hatefull: young plants for their sap had balme, for their yeolow gumme glistering amber. The evening deawd not water on flowers, but honnie. Such a golden age, such a good age, such an honest age was set forth in this banketting house. O *Rome*, if thou hast in thee such soul exalting objects, what a thing is heaven in comparison of thee? Of which *Mercators* globe is a perfecter modell than thou art: yet this I must saie to the shame of us protestants, if good workes may merite heaven they doe them, we talke of them. Whether supersticion or no makes them unprofitable servants, that let pulpits decide: but there you shall have the bravest ladies, in gownes of beaten golde washing pilgrimes and poore souldiers feete, and doing nothing they and their waiting maides all the yeare long, but making shirts and bands for them against they come by in distresse. Their hospitals are more lyke noble mens houses than otherwise, so richly furnished, cleane kept, and hot perfumed, that a souldier would thinke it a sufficient recompence for all his travell and his wounds, to have such a heavenly retyring place. For the pope and his pontificalibus I will not deale with, onely I will dilate unto you what happened whilest I was in *Rome*.

So it fel out, that it being a vehement hot summer when I was a sojourner there, there entered such a hotspurd plague as hath not bin heard of: why it was but a word and a blowe, Lord have mercie upon us and he was gone. Within three quarters of a yeere in that one citie there died of it a hundred thousand looke in *Lanquets* chronicle and you shall finde it. To smell of a nosegay that was poisond, and turne your nose to a house that had the plague, it was all one. The clouds like a number of cormorants that keepe their corne til it stinke and is mustie, kept in their stinking exhalations till they had almost stifeled all *Romes* inhabitants. Phisitions greedines of golde made them greedie of their destinie. They would come to visit those with whose infirmitie their art had no affinitie, and even as a man with a fee should be hired to hang himselfe, so would they quietly go home and die presently after they had bin with their patients. All daye and all night long carre-men did nothing but go up and downe the streets with their carts and cry, Have you anie dead bodies to bury and had many times out of one house their whole loding: one grave was the sepulchre of seven score, one bed was the alter whereon whole families were offered. The wals were hoard and furd with the moist scorching steame of their desolation. Even as before a gun is shot off, a stinking smoake funnels out, and prepares the way for him, so before any gave up the ghost, death araid in a stinking smoak stopt his nostrels, and cramd it selfe ful into his mouth that closed up his fellows eyes, to give him warning to prepare for his funeral. Some dide sitting at their meat, others as they were asking counsell of the phisition for theyr friends. I sawe at the house where I was hosted a maide bring her master warme broth for to comfort him, and shee sinke downe dead her selfe ere he had halfe eate it up.

VIII

During this time of visitation, there was a Spaniard, one *Esdras* of *Granado*, a notable Bandetto, authorised by the pope, because he had assisted him in some murthers. This villain colleagued with one *Bartol* a desperate Italian, practised to breake into those riche mens houses in the night where the plague had most rained, and if there were none but the mistres and maide left alive, to ravish them both, and bring awaie ali the wealth they could fasten on. In an hundred chiefe citizens houses where the hand of God had bene they put this outrage in use. Though the women so ravished cride out, none durst come neere them for feare of catching their deaths by them, and some thought they cried out onely with the tyrannie of the maladie. Amongst the rest, the house where I lay he invaded, where al being snatcht up by sicknes but the good wife of the house, a noble and chaste matrone called *Heraclide* and her zanie, and I and my curtizan, hee knocking at the doore late in the night, ranne in to the matrone, and left me and my love to the mercie of his companion. Who finding me in bed (as the time requird) ranne at me ful with his rapier, thinking I would resist him, but as good luck was I escapt him, and betooke me to my pistoll in the window uncharged. He, fearing it had beene charged, threatned to runne her through if I once offered but to aime at him. Foorth the chamber hee dragde her, holding his rapier at her heart, whilest I cride out, Save her, kill me, and Ile ransome her with a thousande duckets: but lust pervailed, no prayers woulde be heard. Into my chamber I was lockte, and watchmen charged (as hee made semblaunce when there was none there) to knocke mee downe with theyr halberdes if I stirde but a foote downe the stayres. Then threw I my selfe pensive againe on my pallate, and darde all the deviles in hell nowe I was alone to come and fight with mee one after another in defence of that detestable rape. I beat my head against the wals and cald them bauds, because they would see such a wrong committed, and not fall uppon him. To returne to *Heraclide* below, whom the ugliest of all bloud suckers *Esdras* of *Granado* had under shrift. First he assayled her with rough meanes, and slue hir *Zanie* at hir foote, that stept before hir in rescue. Then when all armed resist was put to flight, he assaied her with honie speech, and promised her more jewells and giftes than hee was able to pilfer in an hundred yeres after. He discourst unto her how he was countenanced and borne out by the pope, and how many execrable murthers with impunitie he had executed on them that displeasde him. This is the eight score house (quoth he) that hath done homage unto me, and here I will prevaile, or I will bee torne in pieces. Ah quoth *Heraclide* (with a hart renting sigh), art thou ordained to be a worse plague to me than the plague it selfe? Have I escapt the hands of God to fal into the hands of man? Heare me *Jehovah*, and be merciful in ending my miserie. Dispatch me incontinent dissolute homicide deaths usurper. Here lies my husband stone colde on the dewie floore. If thou beest of more power than God, to strike me speedily, strike home, strike deepe, send me to heaven with my husband. Aie me, it is the spoil of my honor thou seekest in my soules troubled departure, thou art some devill sent to tempt me. Avoid from me sathan, my soule is my saviours, to him I have bequeathed it, from him can no man take it. Jesu, Jesu spare mee undefiled for thy spouse, Jesu, Jesu never faile those that put their trust in thee. With that she fell in a sowne, and her eies in their closing seemed to spaune forth in their outward sharpe corners new created seed pearle, which the world before never set eie on. Soone he rigorously revived her, and told her that he had a charter above scripture, she must yeld, she should yeld, see who durst remove her out of his hands. Twixt life and death thus she faintly replied. How thinkest thou, is there a power above thy power, if there be, he is here present in punishment, and on thee will take present punishment if thou persistest in thy enterprise. In the time of securitie everie man sinneth, but when death substitutes one frend his special baily to arrest another by infection, and dispearseth his quiver into ten thousande hands at once, who is it but lookes about him? A man that hath an unevitable huge stone hanging only by a haire over his head, which he lokes everie Pater noster while to fall and pash him in peeces, will not he be submissively sorrowfull for his transgressions, refraine himselfe from the least thought of folly, and purifie his spirit with contrition and penitence? Gods hand like a huge stone hangs inevitably over thy head: what is the plague, but death playing the Provost Marshall, to execute all those that will not be called home by anie other meanes? This my dere knights bodie is a quiver of his arrowes which alreadie are shot into thee invisibly. Even as the age of goats is knowen by the knots on their hornes, so thinke the anger of God apparently visioned or showne unto thee in the knitting of my browes. A hundred have I buried out of my house, at all whose departures I have been present: a hundreds infection is mixed with my breath: loe, now I breath upon thee, a hundred deaths come uppon thee. Repent betimes, imagine there is a hell though not a heaven: that hell thy conscience is thoroughly acquainted with, if thou hast murdered half so manie, as thou unblushingly braggest. As *Mecænas* in the latter end of his daies was seven yeres without sleepe, so these seven weeks have I tooke no slumber, my eyes have kept continuall watch against the divell my enemie: death I deemed my frend (friends flye from us in adversitie), death, the divell, and all the ministring spirits of temptation are watching about thee to intrap thy soule (by my abuse) to eternall damnation. It is thy soule thou maist save, onely by saving mine honour. Death will have thy bodie infallibly for breaking into my house, that he had selected for his private habitation. If thou ever camst of a woman, or hopest to be saved by the seed of a woman, pittie a woman. Deares oppressed with dogges, when they cannot take soyle, run to men for succour: to whom should women in theyr disconsolate and desperate estate run, but to Men (like the Deare) for succour and sanctuarie. If thou be a man, thou wilt succour mee, but if thou be a dog and a brute beast, thou wilt spoile mee, defile mee, and teare me: either renounce Gods image, or renounce the wicked mind thou bearest

These words might have moovd a compound hart of yron and adamant, but in his hart they obtained no impression: for he sitting in his chaire of state against the doore all the while that she pleaded, leaning his over-hanging gloomie eybrowes on the pommell of his unsheathed sword, he never lookt up or gave hir a word: but when he perceived she expected his answer of grace or utter perdition, he start up and tooke her currishly by the neck, asking how long he should stay for hir Ladiship. Thou telst me (quoth he) of the plague, and the heavie hand of God, and thy hundred infected breaths in one: I tel thee I have cast the dice an hundred times for the gallies in *Spaine*, and yet still mist the ill chance. Our order of casting is this, If there be a Generall or Captaine new come home from the warres, and hath some 4. or 500. crownes overplus of the Kings in his hand, and his soldiers all paid, he makes proclamation, that whatsoever two resolute men will goe to dice for it, and win the bridle or lose the saddle, to such a place let them repaire, and it shall be readie for them. Thither go I, and finde another such needie squire resident. The dice run, I win he is undone. I winning have the crownes, hee loosing is carried to the Galleyes. This is our custome, which a hundred times and more hath paid me custome of crownes, when the poore fellowes have gone to *Gehenna*, had course bread and whipping chere al their life after. Now thinkest thou that I who so oft have escaped such a number of hellish dangers, onely depending uppon the turning of a fewe prickes, can bee scare-bugd with the plague? what plague canst thou name worse than I have had? whether diseases, imprisonment, povertie, banishment. I have past through them all. My owne mother gave I a boxe of the eare too, and brake her necke downe a paire of staires, because she would not goe into a Gentleman when I bad her: my sister I sold to an old Leno to make his best of her: anie kinswoman that I have knew I she were not a whore, my selfe would make her one: thou art a whore, thou shalt be a whore, in spite of religion, or precise ceremonies.

Therewith he flew upon her, and threatned her with his sword, but it was not that he meant to wound her with. He graspt her by the yvorie throat, and shooke her as a mastiffe would shake a yong beare, swearing and staring he would teare out her weasand if shee refused. Not content with that savage constraint, he slipt his sacriligius hand from her lilly lawne skinned necke, and inscarft it in her long silver lockes, which with strugling were unrould. Backward he dragd her even as a man backwarde would plucke a tree downe by the twigs, and then like a traitor that is drawen to execution on a hurdle, he traileth her up and down the chamber by those tender untwisted braids, and setting his barbarous foote on her bare snowy breast, bad her yeld or have her winde stampt out. She cride, stamp, stifle me in my haire, hang me up by it on a beame, and so let me die, rather than I should goe to heaven with a beame in my eye. No quoth he, not stampt, nor stifled, nor hanged, nor to heaven shalt thou go till I have had my wil of thee thy busie armes in these silken fetters Ile infold. Dismissing her haire from his fingers, and pinnioning her elbowes therwithall, she strugled, she wrested, but all was in vaine. So strugling, and so resisting, her jewels did sweate, signifying there was poison comming towards her. On the hard boords he threw her, and used his knee as an yron ramme to beat ope the two leavd gate of her chastitie. Her husbands dead bodie he made a pillow to his abhomination. Conjecture the rest, my words sticke fast in the myre and are cleane tyred, would I had never undertooke this tragicall tale. Whatsoever is borne, is borne to have an end. Thus ends my tale, his whorish lust was glutted, his beastly desire satisfied: what in the house of anie worth was carriageable, he put up, and went his way.

Let not your sorrow die: you that have read the proeme of the narration of this eligiacall historie. Shew you have quick wits in sharp conceipt of compassion. A woman that hath viewed all her children sacrificed before her eyes, and after the first was slaine, wyped the sword with her apron to prepare it for the cleanly murther of the second, and so on forward till it come to the empiercing of the seventeenth of her loynes, will not you give her great allowance of anguish? This woman, this matrone, this forsaken *Heraclide,* having buried fourteene children in five daies, whose eyes she howlingly closed, and caught manie wrinckles with funerall kisses: besides, having her husband within a day after laid forth as a comfortles corse, a carrionly blocke, that could neither eate with her, speak with her, nor weepe with her, is she not to bee borne withall, though her body swell with a Timpany of teares, thogh her speech be as impatient as unhappie *Hecubas,* thogh her head raves, and her braine doate? Devise with your selves that you see a corse rising from his hierce after he is caried to church, and such another suppose *Heraclide* to be, rising from the couch of enforced adulterie.

Her eies wer dim, her cheeks bloodles, her breath smelt earthy, her countnance was gastly. Up she rose after she was deflowred, but loath she arose, as a reprobate soule rising to the day of judgement. Looking on the tone side as she rose, she spide her husbands bodie lying under her head: ah then she bewailed, as *Cephalus* when he had kild *Procris* unwittingly, or *Oedipus* when ignorantly he had slaine his father, and known his mother incestuously: this was her subdued resons discourse.

Have I livd to make my husbands bodie the beere to carrie mee to hell? had filthy pleasure no other pillow to leane upon but his spredded lims? On thy flesh my fault shall be imprinted at the day of resurrection. O beautie, the bait ordained to insnare the irreligious: rich men are robd for their welth, women are dishonested for being too fair. No blessing is beautie but a curse: curst be the time that ever I was begotten, curst be the time that my Mother brought mee foorth to tempt. The serpent in paradice did no more, the serpent in paradice is damned sempiternally: why should not I hold my selfe damned (if predestinations opinions be true) that am predestinate to this horrible abuse. The hog dieth presently if he looseth an eye: with the hog have I wallowed in the myre, I have lost my eye of honestie, it is cleane pluckt out with a strong hand of unchastitie: what remaineth but I dye? Die I will, though life be unwilling: no recompence is there for me to redeeme my compelled offence, but with a rigorous compelled death. Husband, Ile bee thy wife in Heaven: let not thy pure deceased spirit despise me when we meet, because I am tyranously polluted. The divell, the belier of our frailtie, and common accuser of mankinde, cannot accuse mee though hee would of unconstrained submitting. If anie guilt be mine, this is my fault, that I did not deforme my face, ere it should so impiouslie allure. Having passioned thus awhile, she hastely ran and lookt hir selfe in hir glasse, to see if her sin were not written on her forhead: with looking shee blusht, though none lookt upon her, but her owne reflected image.

Then began she againe. *Heu quam difficile est crimen non prodere vultu*: How hard is it not to bewray a mans falt by his forhead. My selfe doo but behold my selfe, and yet I blush: then God beholding me, shall not I be ten times more ashamed? The Angels shall hisse at me, the Saints and Martyrs flye from me: yea, God himselfe shall adde to the divels damnation, because he suffered such a wicked creature to come before him. *Agamemnon*, thou wert an infidell, yet when thou wentst to the *Troian* warre, thou leftst a musitian at home with thy Wif, who by playing the foote *Spondæus* till thy retourne, might keepe her in chastitie. My husband going to warre with the divell and his enticements, when hee surrendred left no musition with me, but mourning and melancholy: had he left anie, as *Ægistus* kild *Agamemnons* Musitian ere he could be successfull, so surely would hee have been kild ere this *Ægistus* surceased. My distressed heart as the Hart when as hee looseth his hornes is astonied, and sorrowfullie runneth to hide himselfe, so be thou afflicted and distressed, hide thy selfe under the Almighties wings of mercie: sue, plead, intreate, grace is never denied to them that aske. It may be denied, I maie be a vessell ordained to dishonor.

The onely repeale we have from Gods undefinite chastisement, is to chastise our selves in this world: and I will, nought but death be my pennance, gracious and acceptable maie it be: my hand and my knife shall manumit mee out of the horrour of minde I endure. Fare-well, life, that hast lent me nothing but sorrowe. Fare-well sinne-sowed flesh, that hast more weedes than flowers, more woes than joies. Point pierce, edge enwiden, I patiently affoorde thee a sheath: spurre forth my soule to mount poste to heaven. Jesu forgive me, Jesu receive me.

So (throughlie stabd) fell she downe, and knockt her head against her husbands bodie: wherewith, he not having been aired his ful foure and twentie howres, start as out of a dreame: whiles I thorough a crannie of my upper chamber unseeled, had beheld all this sad spectacle. Awaking, he rubbed his head too and fro, and wyping his eyes with his hand began to looke about him. Feeling some thing lie heavie on his breast, he turned it off, and getting upon his legs lighted a candle.

Here beginneth my purgatorie. For hee good man comming into the hall with the candle, and spying his wife with hir haire about hir eares defiled and massacred, and his simple Zanie *Capestrano* runne through, tooke a halberd in his hand, and running from chamber to chamber to serch who in his house was likelie to doo it at length found me lying on my bed, the doore lockt to me on the out-side, and my rapier unsheathed in the window: wherewith he straight conjectured it was I. And calling the neighbours hard by, said, I had caused my self to be lockt into my chamber after that sort, sent a way my Curtizane whom I called my wife, and made clean my rapier, because I would not be suspected.

Uppon this was I laide in prison, should have been hanged, was brought to the ladder, had made a Ballad for my Farewell in a readines called *Wiltons wantonnes*, and yet for all that scapde dauncing in a hempen circle. He that hath gone through many perils and returned safe from them, makes but a merriment to dilate them. I had the knot under my eare, there was faire plaie, the hangman had one halter, another about my necke was fastned to the gallowes, the riding device was almost thrust home, and his foote on my shoulder to presse me downe, when I made my saint-like confession as you have heard before, that such and such men at such an howre brake into the house, slew the Zanie, took my Curtizan, lockt me into my chamber, ravisht *Heraclide*, and finallie how she slew her selfe.

Present at the execution was there a banisht English Earle, who hearing that a Countrey-man of his was to suffer for such a notable murder, came to heare his confession, and see if he knew him. He had not heard me tell halfe of that I have recited, but he craved audience, and desired the execution might be staid.

Not two daies since it is, Gentlemen and noble *Romanes* (said he) since going to be let blood in a Barbars shop against the infection, all on sodaine in a great tumult and uproare was there brought in, one *Bartoll* an *Italian* greevously wounded and bloodie. I seeming to commiserate his harmes, curteously questiond him with what ill debters he had met, or how or by what casualtie he came to bee so arraid? O (quoth he) long have I lived sworne brothers in sensualitie with one *Esdras* of *Granado*: five hundred rapes and murders have we committed betwixt us. When our iniquities were growen to the height, and God had determined to counterchecke our amitie, we came to the house of *Johannes de Imola* (whom this yong Gentleman hath named) there did he justifie all those rapes in manner and forme as the prisoner here hath confest. But loe an accident after, which neyther he nor this audience is privie too. *Esdras* of *Granado* not content to have ravisht the Matrone *Heraclide* and robd her, after he had betook him from thence to his heeles, lighted on his companion *Bartol* with his Curtizan: whose pleasing face he had scarce winkingly glanst on, but he pickt a quarrell with *Bartoll* to have her from him. On thys quarrell they fought, *Bartoll* was wounded to the death, *Esdras* fled, and the faire dame left to go whether she would. This, *Bartoll* in the Barbars shop freely acknowledged, as both the Barbar and his man and other here present can amplie depose.

Deposed they were, their oaths went for currant, I was quit by proclamation: to the banisht Earle I came to render thankes. when thus he examined and schoold me.

Countriman, tell me what is the occasion of thy straying so farre out of *England*, to visit this strange Nation? If it bee languages, thou maist learne them at home, nought but lasciviousnesse is to bee learned here. Perhaps, to be better accounted of, than other of thy condition, thou ambitiously undertakest this voyage: these insolent fancies are but *Icarus* feathers, whose wanton waxe melted against the Sunne, will betray thee into a sea of confusion.

The first traveller was *Cain*, and he was called a vagabond runnagate on the face of the earth. Travaile (like the travaile wherein smithes put wilde horses when they shoo them) is good for nothing but to tame and bring men under.

God had no greater curse to lay upon the *Israelites*, than by leading them out of their owne countrey to live as slaves in a strange land. That which was their curse, we Englishmen count our chiefe blessednes, hee is no bodie that hath not traveld: wee had rather live as slaves in another land, croutch and cap, and be servile to everie jelous Italians and proud Spaniards humor, where we may neither speak looke nor doo anie thing, but what pleaseth them: than live as freemen and Lords in our owne Countrey.

IX

He that is a traveller must have the backe of an asse to beare all, a tung like the taile of a dog to flatter all, the mouth of a hogge to eate what is set before him, the eare of a merchant to heare all and say nothing: and if this be not the highest step of thraldome, there is no libertie or freedome.

It is but a milde kinde of subjection to be the servant of one master at once, but when thou hast a thousand thousand masters, as the veriest botcher, tinker or cobler free borne will dominere over a forreiner, and thinke to bee his better or master in companie; then shalt thou finde there is no such hell, as to leave thy fathers house (thy naturall habitation) to live in the land of bondage.

If thou doost but lend half a looke to a *Romans* or *Italians* wife, thy porredge shalbe prepared for thee, and cost thee nothing but thy lyfe. Chance some of them breake a bitter jest on thee, and thou retortst it severely, or seemest discontented: goe to thy chamber, and provide a great banket, for thou shalt be sure to be visited with guests in a mask the next night, when in kindnes and courtship thy throat shall be cut, and the dooers returne undiscovered. Nothing so long of memorie as a dog, these *Italians* are old dogs, and will carrie an injurie a whole age in memorie: I have heard of a boxe on the eare that hath been revenged thirtie yeare after. The *Neopolitane* carrieth the bloodiest mind, and is the most secret fleering murdrer: whereupon it is growen to a common proverbe, *Ile give him the Neopolitan shrug*, when one intends to play the villaine, and make no boast of it.

The onely precept that a traveller hath most use of, and shall finde most ease in, is that of *Epicharmus, Vigila, et memor sis ne quid credas*: Beleeve nothing, trust no man, yet seeme thou as thou swallowedst al, suspectedst none, but wert easie to be gulled by everie one. *Multi fallere docuerunt* (as *Seneca* saith) *dum timent falli*: Manie by showing their jelous suspect of deceit, have made men seek more subtill meanes to deceive them.

Alas, our Englishmen are the plainest dealing soules that ever God put life in: they are greedie of newes, and love to bee fed in their humors, and heare themselves flattred the best that may be. Even as *Philemon* a Comick Poet died with extreme laughter at the conceit of seeing an asse eate figs: so have the *Italians* no such sport, as to see poore English asses, how soberlie they swallow Spanish figges, devoure anie hooke baited for them. He is not fit to travell, that cannot with the *Candians* live on serpents, make nourishing food even of poison. Rats and mice ingender by licking one another, he must licke, he must croutch, he must cog, lye and prate, that either in the Court or a forren Countrey will ingender and come to preferment. Be his feature what it will, if he be faire spoken he winneth frends: *Non formosus erat, sed erat facundus Ulysses : Ulysses* the long Traveller was not amiable, but eloquent. Some alledge, they travell to learne wit, but I am of this opinion, that as it is not possible for anie man to learne the Art of Memorie, whereof *Tully, Quintillian, Seneca* and *Hermannus Buschius* have written so manie Bookes, except hee have a naturall memorie before, so is it not possible for anie man to attain anie great wit by travell, except he have the grounds of it rooted in him before. That wit which is thereby to be perfected or made staid, is nothing but *Experientia longa malorum*, the experience of manie evils: The experience that such a man lost his life by this folly, another by that: such a yong Gallant consumed his substaunce on such a Curtizan: these courses of revenge a Merchant of *Venice* tooke against a Merchant of *Ferrara*: and this poynt of justice was shewed by the Duke upon the murtherer. What is here but we may read in bookes, and a great deale more too, without stirring our feete out of a warme Studie.

> *Vobis alii ventorum prælia narrent,* (saith *Ovid,*)
> *Quasque Scilla infestat, quasque Charybdis aquas.*
> Let others tell you wonders of the winde,
> How *Scilla* or *Charybdis* is inclinde.
> —*vos quod quisque loquetur*
> *Credite.* Beleeve you what they say, but never trie.

So let others tell you strange accidents, treasons, poysonings, close packings in *France, Spaine,* and *Italy*: it is no harme for you to heare of them, but come not nere them.

What is there in *Fraunce* to bee learned more than in *England*, but falshood in fellowship, perfect slovenrie, to love no man but for my pleasure, to sweare *Ah par la mort Dieu* when a mans hammes are scabd. For the idle Traveller, (I meane not for the Souldiour) I have knowen some that have continued there by the space of halfe a dozzen yeares, and when they come home, they have hid a little weerish leane face under a broad French hat, kept a terrible coyle with the dust in the streete in their long cloakes of gray paper, and spoke English strangely. Nought els have they profited by their travell, save learnt to distinguish of the true *Burdeaux* Grape, and knowe a cup of neate *Gascoigne* wine, from wine of *Orleance*: yea and per-adventure this also, to esteeme of the pox as a pimple, to weare a velvet patch on their face, and walke melancholy with their Armes folded.

From *Spaine* what bringeth our Traveller? a scull crownd hat of the fashion of an olde deepe porringer, a diminutive Aldermans ruffe with short strings like the droppings of a mans nose, a close-bellied dublet comming downe with a peake behinde as farre as the crupper, and cut off before by the brest-bone like a partlet or neckercher, a wide paire of gascoynes, which ungatherd wold make a couple of womens ryding kirtles, huge hangers that have half a cow hide in them, a rapier that is lineally descended from halfe a dozen Dukes at the least. Let his cloake be as long or as short as you will: if long, it is faced with Turkey grogeran raveld: if short, it hath a cape like a Calves tung, and is not so deepe in his whole length, nor hath so much cloath in it I will justifie, as only the standing cape of a Dutchmans cloke. I have not yet tutcht all, for he hath in either shoo as much taffatie for his tyings as wold serve for an ancient, which serveth him (if you wil have the mysterie of it) of the owne accord for a shoo-rag. A soldier and a braggart he is (thats concluded) he jetteth strouting, dancing on hys toes with his hands under his sides. If you talk with him, he makes a dishcloth of his owne Country in comparison of *Spaine*, but if you urge him more particularly wherin it exceeds, he can give no instance but in *Spaine* they have better bread than any we have: when (pore hungrie slaves) they may crumble it into water well enough, and make mizers with it, for they have not a good morsell of meate except it be salt piltchers to eat with it all the yere long: and which is more, they are poore beggers, and lye in fowle straw everie night.

Italy the Paradice of the earth, and the Epicures heaven, how doth it forme our yong master? It makes him to kis his hand like an ape, cringe his necke like a starveling, and play at hey passe repasse come aloft when he salutes a man. From thence he brings the art of atheisme, the art of epicurising, the art of whoring, the art of poysoning, the art of Sodomitrie. The onely probable good thing they have to keepe us from utterly condemning it, is, that it maketh a man an excellent Courtier, a curious carpet knight: which is, by interpretation, a fine close lecher, a glorious hipocrite. It is nowe a privie note amongst the better sort of men, when they would set a singular marke or brand on a notorious villaine, to say, he hath beene in *Italy*.

With the Dane and the Dutchman I will not encounter, for they are simple honest men, that with *Danaus* Daughters doe nothing but fill bottomeles tubs, and will be drunke and snort in the midst of dinner: he hurts himself only that goes thither, he cannot lightly be damnd, for the vintners, the brewers, the malt-men and alewives pray for him. Pitch and pay, they will pray all day: score and borrow, they will wish him much sorrow. But lightly a man is nere the better for their prayers, for they commit all deadly sin for the most part of them in mingling their drinke, the vintners in the highest degree.

Why jest I in such a necessarie perswasive discourse? I am a banisht exile from my country, though nere linkt in consanguinitie to the best: an Earle borne by birth, but a begger now as thou seest. These manie yeres in *Italy* have I lived an outlaw. A while I had a liberall pension of the Pope, but that lasted not, for he continued not: one succeeded him in his chaire that cared neither for Englishmen nor his owne countrimen. Then was I driven to pick up my crums among the Cardinals, to implore the benevolence and charitie of al the Dukes of *Italy*, whereby I have since made a poore shift to live, but so live, as I wish my selfe a thousand times dead.

> *Cum patriam amisi, tunc me perisse putato :*
> When I was banisht, thinke I caught my bane.

The sea is the native soile to fishes, take fishes from the sea, they take no joy nor thrive, but perish straight. So likewise the birds remooved from the aire (the abode wheretoo they were borne) the beasts from the earth, and I from *England*. Can a lamb take delight to be suckled at the brests of a she wolfe? I am a lamb nourisht with the milke of wolves, one that with the *Ethiopians* inhabiting over against *Meroe* feed on nothing but scorpions: use is another nature, yet ten times more contentive were nature restored to her kingdom from whence she is excluded. Beleeve me, no aire, no bread, no fire, no water doth a man anie good out of his owne countrey. Cold frutes never prosper in a hot soyle, nor hot in a cold. Let no man for anie transitorie pleasure sell away the inheritance he hath of breathing in the place where hee was borne. Get thee home my young lad, laye thy bones peaceably in the sepulcher of thy fathers, waxe olde in overlooking thy grounds, be at hand to close the eyes of thy kinred. The divel and I am desperate, he of being restored to heaven, I of being recalled home.

Here he held his peace and wept. I glad of any opportunitie of a full poynt to part from him, tolde him I tooke his counsaile in worth; what lay in mee to requite in love should not bee lacking. Some businesse that concerned me highly cald mee away very hastely, but another time I hop'd we should meete. Verie hardly he let me goe, but I earnestly over pleading my occasions, at length he dismist mee, told mee where his lodging was, and charged mee to visite him without excuse verie often.

Heeres a stir thought I to my selfe after I was set at libertie, that is worse than an upbraiding lesson after a britching: certainely if I had bethought me like a rascall as I was, he should have had an Avemarie of me for his cynike exhortation. God plagud me for deriding such a grave fatherly advertiser. List the worst throw of ill luckes. Tracing uppe and downe the Cittie to seeke my Curtizan till the Evening began to grow verie well in age, it thus fortuned, the Element as if it had drunke too much in the afternoone, powrde downe so profoundly, that I was forst to creep like one afraid of the watch close under the

pentises, where the cellar doore of a Jewes house caled *Zadoch*
(over which in my direct way I did passe) being unbard on the
in-side, over head and eares I fell into it, as a man falls in a
shippe from the oreloope into the hold, or as in an earth-quake
the ground should open, and a blinde man come feeling pad pad
over the open Gulph with his staffe, should tumble on a sodaine
into hell.   Having worne out the anguish of my fal a little with
wallowing up and downe, I cast up myne eyes to see under what
Continent I was: and loe, (O destenie) I saw my Curtizane
kissing very lovingly with a prentise.

My backe and my sides I had hurt with my fall, but nowe
my head sweld and akt worse than both.   I was even gathering
winde to come uppon her with a full blast of contumelie, when
the Jewe (awakde with the noyse of my fall) came hastely
busteling downe the staires, and raysing his other tenaunts,
attached both the Curtizane and me for breaking his house,
and conspiring with his prentise to rob him.

It was then the law in *Rome*, that if anie man had a fellon
falne into his hands, either by breaking into his house, or
robbing him by the high way, he might chuse whether he would
make him his bond-man, or hang him.   *Zadoch* (as all Jewes
are covetous) casting with himselfe he should have no benefit
by casting me off the Ladder, had another pollicie in his heade:
he went to one Doctor *Zacharie* the Popes Phisition, that was
a Jew and his Countrey-man likewise and told him he had the
finest bargaine for him that might be.   It is not concealed from
me (saith he) that the time of your accustomed yearely Anatomie
is at hand, which it behooves you under forfeiture of the foundation of your Colledge very carefully to provide for.   The
infection is great, and hardly will you get a sound body to deal
upon: you are my Countryman, therefore I come to you first.
Be it knowen unto you, I have a yong man at home falne to me
for my bond-man, of the age of eighteene, of stature tall, straight
limd, of as cleare a complection as any Painters fancie can
imagine: goe too, you are an honest man, and one of the scattred
children of *Abraham* you shall have him for five hundred crownes.
Let me se him quoth Doctor *Zacharie*, and I will give you as
much as another.   Home he sent for me, pinniond and shackeled
I was transported alongst the streete: where passing under
Julianaes the Marques of *Mantuaes* wives window, that was a
lustie *Bona Roba* one of the Popes concubines, as shee had her
casement halfe open, shee lookt out and spide me.   At the first
sight she was enamoured with my age and beardles face, that

had in it no ill signe of phisiognomie fatall to fetters: after me she sent to know what I was, wherein I had offended, and whether I was going? My conducts resolved them all. Shee having received this answer, with a lustfull collachrimation lamenting my Jewish Premunire, that bodie and goods I should light into the hands of such a cursed generation, invented the means of my release.

X

But first Ile tell you what betided mee after I was brought to Doctor *Zacharies*. The purblind Doctor put on his spectacles and lookt upon me: and when he had throughly viewd my face, he caused me to be stript naked, to feele and grope whether each lim wer sound and my skin not infected. Then he pierst my arme to see how my blood ran: which assayes and searchings ended, he gave *Zadoch* his full price and sent him away, then lockt me up in a darke chamber till the day of anatomie.

O, the colde sweating cares which I conceived after I knewe I should be cut like a French summer dublet. Me thought already the blood began to gush out at my nose: if a flea on the arme had but bit me, I deemed the instrument had prickt me. Wel, well, I may scoffe at a shrowd turne, but theres no such readie way to make a man a true Christian, as to perswade him-selfe he is taken up for an anatomie. Ile depose I praid then more than I did in seven yeare before. Not a drop of sweate trickled downe my breast and my sides, but I dreamt it was a smooth edgd razer tenderly slicing downe my breast and sides. If anie knockt at doore, I supposd it was the Bedle of surgeons hal come for me. In the night I dreamd of nothing but phle-botomie, bloudie fluxes, incarnatives, running ulcers. I durst not let out a wheale for feare through it I should bleede to death. For meat in this distance, I had plumporredge of purgations ministred me one after another to clarifie my blood, that it should not lye cloddered in the flesh. Nor did he it so much for clari-fying Phisicke, as to save charges. Miserable is that Mouse that lives in a Phisitions house, *Tantalus* lives not so hunger starved in hell, as she doth there. Not the verie crums that fall from his table, but *Zacharie* sweepes together, and of them moulds up a Manna. Of the ashie parings of his bread, he would make conserve of chippings. Out of bones after the meate was eaten off, hee would alchumize an oyle, that hee sold for a shilling a dram. His snot and spittle a hundred times hee hath put over to his Apothecarie for snow water. Anie spider hee would temper to perfect Mithridate. His rumaticke eies when hee went in the winde, or rose early in a morning, dropt as coole allome water as you would request. He was dame Niggardize sole heire and executor. A number of old books had he eaten with the moaths and wormes, now all day would not he studie a dodkin, but picke those wormes and moaths out of his Librarie, and of their mixture make a preservative against the plague. The licour out of his shooes hee would wring to make a sacred Balsamum against barrennes.

Spare we him a line or two, and looke backe to *Juliana*, who conflicted in her thoughts about me very doubtfully, adventured to send a messenger to Doctor Zachary in hir name, verie boldly to beg mee of him, and if she might not beg me, to buy me with what summes of money soever hee would aske. *Zacharie* Jewishly and churlishlie denied both her sutes, and said if there were no more Christians on the earth, he would thrust his incision knife into his throate-bowle immediatly. Which replie she taking at his hands most despitefully thoght to crosse him over the shins with as sore an overwhart blow ere a month to an end. The Pope (I know not whether at her entreatie or no) within two daies after fell sick, Doctor *Zacharie* was sent for to minister unto him, who seeing a little danger in his water, gave him a gentle comfortive for the stomach, and desired those nere about him to perswade his holines to take some rest, and he doubted not but he would be forthwith well. Who should receive thys milde phisicke of him but the concubine *Juliana* his utter enemie: she being not unprovided of strong poyson at that instant, in the Popes outward chamber so mingled it, that when his Grand-sublimity-taster came to relish it, he sunke downe stark dead on the pavement. Herewith the Pope cald *Juliana*, and askt her what strong concocted broath she had brought him. She kneeled downe on her knees, and said it was such as *Zacharie* the Jew had delivered her with hys owne hands, and therfore if it misliked his holines she craved pardon. The Pope without further sifting into the matter, would have had *Zacharie* and all the Jewes in *Rome* put to death, but she hung about his knees, and with Crocodile tears desired him the sentence might be lenefied, and they be all but banisht at the most. For Doctor *Zacharie* quoth she, your ten-times ungratefull Phisition, since notwithstanding his trecherous intent, he hath much Arte, and manie sovereigne simples, oyles, gargarismes and sirups in his closet and house that may stand your Mightines in stead, I begge all his goods onely for your Beatitudes perseruation and good. This request at the first was sealed with a kisse, and the Popes edict without delaye proclaimed throughout *Rome*, namely, that all fore-skinne clippers whether male or female belonging to the old *Jurie*, should depart and avoid upon pain of hanging within twentie daies after the date thereof.

Juliana (two daies before the proclamation came out) sent her servants to extend upon *Zacharies* territories, his goods, his mooveables, his chattels and his servants: who performed their commission to the utmost title, and left him not so much as master of an old urinall case or a candle-boxe. It was about sixe a clocke in the evening when those boot-halers entred: into my chamber they rusht, when I sate leaning on my elbow, and my left hand under my side, devising what a kinde of death it might be to bee let blood till a man die. I cald to minde the assertion of some philosophers, who said the soule was nothing but blood: then thought I, what a thing were this, if I should let my soule fall and breake his necke into a bason. I had but a pimple rose with heate in that parte of the veyne where they use to pricke, and I fearfully misdeemed it was my soule searching for passage. Fie upon it, a mans breath to bee let out at a backe doore, what a villanie it is? To die bleeding is all one, as if a man should die pissing, Good drinke makes good blood, so that pisse is nothing but blood under age. *Seneca* and *Lucan* were lobcockes to choose that death of all other: a pig or a hog or any edible brute beast a cooke or a butcher deales upon, dies bleeding. To die with a pricke, wherewith the faintest hearted woman under heaven would not be kild, O God, it is infamous.

In this meditation did they seaze upon me, in my cloke they muffeld me that no man might know me, nor I see which way I was carried. The first ground I toucht after I was out of *Zacharyes* house, was the Countesse *Julianas* chamber: little did I surmise that fortune reserved me to so faire a death. I made no other reckoning all the while they had me on their sholders, but that I was on horsbacke to heaven, and carried to Church on a beere, excluded for ever for drinking any more ale or beer. *Juliana* scornfully questioned them thus (as if I had falne into her hands beyond expectation) what proper apple squire is this you bring so suspitiously into my chamber? what hath he done? or where had you him? They answered likewise a far off, that in one of *Zacharies* chambers they found him close prisoner, and thought themselves guiltie of the breach of her Ladiships commaundement if they should have left him. O quoth shee, yee love to be double diligent, or thought peradventure that I beeing a lone woman, stood in need of a love. Bring you me a princoks beardlesse boy (I know not whence he is, nor whether he would) to call my name in suspense? I tell you, you have abused mee, and I can hardly brooke it at your hands. You should have lead him to the magistrate, no commission received you of mee but for his goods and his servants. They besought her to excuse their error, proceeding of dutious zeale no negligent defalt. But why should not I conjecture the worst quoth she? I tell you troth, I am halfe in a jelozie he is some fantasticke yonkster, who hath hyrde you to dishonor me. It is a likely matter that such a man as *Zacharie* should make a prison of his house. By your leave sir gallant, under locke and key shall you stay with me, till I have enquirde farther of you, you shall be sifted throughly ere you and I part. Go maid, shewe him to the farther chamber at the end of the gallerie that lookes into the garden: you my trim pandors I pray gard him thether as you tooke paines to bring him hether: when you have so done, see the dores be made fast and come your way. Heere was a wily wench had her liripoop without book, she was not to seeke in her knackes and shifts: such are all women, each of them hath a cloke for the raine, and can bleare her husbands eies as she list. Not too much of this Madam Marques at once, let me dilate a little what *Zadoch* did with my curtizan after he had sold me to *Zacharie*. Of an ill tree I hope you are not so ill sighted in grafting to expect good fruite: hee was a Jew, and intreated her like a Jew. Under shadow of enforcing her to tell how much money she had of his prentice so to be trayned to his cellar, hee stript her, and scourged her from top to toe tantara. Day by day he disgested his meate with leading her the measures. A diamond Delphinicall drie leachour it was.

The ballet of the whipper of late days here in England, was but a scoffe in comparison of him. All the Colliers of Romford, who holde their corporation by yarking the blinde beare at Paris garden, were but bunglers to him, he had the right agilitie of the lash, there were none of them could make the corde come aloft with a twange halfe like him. Marke the ending, marke the ending. The tribe of Juda is adjudged from Rome to bee trudging, they may no longer bee lodged ther, al the Albumazers, Rabisacks, Gedions, Tebiths, Benhadads, Benrodans,

Zedechiaes, Halies of them wer banquerouts and turned out of house and home. *Zacherie* came running to Zadochs in sacke cloth and ashes presently after his goods were confiscated and tolde him how he was served, and what decree was comming out against them all. Descriptions stand by, here is to bee expressed the furie of Lucifer when he was turnde over heaven barre for a wrangler. There is a toad fish, which taken out of the water swels more than one would thinke his skin could hold, and bursts in his face that toucheth him. So swelled Zadoch, and was readie to burst out of his skin and shoote his bowels like chaine-shot full at *Zacharies* face for bringing him such balefull tidings, his eies glared and burnt blew like brimstone and *aqua vitæ* set on fire in an egshell, his verie nose lightned glow-wormes, his teeth crasht and grated together, like the joynts of a high building cracking and rocking like a cradle, when as a tempest takes her full but against his broad side. He swore, he curst, and saide, these be they that worship that crucifide God of Nazareth, heres the fruits of their new found Gospell, sulpher and gunpowder carry them al quick to Gehenna. I would spend my soule willingly, to have that triple headed Pope with all his sin-absolved whores, and oilegreased priests borne with a blacke sant on the divells backes in procession to the pit of perdition. Would I might sink presently into the earth, so I might blow up this Rome, this whore of *Babilon* into the aire with my breath. If I must be banisht, if those heathen dogs will needs rob me of my goods, I will poyson their springs and conduit heades, whence they receive al their water round about the citie, ile tice all the young children into my house that I can get, and cutting their throates barrell them up in poudring beefe tubbes, and so send them to victuall the Popes gallies. Ere the officers come to extend, Ile bestow an hundred pound on a doale of bread, which Ile cause to be kneaded with scorpions oyle, that will kill more than the plague. Ile hire them that make their wafers or sacramentary gods, to minge them after the same sort, so in the zeale of their superstitious religion, shall they languish and droup lyke carrion. If there be ever a blasphemous conjurer that can call the windes from their brasen caves, and make the cloudes travell before their time, Ile give him the other hundred pounds to disturbe the heavens a whole weeke together with thunder and lightning, if it bee for nothing but to sowre all the wines in *Rome*, and turne them to vineger. As long as they have eyther oyle or wine, this plague feeds but pinglingly upon them.

Zadoch, Zadoch, sayd Doctor *Zachery*, (cutting him off) thou threatnest the aire, whilest we perish here on earth, it is the countesse *Juliana* the Marques of Mantuas wife, and no other, that hath complotted our confusion, aske not how, but insist in my wordes, and assist in revenge.

As how, as how, sayde *Zadoch*, shrugging and shrubbing. More happie than the patriarches were I, if crushte to death with the greatest torments *Romes* tyrants have tride, there might be quintesenst out of me one quart of precious poison. I have a leg with an issue, shall I cut it off, and from his fount of corruption extract a venome worse than anie serpents? If thou wilt, Ile goe to a house that is infected, where catching the plague, and having got a running sore upon me, Ile come and deliver her a supplication and breath upon her. I knowe my breath stinkes so alredie, that it is within halfe a degree of poison, Ile paie her home if I perfect it with anie more putrifaction.

No, no brother *Zadoch*, answered *Zachery*, that is not the way. Canst thou provide me ere a bond-maide, indued with singular and divine qualified beautie, whom as a present from our synagogue thou mayst commend unto her, desiring her to be good and gracious unto us.

I have, I am for you, quoth *Zadoch*: *Diamante* come forth. Heeres a wench (sayd he) of as cleane a skin as *Susanna*, shee hath not a wem on her flesh from the soale of the foote to the crowne of the head: how thinke you master Doctor, will she not serve the turne?

She will sayde *Zacharie*, and therefore Ile tell you what charge I would have committed to her. But I care not if I disclose it onely to her. Maide (if thou beest a maide) come hether to me, thou must be sent to the countesse of *Mantuaes* about a small peece of service, whereby being now a bond woman, thou shalt purchase freedome and gaine a large dowrie to thy mariage. I know thy master loves thee dearly though he will not let thee perceive so much, hee intends after hee is dead to make thee his heir, for he hath no children: please him in that I shall instruct thee and thou art made for ever. So it is, that the pope is farre out of liking with the countesse of *Mantua* his concubine, and hath put his trust in me his phisition to have her quietly and charitably made away. Now I cannot intend it, for I have many cures in hande which call upon me hourly: thou if thou beest placd with her as her waiting maid or cup-bearer, maist temper poison with hir broth, her meate, her drinke, her oyles, her sirrupes, and never bee bewraid. I will not saie whether the pope hath heard of thee, and thou mayst come to bee his lemman in her place, if thou behave thy selfe wisely. What, hast thou the heart to go through with it or no? *Diamante* deliberating wyth her selfe in what hellish servitude she lived with the Jew, and that shee had no likelyhood to be releast of it, but fall from evil to worse if she omitted this opportunitie, resigned her selfe over wholly to be disposed and emploid as seemed best unto them. Therupon, without further consultation, her wardrop was richly rigd, hir tongue smooth filed and new edgd on the whetstone, her drugs delivered her, and presented she was by *Zadoch* hir master to the countesse, together with some other slight newfangles, as from the whole congregation, desiring her to stand their mercifull mistres, and solicite the pope for them, that through one mans ignoraunt offence, were all generally in disgrace with him, and had incurred the cruel sentence of losse of goods and of banishment.

Juliana liking well the pretie round face of my black browd *Diamante*, gave the Jew better countenance than otherwise she would have done, and told him for her owne part she was but a private woman, and could promise nothing confidently of his holines: for though he had suffered himselfe to be overruled by her in some humors, yet in this that toucht him so nerely, she knew not how he would be inclinde: but what laie in her either to pacifie or perswade him, they should bee sure off, and so cravde his absence.

His backe turnd, she askt *Diamante* what countrie woman she was, what friends she had, and how shee fell into the hands of that Jew? She answered that she was a Magnificos daughter of Venice, stolne when she was young from her friends and sold to this Jew for a bond-woman, who (quoth she) hath usde me so jewishly and tyrannously, that for ever I must celebrate the memorie of this daie, wherein I am delivered from his jurisdiction. Alas (quoth she, deep sighing) why did I enter into anie mention of my owne misusage? It wil be thought that that which I am now to reveale, proceeds of mallice not truth. Madam, your life is sought by these Jews that sue to you. Blush not, nor be troubled in your minde, for with warning I shall arme you against all their intentions. Thus and thus (quoth she) said Doctor *Zachery* unto me, this poyson he delivered me. Before I was calde in to them, such and such consultation through the crevise of the doore hard lockt did I heare betwixt them. Denie it if they can, I will justifie it: onely I beseech you to be favorable ladie unto me, and let me not fall againe into the hands of those vipers.

Juliana said little but thought unhappily, onely she thankt her for detecting it, and vowed though she were her bond-woman to be a mother unto her. The poison she tooke of her, and set it up charely on a shelfe in her closet, thinking to keepe it for some good purposes: as for example, when I was consumed and worne to the bones through her abuse, she wold give me but a dram too much, and pop mee into a privie. So shee had served some of her paramors ere that, and if God had not sent *Diamante* to be my redeemer, undoubtedly I had dronke of the same cup.

In a leafe or two before was I lockt up: here in this page the foresayd good wife Countesse comes to me, she is no longer a judge but a client. Howe she came, in what manner of attyre, with what immodest and uncomely wordes she courted me, if I should take upon me to inlarge, all modest eares would abhorre me. Some inconvenience she brought me too by her harlot-like behavior, of which inough I can never repent me.

Let that be forgiven and forgotten, fleshly delights could not make her slothfull or slumbring in revenge against *Zadoch.* She set men about him to incense and egge him on in courses of discontentment, and other supervising espialls, to plie, follow, and spurre forward those suborning incensers. Both which playde their partes so, that *Zadoch* of his owne nature violent, swore by the arke of *Jehova* to set the whole city on fire ere he went out of it. *Zacharie* after he had furnisht the wench with the poyson, and given her instructions to goe to the devill, durst not staie one houre for feare of disclosing, but fled to the duke of *Burbon* that after sackt *Rome,* and ther practised with his bastardship all the mischiefe against the pope and *Rome* that envy could put into his mind. *Zadoch* was left behind for the hangman. According to his oath he provided balls of wild fire in a readinesse, and laid traines of gunpowder in a hundred severall places of the citie to blow it up, which he had set fire to and also bandied his balls abroad, if his attendant spies had not taken him with the manner. To the straightest prison in *Rome* he was dragged, where from top to toe he was clogd with fetters and manacles. *Juliana* informed the pope of *Zachary* and his practise, *Zachary* was sought for, but *Non est inventus,* he was packing long before. Commandement was given, that *Zadoch* whom they had under hand and seale of lock and key, should be executed with al the firy torments that could be found out.

Ile make short worke, for I am sure I have wearyed all my readers. To the execution place was he brought, where first and formost he was stript, then on a sharp yron stake fastened in the ground, he had his fundament pitcht, which stake ran up along into the bodie like a spit, under his arme-holes two of lyke sort, a great bon-fire they made round about him, wherewith his flesh roasted not burnd: and ever as with the heate his skinne blistred, the fire was drawen aside, and they basted him with a mixture of Aqua fortis, allum water, and Mercury sublimatum, which smarted to the very soul of him and searcht him to the marrowe. Then dyd they scourge his backe partes so blistred and basted, with burning whips of red hot wier: his head they nointed over with pitch and tar, and so inflamed it. To his privie members they tied streaming fire-workes, the skinne from the crest of the shoulder, as also from his elbowes, his huckle bones, his knees, his anckles, they pluckt and gnawed off with sparkling pincers: his breast and his belly with seale skins they grated over, which as fast as they grated and rawed, one stood over and laved with smiths syndry water and Aqua vitæ: his nailes they halfe raised up, and then under-propt them with sharpe prickes like a Tailers shop window halfe open on a holy daie: every one of his fingers they rent up to the wrist: his toes they brake off by the rootes, and let them still hang by a little skinne. In conclusion they had a small oyle fire, such as men blow light bubbles of glasse with and beginning at his feete, they let him lingringly burne up lim by lim, till his heart was consumed, and then he died. Triumph women, this was the end of the whipping Jew, contrived by a woman, in revenge of two women, her selfe and her maide.

XI

I have told you or I should tel you in what credit *Diamante* grew with hir mistres. *Juliana* never dreamed but she was an authenticall maide: she made her the chiefe of her bed-chamber, she appoynted none but her to look in to me, and serve mee of such necessaryes as I lacked. You must suppose when wee met there was no small rejoycing on eyther parte, much like the three brothers that went three severall wayes to seeke their fortunes, and at the yeeres end at those three crosse waies met againe, and told one another how they sped: so after wee had bin long asunder seeking our fortunes, wee commented one to another most kindly, what crosse haps had encountred us. Neare a six houres but the Countesse cloyd me with her companie. It grew to this passe that either I must finde out some miraculous meanes of escape, or drop awaie in a consumption, as one pinde for lacke of meate: I was clean spent and done, there was no hope of me.

The yere held on his course to doomes day, when Saint *Peters* daie dawned: that day is a day of supreme solemnity in Rome, when the Embassador of Spaine comes and presents a milke white jennet to the pope, that kneeles downe uppon his owne accord in token of obeisaunce and humilitie before him, and lets him stride on his back as easie as one strides over a blocke: with this jennet is offered a rich purse of a yard length full of *Peter* pence. No musicke that hath the gifte of utterance but sounds all the while: coapes and costly vestments decke the hoarsest and beggerlyest singing-man, not a clarke or sexten is absent, no nor a mule nor a foot-cloth belonging to anie Cardinall but attends on the taile of the triumph. The pope himselfe is borne in his pontificalibus thorough the Burgo (which is the chiefe streete in Rome) to the Embassadours house to dinner, and thether resortes all the assembly: where if a poet should spend all his life time in describing a banket, he could not feast his auditors halfe so wel with wordes, as he doth his guests with junkets.

To this feast *Juliana* addressed her selfe like an angel, in a litter of greene needle worke wrought like an arbour, and open on everie side was she borne by foure men, hidden under cloth rough plushed and woven like eglentine and wodbine. At the foure corners it was topt with foure rounde christall cages of Nightingales. For foote men, on either side of her went foure virgins clad in lawne, with lutes in their hands playing. Next before her two and two in order, a hundred pages in sutes of white cipresse, and long horsemens coates of cloth of silver: who being all in white, advanced everie one of them his picture, enclosed in a white round screene of feathers, such as is carried over greate princesses heads when they ride in summer to keepe them from the heate of the sun, before them went a foure score bead women shee mantayned in greene gownes, scattering and strawing hearbes and floures. After her followed the blinde, the halte and the lame sumptuously apparelled like Lords, and thus past she on to S. *Peters*.

Interea quid agitur domi, how ist at home all this while. My curtizan is left my keeper, the keyes are committed unto hir, she is mistres *fac totum*. Against our countesse we conspire, packe up all her jewels, plate, mony that was extant, and to the water side send them: to conclude, couragiously rob her, and run away. *Quid non auri sacra fames?* what defame will not golde salve. Hee mistooke himselfe that invented the proverbe, *Dimicandum est pro aris et focis*: for it should have been *pro auro et fama*: not for altares and fires we must contend, but for gold and fame.

Oares nor winde could not stirre nor blow faster, than we toyld out of *Tiber*; a number of good fellowes would give size ace and the dice that with as little toyle they could leave Tyburne behinde them. Out of ken we were ere the Countesse came from the feast. When she returned and found her house not so much pestred as it was wont, her chests her closets and her cupbords broke open to take aier, and that both I and my keeper was missing: O then shee fared like a franticke Bacchinall, she stampt, she star'd, shee beate her head against the walls, scratcht her face, bit her fingers, and strewd all the chamber with her haier. None of her servants durst stay in her sight, but she beate them out in heapes, and bad them goe seeke search they knew not where, and hang themselves, and never looke her in the face more, if they did not hunt us out. After her furie had reasonably spent it selfe, her breast began to swell with the mother, caused by her former fretting and chafing, and she grew verie ill at ease. Whereuppon shee knockt for one of her maids, and bad her run into her closet, and fetch her a little glasse that stood on the upper shelfe, wherein there was *spiritus vini*. The maid went, and mistaking tooke the glasse of poyson which *Diamante* had giv'n her and she kept in store for me. Comming with it as fast as her legs could carrie her, her misterres at hir returne was in a sownd, and lay for dead on the floore, wherat she shrikt out, and fel a rubbing and chafing her very busily. When that would not serve, she tooke a keye and opened her mouth, and having heard that *spiritus Vini* was a thing of mightie operation, able to call a man from death to life, shee tooke the poyson, and verely thinking it to be *spiritus vini* (such as she was sent for) powrd a large quantitie of it into her throate, and jogd on her backe to digest it. It revived her with a verie vengeaunce, for it kild her outright, onely she awakend and lift up her hands, but spake nere a worde. Then was the maid in my grandames beanes, and knew not what should become of her, I heard the Pope tooke pittie on her, and because her trespasse was not voluntarie but chance-medly, he assigned hir no other punishment but this, to drinke out the rest of the poison in the glasse that was left, and so go scot-free. Wee carelesse of these mischances, helde on our flight, and saw no man come after us but we thought had pursued us. A theefe, they saie, mistakes everie bush for a true man, the winde ratled not in any bush by the way as I rode, but I straight drew my rapier. To *Bologna* with a mery gale we poasted, where wee lodged our selves in a blinde streete out of the waie, and kept secret many daies: but when we perceived we saild in the haven, that the winde was laid, and no allarum made after us, we boldly came abroad: and one day hearing of a more desperate murtherer than *Caine* that was to be executed, we followed the multitude, and grutcht not to lend him our eyes at his last parting.

Who shoulde it be but one *Cutwolfe*, a wearish dwarfish writhen facde cobler, brother to *Bartol* the Italian, that was confederate with *Esdras* of *Granado*, and at that time stole away my curtizan when he ravisht *Heraclide*.

It is not so naturall for me to epitomize his impietie, as to heare him in his owne person speak upon the wheele where he was to suffer.

XII

Prepare your eares and your teares, for never tyll this thrust I anie tragecall matter upon you. Strange and wonderfull are Gods judgements, here shine they in their glory. Chast *Heraclide*, thy bloud is laid up in heavens treasury, not one drop of it was lost, but lent out to usurie: water powred forth sinkes downe quietly into the earth, but bloud spilt on the ground sprinkles up to the firmament. Murder is wide-mouthd, and will not let God rest till he grant revenge. Not onely the bloud of the slaughtred innocent, but the soul ascendeth to his throne, and there cries out and exclaimes for justice and recompence. Guiltlesse soules that live every houre subject to violence, and with your dispairing feares doe much empaire Gods providence: fasten your eies on this spectacle that will adde to your faith. Referre all your oppressions, afflictions, and injuries to the even ballanced eie of the Almightie, he it is that when your patience sleepeth, will be most exceeding mindfull of you.

This is but a glose upon the text: thus *Cutwolfe* begins his insulting oration.

Men and people that have made holy day to beholde my pained flesh toil on the wheele, expect not of me a whining penitent slave, that shal do nothing but cry and say his praiers and so be crusht in peeces. My bodie is little, but my minde is as great as a gyants: the soule which is in mee, is the verie soule of *Julius Cæsar* by reversion, my name is *Cutwolfe*, neither better nor worse by occupation, but a poore Cobler of *Verona*, Coblers are men and kings are no more. The occasion of my comming hether at this present, is to have a few of my bones broken (as we are all borne to die) for being the death of the Emperour of homicides *Esdras* of *Granado*. About two yeeres since in the streets of *Rome* he slew the only and eldest brother I had named *Bartoll*, in quarrelling about a curtizan. The newes brought to me as I was sitting in my shop under a stal knocking in of tacks, I thinke I raisd up my bristles, solde pritch-aule, spunge, blacking tub, and punching yron, bought mee rapier and pistoll, and to goe I went. Twentie months together I pursued him, from *Rome* to *Naples*, from *Naples* to *Caiete* passing over the river, from *Caiete* to *Syenna*, from *Syenna* to *Florence*, from *Florence* to *Parma*, from *Parma* to *Pavia*, from *Pavia* to *Syon*, from *Syon* to *Geneva*, from *Geneva* backe again towards *Rome*: where in the way it was my chance to meet him in the nicke here at *Bolognia*, as I will tell you how. I sawe a great fraie in the streetes as I past along, and many swordes walking, whereupon drawing neerer, and enquiring who they were, answer was retourned me it was that notable Bandetto *Esdras* of *Granado*. O so I was tickled in the spleene with that word, my hart hopt and danst, my elbowes itcht, my fingers friskt, I wist not what should become of my feete, nor knewe what I did for joy. The fray parted, I thought it not convenient to single him out (beeing a sturdie knave) in the street but to stay til I had got him at more advantage. To his lodging I dogd him, lay at the dore all night where hee entred, for feare hee should give me the slip anye way. Betimes in the morning I rung the bel and craved to speke with him, now to his chamber dore I was brought, where knocking hee rose in his shirt and let me in and when I was entred, bad me lock the dore and declare my arrant, and so he slipt to bed againe.

Marrie this quoth I is my arrant. Thy name is *Esdras* of *Granado*, is it not? Most treacherously thou slewest my brother *Bartoll* about two yeres agoe in the streetes of *Rome*: his death am I come to revenge. In quest of thee ever since a bove three thousand miles have I travaild. I have begd to maintaine me

the better part of the waye, onely because I would intermit no
time from my pursute in going backe for monie. Now have I
got thee naked in my power, die thou shalt, though my mother
and my grandmother dying did intreate for thee. I have
promist the divell thy soule within this houre, breake my word
I will not, in thy breast I intend to burie a bullet. Stirre not,
quinch not, make no noyse: for if thou dost it will be worse
for thee.

Quoth *Esdras*, what ever thou best at whose mercie I lye spare
me, and I wil give thee as much gold as thou wilt aske. Put
me to anie paines my life reserved, and I willingly will sustaine
them: cut off my armes and legs, and leave me as a lazer to some
loathsome spittle, where I may but live a yeare to pray and
repent me. For thy brothers death the despayre of mind that
hath ever since haunted mee, the guiltie gnawing worme of
conscience I feele may bee sufficient penance. Thou canst not
send me to such a hell, as alreadie there is in my hart. To
dispatch me presently is no revenge, it will soone be forgotten:
let me dye a lingring death, it will be remembred a great deale
longer. A lingring death maye availe my soule, but it is the
illest of ills that can befortune my bodie. For my soules
health I beg my bodies torment: bee not thou a divell to
torment my soule, and send me to eternall damnation. Thy
over-hanging sword hides heaven from my sight, I dare not
looke up, least I embrace my deathes-wounde unwares. I
cannot pray to God, and plead to thee both at once. Ay mee,
alreadie I see my life buried in the wrinckles of thy browes:
say but I shall live, though thou meanest to kill me. Nothing
confounds like to suddaine terror, it thrusts everie sense out of
office. Poyson wrapt up in sugred pills is but halfe a poyson:
the feare of deaths lookes are more terrible than his stroake.
The whilest I viewe death, my faith is deaded: where a mans
feare is, there his heart is. Feare never engenders hope: how
can I hope that heavens father will save mee from the hell
everlasting, when he gives me over to the hell of thy furie.

Heraclide now thinke I on thy teares sowne in the dust, (thy
teares, that my bloudie minde made barraine). In revenge
of thee, God hardens this mans heart against mee: yet I did not
slaughter thee, though hundreds else my hand hath brought
to the shambles. Gentle sir, learne of mee what it is to clog
your conscience with murder, to have your dreames, your
sleepes, your solitarie walkes troubled and disquited with
murther: your shaddowe by daie will affright you, you will

not see a weapon unsheathde, but immediatly you will imagine it is predestinate for your destruction.

This murther is a house divided within it selfe: it subbornes a mans owne soule to infourme against him: his soule (beeing his accuser) brings foorth his two eyes as witnesses against him, and the least eie witnesse is unrefutable. Plucke out my eyes if thou wilt, and deprive my traiterous soule of her two best witnesses. Digge out my blasphemous tongue wyth thy dagger, both tongue and eyes wyll I gladly forgoe to have a lyttle more time to thinke on my journey to heaven.

Deferre a while thy resolution, I am not at peace wyth the world, for even but yesterdaie I fought, and in my furie threatned further vengeance: had I a face to aske forgivenesse, I shoulde thinke halfe my sinnes were forgiven. A hundred devils haunt mee dayly for my horrible murthers: the devilles when I die will bee loth to goe to hell with mee, for they desired of Christ he would not send them to hel before their time: if they goe not to hell, into thee they will goe, and hideously vex thee for turning them out of their habitation. Wounds I contemne, life I prize light, it is another worlds tranquilitie which makes me so timerous: everlasting damnation, everlasting houling and lamentation. It is not from death I request thee to deliver me, but from this terror of torments eternitie. Thy brothers bodie only I pearst unadvisedly, his soule meant I no harme to at all: my bodie and soule both shalt thou cast awaie quite, if thou doest at this instant what thou maist. Spare me, spare me I beseech thee, by thy owne soules salvation I desire thee, seeke not my souls utter perdition: in destroying me, thou destroyest thy selfe and me. Eagerly I replid after this long suppliant oration: Though I knew God would never have mercy upon me except I had mercie on thee, yet of thee no mercy would I have. Revenge in our tragedies is continually raised from hell: of hell doe I esteeme better than heaven, if it afford me revenge. There is no heaven but revenge. I tel thee, I would not have undertoke so much toile to gaine heaven, as I have done in pursuing thee for revenge. Divine revenge, of which (as of the joies above) there is no fulnes or satietie. Looke how my feete are blistered with following thee from place to place. I have riven my throat with overstraining it to curse thee. I have ground my teeth to pouder with grating and grinding them together for anger when any hath namde thee. My tongue with vaine threates is bolne, and waxen too big for my mouth: my eyes have broken their strings with staring and

looking ghastly, as I stood devising how to frame or set my
countenance when I met thee. I have neere spent my strength
in imaginarie acting on stone wals, what I determined to execute
on thee: intreate not, a miracle may not reprive thee: villaine,
thus march I with my blade into thy bowels.

Stay, stay exclaimed *Esdras*, and heare me but one word
further. Though neither for God nor man thou carest, but
placest thy whole felicitie in murther, yet of thy felicity learn
how to make a greater felicitie. Respite me a little from thy
swordes point, and set me about some execrable enterprise,
that may subvert the whole state of christendome, and make all
mens eares tingle that heare of it. Commaund me to cut all
my kindreds throats, to burne men, women and children in
their beds in millions, by firing their Cities at midnight. Be it
Pope, Emperor or Turke that displeaseth thee, he shall not
breath on the earth. For thy sake will I sweare and forsweare,
renounce my baptisme, and all the interest I have in any other
sacrament, onely let mee live howe miserable so ever, be it in a
dungeon amongst toads, serpents, and adders, or set up to the
necke in dong. No paines I will refuse howe ever proroged, to
have a little respite to purifie my spirit: oh, heare me, heare me,
and thou canst not be hardned against mee.

At this his importunitie I paused a little, not as retiring from
my wreakfull resolution, but going backe to gather more forces
of vengeaunce, with my selfe I devised how to plague him double
in his base minde: my thoughtes traveld in quest of some notable
newe Italionisme, whose murderous platforme might not onely
extend on his bodie, but his soul also. The ground worke of
it was this: that whereas he had promised for my sake to sweare
and forsweare, and commit *Julian*-like violence on the highest
seales of religion: if he would but this farre satisfie me, he should
be dismist from my furie. First and formost he should renounce
God and his laws, and utterly disclaime the whole title or interest
he had in anie covenant of salvation. Next he should curse
him to his face, as Job was willed by his wife, and write an
absolute firme obligation of his soule to the devill, without
condition or exception. Thirdly and lastly, (having done
this,) hee shoulde pray to God fervently never to have mercie
upon him, or pardon him. Scarce had I propounded these
articles unto him, but he was beginning his blasphemous ab-
jurations. I wonder the earth opened not and swalowed us
both, hearing the bolde tearmes he blasted forth in contempt
of Christianitie: heaven hath thundered when halfe lesse

contumelies against it hath bene uttered. Able they were to raise Saintes and martyrs from their graves, and plucke Christ himselfe from the right hand of his father. My joints trembled and quakt with attending them, my haire stood upright, and my hart was turned wholy to fire. So affectionatly and zealously dyd hee give himselfe over to infidelity, as if sathan had gotten the upper hand of our high maker. The veyne in his left hand that is derived from the hart with no faint blow he pierst, and with the full bloud that flowed from it, writ a full obligation of his soule to the devill: yea, he more earnestly praid unto God never to forgive his soule, than many christians do to save their soules. These fearefull ceremonies brought to an end, I bad him ope his mouth and gape wide. He did so (as what wil not slaves do for feare?) therewith made I no more ado, but shot him full into the throat with my pistoll: no more spake he after, so did I shoot him that he might never speake after or repent him. His bodie being dead lookt as blacke as a toad: the devill presently branded it for his owne. This is the falt that hath called me hether, no true Italian but will honor me for it. Revenge is the glorie of armes, and the highest performance of valure, revenge is whatsoever we call law or justice. The farther we wade in revenge the neerer come we to the throne of the almightie. To his scepter it is properly ascribed, his scepter he lends unto man, when he lets one man scourge an other. All true Italians imitate me in revenging constantly and dying valiantly. Hangman to thy taske, for I am readie for the utmost of thy rigor. Herewithall the people (outragiously incensed) with one conjoyned outcrie, yelled mainely, Awaie with him, away with him. Executioner torture him, teare him, or we will teare thee in peeces if thou spare him.

The executioner needed no exhortation hereunto, for of his owne nature was he hackster good inough: olde excellent he was at a bone-ach. At the first chop with his wood-knife would he fish for a mans heart, and fetch it out as easily as a plum from the bottome of a porredge pot. He woulde cracke neckes as fast as a cooke cracks egges: a fidler cannot turne his pin so soone as he would turne a man of the ladder: bravely did he drum on this *Cutwolfes* bones, not breaking them outright, but like a sadler knocking in of tackes, jarring on them quaveringly with his hammer a great while together. No joint about him but with a hatchet he had for the nones he disjoynted halfe, and then with boyling lead souldered up the wounds from bleeding: his tongue he puld out, least he should blaspheme in his torment: venimous stinging wormes hee thrust into his eares to keep his head ravingly occupied: with cankers scruzed to peeces hee rubd his mouth and his gums: no lim of his but was lingeringly splinterd in shivers. In this horror left they him on the wheele as in hell: where yet living he might beholde his flesh legacied amongst the foules of the aire. Unsearchable is the booke of our destinies, one murder begetteth another: was never yet bloud-shed barren from the beginning of the world to this daie. Mortifiedly abjected and danted was I with this truculent tragedie of *Cutwolfe* and *Esdras*. To such straight life did it thence forward incite me, that ere I went out of *Bolognia* I married my curtizan, performed many almes deedes, and hasted so fast out of the *Sodom* of *Italy*, that within fortie daies I arrived at the king of *Englands* campe twixt *Ardes* and *Guines* in *France*: where he with great triumphs met and entertained the Emperour and the French king, and feasted many daies. And so as my storie began with the king at *Turnay* and *Turwin*, I thinke meete here to end it with the king at *Ardes* and *Guines*. All the conclusive epilogue I wil make is this, that if herein I have pleased anie, it shall animat mee to more paines in this kind.

Otherwise I will sweare upon an English Chronicle never to bee out-landish Chronicler more while I live. Farewell as many as wish me well.

FINIS.

June 27, 1593.

EVERYMAN'S LIBRARY: A Selected List

BIOGRAPHY

ESSAYS AND CRITICISM

FICTION

1

Brontë, Anne (1820–49). THE TENANT OF WILDFELL HALL and AGNES GREY. 685
Brontë, Charlotte (1816–55). For Mrs Gaskell's 'Life' *see* Biography. JANE EYRE, 1847. 287. THE PROFESSOR, 1857. 417. SHIRLEY, 1849. 288. VILLETTE, 1853. 351
Brontë, Emily (1818–48). WUTHERING HEIGHTS, 1848; and POEMS. 243
Butler, Samuel (1835–1902). EREWHON, 1872 (revised 1901); and EREWHON REVISITED, 1901. 881. THE WAY OF ALL FLESH, 1903. 895
Cervantes Saavedra, Miguel de (1547–1616). DON QUIXOTE DE LA MANCHA. Translated by *P. A. Motteux*. 2 vols. 385–6
Collins, Wilkie (1824–89). THE MOONSTONE, 1868. 979. THE WOMAN IN WHITE, 1860. 464
Conrad, Joseph (1857–1924). LORD JIM, 1900. Typically set in the East Indies. 925. THE NIGGER OF THE 'MARCISSUS'; TYPHOON; and THE SHADOW LINE. 980. NOSTROMO, 1904. New edition of Conrad's greatest novel. 38. THE SECRET AGENT, 282
Defoe, Daniel (1661?–1731). THE FORTUNES AND MISFORTUNES OF MOLL FLANDERS, 1722. 837. JOURNAL OF THE PLAGUE YEAR, 1722. 289. LIFE, ADVENTURES OF THE FAMOUS CAPTAIN SINGLETON, 1720. 74. ROBINSON CRUSOE, 1719. Parts 1 and 2 complete. 59
Dickens, Charles (1812–70). WORKS. (*See also* Biography.)
Dostoyevsky, Fyodor (1821–81). THE BROTHERS KARAMAZOV, 1879–80. Translated by *Constance Garnett*. 2 vols. 802–3. CRIME AND PUNISHMENT, 1866. *Constance Garnett* Translation. 501. THE IDIOT, 1873. Translated by *Eva M. Martin*. 682. LETTERS FROM THE UNDERWORLD, 1864; and OTHER TALES. 654. POOR FOLK, 1845; and THE GAMBLER, 1867. 711. THE POSSESSED, 1871. Translated by *Constance Garnett*. 2 vols. 861–2
Dumas, Alexandre (1802–70). THE BLACK TULIP, 1850. The brothers De Witt in Holland, 1672–5. 174. COUNT OF MONTE CRISTO, 1844. 2 vols. Napoleon's later phase. 393–4. MARGUERITE DE VALOIS, 1845. The Eve of St Bartholomew. 326. THE THREE MUSKETEERS, 1844. The France of Cardinal Richelieu. 81
Eliot, George. ADAM BEDE, 1859. 27. DANIEL DERONDA, 1876. 2 vols. 539–40. MIDDLEMARCH, 1872. 2 vols. 854–5. THE MILL ON THE FLOSS, 1860. 325. ROMOLA, 1863. The Florence of Savonarola. 231. SILAS MARNER, THE WEAVER OF RAVELOE, 1861. 121
Fielding, Henry (1707–54). AMELIA, 1751. 2 vols. Amelia is drawn from Fielding's first wife. 852–3. JONATHAN WILD, 1743; and JOURNAL OF A VOYAGE TO LISBON, 1755. 877. JOSEPH ANDREWS, 1742. A skit on Richardson's *Pamela*. 467. TOM JONES, 1749. 2 vols. The first great English novel of humour. 355–6
Flaubert, Gustave (1821–80). MADAME BOVARY, 1857. Translated by *Eleanor Marx-Aveling*. 808. SALAMMBO, 1862. Translated by *J. C. Chartres*. 869. SENTIMENTAL EDUCATION, 1869. Translated by *Anthony Goldsmith*. 969
Forster, Edward Morgan (*b.* 1879). A PASSAGE TO INDIA, 1924. 972
Galsworthy, John (1867–1933). THE COUNTRY HOUSE. 917
Gaskell, Mrs Elizabeth (1810–65). CRANFORD, 1853. 83
Gogol, Nikolay (1809–52). DEAD SOULS, 1842. 726
Goldsmith, Oliver (1728–74). THE VICAR OF WAKEFIELD, 1766. 295
Gorky, Maxim (1868–1936). THROUGH RUSSIA. 741
Hugo, Victor Marie (1802–85). LES MISÉRABLES, 1862. 2 vols. 363–4. NOTRE DAME DE PARIS, 1831. 422. TOILERS OF THE SEA, 1866. 509
James, Henry (1843–1916). THE AMBASSADORS, 1903. 987. THE TURN OF THE SCREW, 1898; and THE ASPERN PAPERS, 1888. 912
Jerome, Jerome K. (1859–1927). THREE MEN IN A BOAT and THREE MEN ON THE BUMMEL. 118
Kingsley, Charles (1819–75). HEREWARD THE WAKE, 1866. 296. WESTWARD HO!, 1855. 20
Lytton, Edward Bulwer, Baron (1803–73). THE LAST DAYS OF POMPEII, 1834. 80
Maugham, W. Somerset (*b.* 1874). CAKES AND ALE, 1930. 932
Maupassant, Guy de (1850–93). SHORT STORIES. Translated by *Marjorie Laurie*. 907
Melville, Herman (1819–91). MOBY DICK, 1851. 179. TYPEE, 1846; and BILLY BUDD (*published*) 1924. South Seas adventures. 180
Meredith, George (1828–1909). THE ORDEAL OF RICHARD FEVEREL, 1859. 916
Modern Short Stories. Selected by *John Hadfield*. Twenty stories. 954
Moore, George (1852–1933). ESTHER WATERS, 1894. 933
Priestley, J. B. (*b.* 1894). ANGEL PAVEMENT, 1931. A finely conceived London novel. 938
Rabelais, François (1494?–1553). THE HEROIC DEEDS OF GARGANTUA AND PANTAGRUEL, 1532–5. 2 vols. *Urquhart and Motteux's* unabridged Translation, 1653–94. 826–7
Russian Short Stories. Translated by *Rochelle S. Townsend*. 758
Scott, Sir Walter (1771–1832). WORKS.
Shelley, Mary Wollstonecraft (1797–1851). FRANKENSTEIN, 1818. 616
Smollett, Tobias (1721–71). THE EXPEDITION OF HUMPHRY CLINKER, 1771. 975. PEREGRINE PICKLE, 1751. 2 vols. 838–9. RODERICK RANDOM, 1742. 790
Stendhal (pseudonym of Henri Beyle, 1783–1842). SCARLET AND BLACK, 1831. Translated by *C. K. Scott Moncrieff*. 2 vols. 945–6
Stevenson, Robert Louis (1850–94). DR JEKYLL AND MR HYDE, 1886; THE MERRY MEN, 1887; WILL O' THE MILL, 1878; MARKHEIM, 1886; THRAWN JANET, 1881; OLALLA, 1885; THE TREASURE OF FRANCHARD. 767. THE MASTER OF BALLANTRAE,

HISTORY

LEGENDS AND SAGAS

POETRY AND DRAMA

DATE DUE

OCT 25 1999			
GAYLORD			PRINTED IN U.S.A.